TAKE A
DEEP BREATH

TAKE A
DEEP BREATH

Insight Into a Medical Practice

By

Elmer E. Cooper, M.D.

NORTEX PRESS   ★   Austin, Texas

FIRST EDITION

Copyright © 1992
By Elmer E. Cooper, M.D.

Manufactured in the United States of America
By Nortex Press
A Division of Sunbelt Media, Inc.
Austin, Texas

ISBN 0-89015-886-X

Names and identifying information of individuals have been changed to protect confidentiality. Any identifications are conjectural.

This book is dedicated to my wife,
Sally,
whose encouragement, patience, and
grammatical corrections
guided me to the final period.

The book is also dedicated to those doctors
who have helped people and thanked God,
rather than to those who have helped and think they are Gods.

Contents

Prologue

From the age of three I always knew I was going to be a doctor. I remember my mother introducing me to her friends as, "My boy, 'Sonny,' who is going to be a doctor." My parents were immigrants; Mother came from Russia and Dad from Rumania. We were poor and lived in a tough neighborhood in East Cleveland. The Italian and Polish kids took delight in calling us "Shinnies" or "Jew Boys," and took even greater delight in beating us up. But their best fun came from throwing rocks as they chased us. In order to preserve life and limb, I learned to run very fast; so fast, indeed, that I made the track team in junior high and high school, and was considered quite good until I ran against Jesse Owens.

Growing up during the depression was difficult, but my friends were also poor, and we accepted that condition as the norm. Dad worked in the garment district as a cutter of dress patterns. The work was seasonal. That meant that for weeks during the off season he was unemployed.

Our next door neighbor, Mr. Gordon, was blind. He made a living selling brooms door-to-door. After school I drove his truck for him and helped him on his rounds. For this, I was paid fifty cents a day. I was only thirteen, but when I applied for the job, confident he could not see how small I was, I told him I was sixteen. This was my first experience as a salesman. Later, on my own, I tried to sell magazine subscriptions, ties, and perfumed soaps. I did poorly in all those endeavors, and it reconfirmed that I was not a good business man — I had to be a professional.

Although Mom, Dad, and I knew I was going to someday become a doctor, our limited finances precluded entering pre-med in the fall after high school graduation.

Job hunting was frustrating during the depression. The only

bread winner in the family was my sister, Molly, who had a secretarial position of $16 per week. When the company needed a new truck driver, she told them I was eighteen. I put on my cousin's oversized suit, shirt and tie and presented myself for the interview. I looked comical with my skinny neck, sleeves reaching to my fingertips, and rolled up pant's cuffs. But my "Charlie Chaplin Look" amused the boss and he gave me the job. I drove a truck from 7:00 A.M. to 7:00 P.M. for $13 per week. On Thursdays I worked at night until 10:00 P.M. and the boss gave me thirty-five cents for supper at the Blue Plate Diner across the street, and fifty cents for the extra hours. I learned about women, sex, the art of cussing, and how to shoot craps with the older truck drivers. The job lasted nine months, until I had a fist fight with the boss' son. He had always looked down on me as though I were of a lower caste. After one too many of his sneering remarks about my being poor, I caught him on the back freight elevator and challenged him. I won the fight, but lost the job.

When I learned about the fancy new Krogers Grocery Store opening in the rich section of Cleveland, I applied and was accepted to be their stockboy and fruit and vegetable trimmer. The job paid only $8.50 per week, but I was glad to get it. I shared the job with Tony, who was nineteen-years-old, and we worked together in the basement. I taught him to call everyone we did not like a "momser" (bastard in Yiddish), and he gave me the equivalent in Italian, "brutano." The clerks upstairs thought those were our nicknames for them!

A year after graduation I had saved enough money to enter the freshman class of 1932 at Ohio State University. I quickly took a N.Y.A. (National Youth Administration) job at the school at thirty-five cents an hour, and tutored pre-med students in chemistry. On Saturdays I sold shoes downtown, and on Sundays, fruits and vegetables at the market at the edge of the campus. But I was "pre-med"! and beginning to believe I would become a doctor after all!

Now, years later after completion of medical school, and all of my training, and over forty years of the practice of internal medicine, it has occurred to me that I have performed approximately 100,000 physicals. Each time I examine a chest, I request the patient to take at least six *Deep Breaths,* and when I palpate the abdomen the patient is asked to take four more *Deep Breaths,* making an average of ten *Deep Breaths* per physical. Therefore, I have observed approximately one million *Deep Breaths!*

During the observation of all these inspirations and expirations, I had become a participant in the management of their medical problems and often of their lives. They, along with my teachers, fellow students, and colleagues became inextricably woven into the fabric of my profession and personal life. We shared successes and failures, happiness and sadness. In this collection of remembrances I have chronicled my personal odyssey in an enormously demanding but immeasurably rewarding discipline wherein I wore three hats: Practicing, Teaching, and Clinical Research.

Dr. Elmer and Sally Cooper

Murder Under the Oaks

It was 11:00 A.M. on Sunday, June 17, 1947. The day promised to be bright, sunny and hot. I had finished early morning rounds at the Santa Rosa Hospital and was looking forward to a relaxing family day around the pool at Hillcrest Country Club. The piercing ring of the telephone shattered the stillness. Resignedly, I answered, totally unprepared for the shocking news I was to hear. My colleague and good friend, Dr. Lloyd Ross, had murdered four persons of one family and injured a fifth.

Lloyd Ross was a gifted surgeon. He arrived in San Antonio in the early '40s with impressive credentials, having trained at Boston's Lahey Clinic and Massachusetts General Hospital. His technique was superb and his surgical judgment impeccable. Predictably, his results were excellent. He had the patience and concentration of a Swiss watch repairman.

A typical "Type A" personality, Lloyd was the greatest perfectionist I have ever known. He was obsessive, comprehensive, compulsive, brilliant, and extremely correct in manner. A quick sense of humor and capacity for comraderie with his colleagues saved him from being resented. Always meticulously groomed, moderately tall, round faced, with brown hair, steady myopic brown eyes behind thick horn-rimmed glasses, he looked every inch the imposing doctor-deity as he strode authoritatively through the corridors of the Santa Rosa Medical Center. The Catholic nun nursing staff adored him, patients idolized

1

him, and the medical community held him in the greatest respect. His preoperative, operative, and postoperative care were almost fanatically obsessive. He paid rigorous attention to details. Patients were "prepped" for surgery twice under his auspices, for fear the first preparation might have been imperfect. Following surgery, he observed the patient in the recovery room for a minimum of one hour to make certain there were no immediate postoperative complications. And for the first three days after one of his surgical procedures, or longer if indicated, he visited his patients three times daily, checking and rechecking ad infinitum. As his reputation grew, patients who came from all over the Southwest bragged about his surgery as though it were some kind of status symbol. Sister Dorothea, chief of the Santa Rosa surgical department, declared him the most talented, exquisitely conscientious, successful surgeon she had ever encountered.

Responding to one another's perfectionistic approach to medicine, Lloyd and I soon developed a beautiful reciprocal relationship. When I referred surgical cases to him, I did so knowing my patients would receive treatment as fine as was available anywhere in the country. He had the same admiration for my medical capabilities, and called me as consultant when confronted with internal medical problems. Given his perfectionism, he automatically asked me to check each patient for the possibility of medical complications before operating. In unusually difficult cases, he always requested that I be present during the actual surgical procedure to cope with any medical exigencies that might arise.

Our close professional association led to personal friendship. My wife and Gladys Ross, a vivacious brunette, enjoyed one another's company and our social life frequently included dinner with the Rosses. Their home was beautiful and compulsively orderly. It was so perfect that to us it seemed sterile. We found it difficult to believe that anyone actually lived in those exquisitely decorated rooms. In all the years of our friendship, we never saw a pillow rumpled, a flower wilted, or a magazine askew. Their only daughter, an honor student and gifted pianist, seemed immune from the usual adolescent problems. They appeared a perfect family, living in a perfect house in a perfect little personal world — envied, admired, and respected by their peers. To all of us, it seemed that the Rosses led a charmed life, free of the problems and frailties that beset the rest of the human race.

Before long, Dr. Ross had amassed a considerable fortune in practice and became interested in finding some lucrative investment opportunities. He had operated on Willard "Mike" York, a bright investment banker with a magnetic personality and they developed a close friendship. Lloyd had great confidence in Mike and soon began to utilize his services as an investment counselor. The York and Ross families became inseparable. They attended the same church, sat together at the Saturday night symphony concerts, and were frequent guests in one another's homes. Their daughters were the same age and shared many interests.

I first met Mike York when he was referred to me by Dr. Ross for cardiac arrhythmia. An attractive man in his early 40s, Mike had a round cherubic face with ruddy cheeks, thinning sandy hair, and eyes of a deep, arresting blue. I found him to be a cooperative, intelligent patient, with great personal charm, an interesting conversationalist, and quite knowledgeable in a variety of subjects, including finance. Small of stature, he nonetheless had great presence. In due time, both Lloyd and I made investments with him.

Mike's procedure was straightforward. We supplied him with specific sums of money, which he was to invest for us in stocks and bonds, thus freeing us from decision-making and allowing us to devote our full time and attention to our profession. At the end of each month, he presented us with worksheets reporting what our investments were worth. We trusted him completely and felt fortunate to have our financial affairs in such competent hands, as did his numerous other clients.

One day, a small article in the *San Antonio Light* newspaper reported that the SEC was investigating Willard York. I was sure it was an error. The report contended that instead of purchasing stocks and bonds for which he had been funded, York was speculating on the market with everyone else's money. He lost most of the money, and in addition, used his customers' funds for personal use, including the purchase of a beautiful oak-studded 1,600 acre ranch in Comal County, approximately twenty miles north of San Antonio.

I was shocked and disbelieving. When the allegations in the article turned out to be true I was disturbed but philosophical. I had lost a little over $12,000, accepted it as bad luck and a consequence of poor judgment on my part, and dismissed it from my mind.

Lloyd Ross, on the other hand, had lost over $100,000. Worse than the blow of the monetary loss was the blow to his ego. He was devastated by the fact that he had been swindled by this man who had become his best friend. With his zeal for perfection, his obsessive overly-compulsive nature, he could not accept this evidence of his own fallibility in so grossly misjudging York's character.

He brooded over the situation, becoming increasingly disturbed and frustrated, and engaged counsel to institute suit against York. As the weeks passed, Dr. Ross became more and more upset and paranoid about the situation. His work began to deteriorate and he refused to undertake difficult surgical procedures, electing instead to sit in his darkened study at home, brooding. Gladys and those of us who were his friends tried to ease his depression by reminding him that with his superb surgical skills, he could soon recoup his loss and go forward in his career. Heedless of our advice, he continued to recriminate himself for being so unperceptive — for not recognizing the "con" man in Willard York.

The phone call that disrupted my peaceful Sunday morning came from Dr. Johnson, a longtime friend and confidante of the Ross family. In a shaking voice, barely coherent, he told me the horrible story: Lloyd Ross, the most correct, proper man I had ever known, had just murdered four members of the York family and injured a fifth.

That glorious June morning, Lloyd Ross drove to the York ranch and parked under a gnarled oak tree in the rough, lonely, twisting lane leading to the house. The front of his vehicle protruded into the road, effectively blocking any car coming from the house. Presently York appeared at the wheel of his new Buick sedan, en route to church. With him were his wife Gertrude, his mother Mary, and his two children, John and Ann. York slowed when he saw the Ross car, stopped, put his head out the window on the driver's side and greeted Lloyd in a friendly manner. Dr. Ross approached the car slowly, and when he came abreast of the open window, poked in the head of a rifle which he had held hidden behind him, and blasted away. Willard sustained three bullet holes in his body and died instantly, slumping under the wheel of his new Buick. Gertrude York's bullet-ridden body was found huddled in a pool of blood in the passenger's side of the front seat. A white hat and her white gloves, intended for church, were found, unstained, on the seat. Their nine-year-old son John had two bullet wounds in his body and was found near the right hand door, clutching a bouquet of colorful wild flowers, intended for church. York's mother Mary, age sixty-seven, seated in the back between the two children, was shot five times. Her body lay crumpled on the seat.

Ann York, eleven, the sole survivor of the massacre, jumped from the car when the shooting began, having managed to open the left rear door, and fled for her life through the rock-strewn road into the woods. She was shot in the right hip as she jumped from the car. In the insane melee of the moment, Ross' glasses fell and shattered on the stony road. Being extremely myopic, he was unable to follow Ann as she raced, dripping blood from the hip wound, through the woods to the nearest ranch house approximately a mile away. In partial shock, she weakly pounded on the door, attracted the attention of the startled neighbor and, gasping for breath, blurted incoherent details of the terrible tragedy before collapsing.

An hour after the event, a dazed Dr. Ross appeared at the San Antonio Police Department and said: "There is a rifle in the trunk of my car and apparently it has been fired." Ross was taken into custody immediately. He was charged in Comal County with the murder of four persons and wounding with intent to kill young Ann York. After a lengthy, sensational sanity hearing, Ross was declared insane, thus escaping the death sentence. He was remanded to the Texas State Hospital for the criminally insane in Wharton, Texas. His spinster sister, Renna Ross, moved from her Ohio home to Wharton in order to visit her adored brother whenever possible.

The repercussions following this brutal multiple slaying by a man of Lloyd Ross' stature continued for years. Of all the doctors in San Antonio, he would have seemed the least capable of committing so heinous a crime. It was incomprehensible that this assured, dignified gentleman could have become an insane, brutal killer. The Sister nurses at the Santa Rosa mourned him as though he were dead. Patients and friends were shocked and grief stricken, unable to connect this cruel deed with the gentle Lloyd Ross they had known and loved. My wife and I were among the most disturbed and it took several months for us to recover from the emotional trauma.

The Sisters of the Santa Rosa visited Ross at the prison hospital regularly and included him in their prayers. I too visited him occasionally and found him totally unrepentant; convinced that his act was justified by the heavenly voices that commanded him to eradicate the York family from the earth.

That Sunday evening, June 17, 1947, I sat alone in my green leather chair, in the stillness of my den, quietly agonizing over the unbelievable, incomprehensible, irrational behavior of that medical deity, that revered, skilled, trained surgical genius. And then the truth of the tragedy dawned on me. Lloyd Ross typified the psychologically unwavering perfected individual whose family background and

precise professional technical training denied him the acceptance of im-
perfections, errors, variances or disappointments. Like honed steel this
ramrod precise personality could not flex, or give with tension, or exi-
gency, but instead must break, and break he did.

It also occurred to me that despite the fact that I engaged daily in
physical exams, hospital rounds, x-rays, EKGs, lab reports, etc., it is
necessary to interact with people, with humanity in concert, and to
understand their psychological behaviors. And this fascinating opportunity to interrelate with human beings was initiated by the letter I received dated March 15, 1935!

Blood, Sweat and Fears

Medical School — The Agony and the Ecstasy

The letter was delivered to me during my junior year as a pre-med at Ohio State University. I was nineteen-years-old. It was a single typed sheet that said, tersely:

3-15-1935

Dear Sir:

I am glad to report that the committee has authorized a scholarship admission to the medical school in the autumn of 1935. A place in the first year class will be reserved for you in the autumn quarter. Attention is invited to the fact that in the first two years there is a fixed program of required medical courses given only once a year. It will be difficult or impossible for students to do outside work for self-support. They should give all their time and energy to the work of the medical school. A certificate of admission will be issued to you on receipt of transcript covering work now in progress.

Yours sincerely,

BCH Harvey, Dean of Medical Students
University of Chicago
Division of Biological Sciences
School of Medicine

That was the total substance of my permission to enter the world of medicine. With those few sentences, the direction of the rest of my life was set.

I had already received an admission to the medical school at Ohio State University where I was doing my pre-med work, as well as to the University of Indiana medical school, where I had applied as an alternate possibility. Imagine my euphoria at being admitted on full tuition scholarship to one of the top medical schools in the country. I thanked God for the scholarship, for only with that help could medical school be feasible.

However, the clause that required "complete attention for the first two years, without any time to do outside work for self-support" was a little worrisome, as somehow I had to sustain myself for room and board. A subsequent letter from Dean Harvey somewhat reassured me on that score as he intimated that he had some ideas for solution of that problem. I was to see him one week prior to the start of classes in September.

I was also beset by problematic questions and self-doubt. I realized that my role in life was to be permanently and completely altered. I questioned myself about the consequences of this move. Was I ready for the serious responsibilities with their practical, social, emotional

First year medical student.

and physical demands? Could I endure the relentless regime, the hard study, the slave labor in internships and residencies? (Internships and residencies are entirely different today. Working conditions, hours in attendance, and the salaries are much more compatible with present-day living.) Would I do justice to my sacrificing parents? Could I justify the time and energy expended upon me by the teachers I was to meet in medical school? Would I be able to warrant the energy extended by my predecessors who molded medicine as it existed at the time? Would I constantly be aware of the ensuing changes and the new frontiers inevitably presented as science marched forward? Could I accept the evolution of the social and economic changes in medical practice?

Could I prepare myself with emotional stability to handle patients who would become ill and who might or might not recover, or become disabled? How would I attend the dying patients and their families? I asked myself these questions and hoped that I could meet the challenge.

I found the Midway, the site of the University of Chicago Medical School on the southside of Chicago, after eight long tedious hours on a Greyhound bus, and a thirty minute street car ride from the depot. There I was, a scared, shabby, skinny nineteen-year-old, standing in front of awe-inspiring Gothic buildings stretching one-half mile along the Midway, the grassy stretches that were the original site of the 1893 World's Fair.

Behind those massive walls were my teachers who had amassed the knowledge of their predecessors and added their own findings to the total. I was to be the recipient of this medical bounty. During my lifetime, would I add to it or, parasitically, merely use what I assimilated from others?

I located the Anatomy Building and stood in front of it, looking up at the three stories of cold granite Gothic architecture with the gargoyles looking down at me. As I looked up at the building I felt what Hilary and Tensing must have felt when they stood at the bottom of Mt. Everest prior to their climb. I was there and therefore it had to be assaulted, and I had to do the climbing. True, the building looked foreboding and mysterious, but it was stable, immobile, and looked enduring.

This was the university where Robert Maynard Hutchins inaugurated his revolutionary new philosophy of education. Each student should proceed at the rate at which he or she was capable. Once they were accepted at the university, they could select classes, attend lectures, study in the library, and whenever they felt prepared, they could take their exams. If they passed the comprehensives, they could advance to the next subject. It was a thrilling system, challenging the student to do his utmost without pressure or boredom. It promised to be an exhilarating intellectual voyage.

Once I entered the Anatomy Building, I found the interior entirely different from what I expected. I saw old oak panels, large white banisters, and wooden steps that creaked as you ascended. Consulting the large directory, I found that the office of Dr. BCH Harvey, Dean of Medical School, was on the fourth floor, and I started up the steps with increasing trepidation and palpitations. The palpitations, sensation of cardiac awareness, and the increased rate were not due to any cardiac decompensation, as I was to learn later on in physiology, but were simply an emotional response triggered by a new and awesome experience. I felt a mixture of fear and expectation. Would I live up to his standards for the tuition scholarship awarded me? It was earned on the basis of my academic standing for the three years of pre-med as well as the medical aptitude test score and letters of recommendation from my pre-med professors at Ohio State University.

I was ushered into the inner office to meet Dean Harvey after a twenty-minute wait in the outer reception area. He was a pleasant surprise, about five-feet, five or six inches tall, with curly grayish hair, round face, rosy cheeks, cherubic-looking with a wide, friendly, fatherly smile, reminding me of the angel in the Jimmie Stewart film "It's a Great Life." I was to learn later that this man with his pleasant expression was actually a stern tactician, famous anatomist, and Chairman of the Department of Anatomy. This was the Moses who was to lead his flock of 100 naive medical student followers, waiting to be ushered into the world of medicine, our Land of Milk and Honey. The manna did not, however, fall from heaven, as I soon learned. It came from long hours of study, long hours of lectures, tedious hours of laboratory work, and very little sleep. For it was learn, learn, learn, and learn! We shared some pleasantries in the Dean's office, and then he told me that he was particularly impressed with one statement I made on my application: I had written that I wanted to be a doctor for many reasons but, important among them, I wanted to enter a scientific field where I would never stop learning.

Dr. Harvey then entered freely in the discussion about the restriction of Jewish applicants to medical schools. He readily admitted that there was a quota in all medical schools in the USA at that time, the maximum being approximately ten percent outside of New York City. But he explained clearly that this wasn't unexpected since the population of Jewish people versus the entire population percentage-wise was probably only three or four percent at that time. He recognized, however, that the competition around many Jewish applicants was very stressful. The dean, I learned, was eclectic, educated, and derived pleasure from the medical school world about him. I also learned at that time that the usual ratio of women in medicine was approximately three percent. Today it has reached forty to forty-five percent. Dr. Harvey, being aware of my financial problems, felt he had an answer. There was a young lady with chronic rheumatic heart disease, living less than a mile from the school who had, for the last four years, employed a medical student to function in the capacity of a companion in her home. Mary Stein was her name and I was told that she was quite wealthy, had a large apartment in the nicest section of Drexel Avenue, and she had arranged for the student to have his own room on the second floor, with a private bath, and board, and a stipend of $20 per week. In return he was to serve as a companion. He was to be with her after returning from school, join her for supper and when she went to bed at 9:00 P.M., he was free to go to his room and do his studies, and wouldn't need to be with her again until the following day, after classes. He was to be aware of her physical condition, alert to the possibilities of early cardiac congestive failure and be able to treat any emergency which presented itself. The student would be instructed by Stein's internist as to what need be done and how it should be done for any medical exigency. During the daytime she had a very responsible capable maid on duty to give her complete security. This all seemed much too good to be true. Certainly I could learn what had to be done from her internist, and I felt energetic and outgoing and sure I could become a companion for the few hours daily and certainly I needed that $20 a week for books, laundry, food, entertainment, etc. I shook Dr. Harvey's hand gratefully and rushed out to meet Mary Stein in the fancy upper section of Drexel Avenue.

Most of the apartments on Drexel Avenue were three and four stories high and consisted of a separate flat on each floor. The section where Miss Stein lived consisted of individual apartments each two to three stories high. The steps were white marble. There were wide windows and a beautiful leaded glass door at the entrance. I rang the bell with trepidation. I wasn't prepared for the individual who opened the door admitting me, a very pretty black woman, hair neatly groomed, wearing a black uniform with a white apron and white blouse with cuffs. She ushered me into the living room, passing through a beautiful stained glass foyer with luxuriant plants along the walls. I was told Miss Stein would see me shortly, and that I was to sit there and she would return for me. I walked across the plush carpeting, my feet sinking into the thick rug. We had linoleum floors at home. I buried myself in one of the inviting French armchairs and sat looking around at the wonders that presented themselves in this beautiful room.

There were two sculptures on pedestals, one on each side of an archway leading to the dining room. They were both figurines, each one was different, both very appealing. One sculpture was of mother and child — the mother was holding the child aloft with her arms outstretched and upwards, as though she had just playfully flung her in the air and caught the child on the downward motion with the child's legs extended in playful fright. The other sculpture was a four-foot bronze female nude with an ethereal, perfectly molded, very sensuous body. A large crystal chandelier hung from the ceiling. There were beautiful well-lit paintings on the walls. A library stretched to the right of the entrance to the dining room, with shelves from floor to ceiling crowded with books. The Steinway baby grand piano held open sheet music, I saw that it was Bach. One of the large oil paintings that I was able to see from where I sat was signed by Camille Pissarro. I thought the other painting was a Renoir, but I was too far away to determine for sure if it was signed by him. Truthfully, I would not recognize the authenticity of any of these paintings, as I had had very little exposure to Renoir, Pissarro, etc.

After an uncomfortable fifteen minutes the maid ushered me into a large warm bedroom to meet Mary Stein. She was smiling and held her hand out gracefully to shake mine, and told me that she knew my background, having had a lengthy telephone conversation with the dean. She removed two opened books from the chair that was next to her bed, and bade me sit down close to her. She was quite attractive, was about thirty-four years of age, with a flawless complexion and shiny black hair tied behind her head in a knot held in place by a red ribbon. She had large brown eyes with lashes thick with mascara. She was lying in bed propped up on two pillows, but did not seem to be in any discomfort. I noticed that she was voluptuous and made no effort to close her upper gown in spite of her exposed cleavage. Miss Stein said she lived alone in this house, the maid left after dinner. Her parents had died and left her an estate, and she objected strenuously to having nurses about her as they reminded her of her terrible experiences in hospitals. And that was why she preferred to have a medical student. She said she had acquired acute rheumatic fever as a child following a strep throat infection, followed by scarlet fever, and then an episode with generalized joint pains followed months later with cardiac involvement. She was quite intelligent and discussed her rheumatic heart condition with ease. I learned that her mitral valve was involved and that it was stenotically narrowed: This interfered with the amount of blood that was to get into the left ventricle and ejected through the aortic system. She also knew that on occasion, after stress or strain, or for other reasons for which she knew no explanation, she had occasional attacks of cardiac congestive failure and would develop some fluid in the lungs, requiring energetic and aggressive therapy for relief. She said she rarely had painful attacks, but when she had these rare respiratory failure problems, she did need an injection of an opiate, but in small doses, and never more than once a month. She took great pains to impress me with the knowledge that the attacks were very infrequent. This relieved me immediately, as I was concerned about the possibility that she might have some addiction. She was bright, had a cheery expression, smiled often, and had a melodious voice. She was likable and I hoped she would like me.

She told me that if I were to be accepted for the position, I would meet with her internist who would describe her periodic use of oxygen, the occasional use of opiates, and the use of medication by injection to wash out fluids, which should be given intravenously. I reassured her that I would have no problem coping with any of these conditions that needed attention.

With all this luxury around me, I felt somewhat uncomfortable as I sat there in my Sears & Roebuck corduroy pants, a white sportshirt which had been mended, and my recently shined shoes. I had spent only a few minutes preparing for this interview, but my hair was combed nicely, and I was freshly shaven, and hoped that I was presenting a dependable personality. After we each had a cup of tea, she told me that her pleasures in life at this time revolved primarily around art and music. She also told me that although she had some cardiac problems, her other bodily functions were quite normal. She had no urinary complaints, none with reference to her gastrointestinal system, and she emphasized twice that she had a very normal hormone balance. I reflected on this a bit, but then reassured myself that she merely wanted me to know that she was healthier than one would believe.

She motioned me to bring my seat a little closer to the bed and then she said to me, "Did you notice the paintings in my living room?" She said, "I am very proud because I have a Monet, a Renoir, and a Pissarro hanging on my walls." I was more familiar with the cartoons of Al Capp and Norman Rockwell paintings at that time, and began to feel a bit uncomfortable. Then casually she asked me if I knew what period the artists represented. Of course, she wanted me to say they were representative of the era of the Impressionists. But I was unfamiliar with art at that time and naively said they represented a deep intensity of color. I noticed her look of dismay.

She said that occasionally when she felt good she could go to the piano and play classical music, that she loved Liszt, Beethoven, and Tchaikovsky. Then she said, "It is interesting that they all have this one great thing in common." She waiting for me to fill in the answer, but I was not prepared to respond that they had all composed some of the finest piano concertos ever.

Trying desperately to change the subject I said that I noticed she had an extensive library, and wanted to know if it was all right to borrow any of the books. "But of course, I want you to feel free to read, and we shall discuss some of the books you read." Then she hit me below the belt and asked me casually, "What do you think of Dickens, Victor Hugo, and Harriet Beecher Stowe in their writings compared, for example, to Somerset Maugham, Henry James, and F. Scott Fitzgerald?" Musing later I realized that she wanted to discover if I knew that the first three authors wrote about poor people and the oppressed, while on the other hand, the latter authors always wrote about the upper classes. Blushing freely I began to realize that I was not favorably passing this interview.

She then told me that she was a bit tired, and I noticed that she was breathing a little more rapidly, that there was some beginning distention of her neck veins, indicating a bit of stress. I told her that I thought perhaps she needed to rest and that I had to get back to the medical school. She told me that she would call Dr. Harvey and discuss further plans. We shook hands, and I told her how delighted I was to meet her and that I was sure I could be of help to her and hoped she felt that I wouldn't disappoint her. With that I walked out of the bedroom, through the living room, and was ushered past the foyer to the outside by the maid, who closed the front door gingerly as I rapidly descended the marble steps.

When I returned from the interview, feeling uncomfortable and let-down in my self-esteem, I thought I should talk to the student who had spent four years with Mary Stein and see if by chance I had handled myself correctly. I found him at home packing, ready to go off to his internship, and discussed my Mary Stein interview with him in great detail. I told him how badly I floundered in the cultural areas. But when I asked him about her emphasis on her normal hormone balance, he reported confidentially that she desired sexual contact at least once or sometimes twice a week. Startled, all I could ask him at that time was, "Wouldn't it throw her into cardiac congestive failure?" He said, no, he thought that seemed to improve her general status. I pondered for several days about this interview and wondered if I could psychologically perform the function that I would be required to do, especially the sexual part. Certainly the entire project was not what I thought it was to be. I didn't have to resolve this dilemma because Mary Stein never called. For some time I wondered, did I fail to meet her cultural standards, or was it because I did not respond to her sexual signals?

*   *   *   *   *

My angel, Dr. Harvey, phoned me several days after the interview. He had heard from Mary Stein and reassured me that he had an alternate proposition for me. Although not as lucrative, it would be enduring and worthwhile. It was then I was introduced to Robert Wilson. Robert was a delightful young man, approximately my age, perhaps a year or two older, who according to Dr. Harvey was very bright, but had very poor study habits. He was involved in too much social life and he needed discipline and study companionship. In return for studying with him for two or three hours daily, I was to receive fifteen dollars per week, the suits that he no longer wore, and a promise to be introduced to nice social contacts in Chicago.

Robert was smart and retentive and learned easily. His problem fell into the category of very poor study discipline habits. He was a spoiled rich boy from Eggertsville outside of Buffalo, New York, the son of Jack Wilson, a prominent attorney in Buffalo, whose brothers were the Wilson Brothers of Hollywood fame.

Robert lived in the dormitory on campus, but he had a corner suite which consisted of a separate sitting room, a bedroom and a private bath. The rest of the dormitory rooms were single study rooms with a bath down at the end of the corridor, used in common by eight to ten students. By virtue of my sitting and studying with him, Rob-

ert would be forced to discipline himself. Otherwise, he would be off
enjoying his many social activities. He had important social connections in Chicago. Through him, I met Mary Lasker, the famed philan-
thropist, as their families were very close friends. I also had the pleasure of meeting Edgar Bergen, the famous ventriloquist who, with his
dummy, Charlie McCarthy, entertained for years on radio and later on
television, and whose daughter Candice is one of today's celebrities.

Robert was slim, about my weight and height. His cast off suits
did indeed fit me. He had black curly hair, black beady eyes, some old
juvenile acne-pitting of his face, and very white straight teeth, apparently well taken care of by orthodontists. He was quite conservative in
spite of his wealthy background. I recall his purchasing suits from
Stein's downtown "off the rack" and paying seventeen dollars a suit.
His comment was, "Everyone knows how rich I am, and when I wear a
suit they assume it costs one hundred dollars. Who would know the
difference?" Of course, I knew the difference when he was tired of some
of those seventeen dollar suits, he would hand them over to me saying,
"I hope you enjoy the suit as much I did."

My stint with Robert lasted two years, through freshman and
sophomore years, and then he was on his own. My employment with
Bob wasn't as lucrative as it could have been with Mary Stein, but our
relationship was a much more wholesome one, and it helped me learn
anatomy so well that I was hired as an anatomy assistant for the next
two years. I was thus able to earn extra money by doing what I enjoyed.

Three nights a week I was employed as a so-called lab technician
at the Woodlawn Hospital. This was a small hospital on the other side
of the Midway, and a short distance from my rooming house. It was a
small hospital with 100 beds, and not nearly as sophisticated as the famous Billings Hospital at the University of Chicago. But they needed
a technician at night to do routine blood counts and urinalysis, and I
needed the money, and knew how to do the tests. I studied between
calls and slept on a cot in the lab. In the late afternoons several times
weekly, I cleaned glassware in the lab of Dr. Charles Huggins, who became a Nobel recipient at a later date.

Medical research was constantly in progress in the labs of the
medical school and in the adjacent Billings Hospital. Dogs, rabbits,
small monkeys, guinea pigs, and horses were used in various experiments for developing pharmacological drugs, for vaccines, and for experimental surgical procedures. Animals seemed to sense what was

going on in the research labs. When we would walk home from school or the hospital, reeking from formaldehyde or other chemicals, a dog passing us on the same side of the street would quickly run to the other side. Often if they saw us coming a half a block away or more they would quickly turn tail and run off, yelping in fear! The widespread use of tissue cultures, biotechnology advances in gene manipulations, and D.N.A. experiences have today largely and judiciously reduced animal experimentation.

In the later half of my freshman year at the medical school I also obtained a position with Dr. Gustave, who was experimenting with rabbits. He attempted to learn if cobalt was a stimulant to the bone marrow. Would it increase the production of red blood cells? Initially, he made his rabbits partially anemic by bleeding procedures, and then injected a cobalt solution intravenously. He then checked the ensuing blood counts over a period of weeks to see if the injections stimulated red cell production. None of the animals were destroyed, and after a year of intense study, the research was discontinued as there was no improvement in the blood status. Dr. Gustave was tall, lean and athletic, and a delight to work with. He was jovial and told the best off color jokes. As he was a member of the Department of Medicine, he would often discuss hematological clinical disorders, and fascinated me with his descriptive presentations. I learned to recognize pernicious anemias, leukemias, and various bone marrow disorders early in my medical training.

Under his guidance, I developed excellent technique in injecting solutions into small veins of rabbits' ears. Dr. Gustave was very efficient and obsessive and disliked wasting time. A classical example of a "Type A" individual, he refused to leave the lab to go to the rest room to void, and constantly used the sink. Fortunately, he was six feet three and could easily reach the high lab sinks. I'm five-ten and tried it once and bruised myself. Since I preferred my deep masculine voice, I decided to use the rest rooms.

Upon completion of this research, I was reassigned to Dr. Sam Milson who was working with horses, attempting to develop an antiserum for meningitis. In this lab we injected increasing doses of partially attenuated (weakened) meningococcic organisms. These were injected intravenously, increasing the doses weekly in an attempt to develop antibodies to the devastating bacteria. We hoped to produce a serum that would have sufficient antibodies to counteract the ill effects of the meningococcic organism when it infected humans. The theory was to reproduce what was accomplished for tetanus (lockjaw). The tetanus antitoxin was developed by injection of increasing dosages of the gram negative organism into a horse, and serum was developed that contained high titers of antibodies. This serum was used for prophylaxis and for the treatment of tetanus infection.

Dr. Milson was a rather effeminate, precise prim and proper researcher. In appearance and manner, he bore marked resemblance to the late Truman Capote. His voice was high pitched and scratchy, and he was extremely irritable, excessively fussy and fidgety, and very apprehensive and fearful of any contamination. He took his temperature four or five times daily and was continually checking his scrawny neck to be sure he hadn't become infected with the meningococcic bug. Actually, given his peculiarities, I was more frightened of being attacked by "Prissy Milson" than I was of being infected by the meningitis bacteria.

The research was very delicate, and we had to be extremely careful, using meticulous prophylactic measures, for inhalation or accidental injection of the organism would produce a case of active meningitis. The techniques we mastered were invaluable! We learned surgical aseptic technique and practiced it thoroughly. Fortunately, during the months we worked on this project, there were no incidences of cross-infection. Coincidentally, during that same year, the sulfonamides were discovered by Domagk and were very successful in combating the meningococcic organism, both prophylactically and therapeutically. At this point, our program was discontinued.

Thus by selling shoes on Saturdays, working at the Woodlawn Hospital, tutoring Bob, and assisting in the various research projects, I was able to maintain myself.

*   *   *   *   *

In the first semester we studied anatomy, biochemistry, histology, and physiology. We were told to report to the Anatomy Lab on the first Monday in September at 8:00 A.M. Eagerly, all hundred of us climbed the four flights up the wooden staircase and entered the Anatomy Lab to be immediately overwhelmed by our first exposure to the pungent fumes of formaldehyde. It really was brutal to be thus initiated. There they were, twenty-five nude bodies stretched out on metal slabs high enough so that dissection could be done in the standing position. The letter we received had instructed us to purchase either *William's* or *Gray's Anatomy* book, and a book on dissection (either the legendary *Sabotta* or the newer *Spalteholtz Atlas*). I had no problem choosing between those books because I couldn't afford either of them and planned on borrowing and utilizing the library. I did, however, bring my dissecting set, which I had acquired during my third year in pre-med. It consisted of one hemostat, a dull scalpel, a pair of scissors, two probes, a tissue tweezers, and a small ruler.

We found our names on little cards set at the various tables. Our group of four was assigned to an elderly emaciated female cadaver with long gray sparse hair, dry skin, and an open jaw that seemed to sneer at us in a creepy way. I persuaded myself to think of her strictly as an anatomy specimen, not a former living human being. This was not the atmosphere of a quiet clean funeral home surrounded by scented flowers and loving mourners; it was a cold morgue with twenty-five unknown deads with whom we were soon to develop a very close association!

We looked about, but there were no instructors around. We stood patiently and waited and waited, but no one appeared to discuss the approach to the dissection. Apparently this was done by design; the purpose was to test our initiative, and to remind us that we were not going to be "spoon-fed" as we were medical students of the University of Chicago under Robert Maynard Hutchins' philosophy of education. My three lab partners and I stood around avoiding looking at the body, scratching our heads, frustrated and wondering what to do first. Finally, we introduced ourselves, read the dissecting manual, and decided to proceed. One of the partners was Sidney Smith, a native of Chicago, the nephew of a prominent obstetrician-gynecologist who headed the department at the prestigious Michael Reese Hospital. Louis Jacobson, a Swedish former school teacher from Nebraska, was the other partner, and the fourth was a young man from the Bronx, Morris Katz.

Louis had an air of authority and maturity about him and we felt encouraged by his presence. He opened the book and said, "Gentlemen, it appears we have to start dissecting the extremities." So, unsupervised and tremulous, we proceeded to read, cut, probe, and tear. Studying the drawings in the dissecting book we searched for muscles, ligaments, tendons, blood vessels, lymphatics, and nerves of the extremities. Sidney was very agile with his probe, had no hesitation in removing the skin and proceeding with accurate identification of the various structures. Morris was hesitant and I noticed he avoided looking at the face and kept looking about for an assistant or a professor for guidance. Apparently he had been "spoon-fed" during his pre-med courses in New York, and he seemed agitated and insecure. An hour passed and still no instructor appeared to help in our struggle to dissect. The quietness of the lab and the anxiety that was ever present among us was suddenly interrupted by the giggling of four female students who had been assigned to the body of a huge, black, middle-aged male. Our group was close enough to the girls' table to see the source of their humor. It seems that one of them had the temerity to lift the cadaver's huge penis, and the other three were ogling at its unbelievable size. Sidney went to their table and told the girls: "If you think they're all that way, you're going to have a surprise coming." With that, the rest of the students burst out laughing, and this helped to ease the tension.

A KNIFE IN THE HEART

Morris Katz was ascetic in appearance, chubby, short, and unathletic. Extremely myopic, he wore horn-rimmed thick lenses. He smiled frequently but inappropriately and never looked at the person he addressed. He perspired freely and had a hesitant tremor of the hand. During dissection he would identify a nerve or muscle, verify it in the dissecting manual, go back and reidentify the nerve or muscle, and once again return to the manual and again back to the anatomy specimen. This hesitancy, accompanied by perspiration and the nervous grin was a bit annoying to the rest of us. But we ignored this irritating habit because we liked him, and soon realized that he was an obsessive-compulsive person, aiming for perfection. Sensing that Morris was a dependent type, I tried to assume the role of the big brother.

On several occasions after classes and before I went to my various jobs, I would walk with him along the Midway and discuss his family background, his thoughts, ambitions, and his reactions to the medical school environment. He was a very poor boy from the Bronx, also on scholarship, and pre-med Phi Beta Kappa. He admitted that he had worked very, very hard at Columbia to obtain this enviable record. His scholarship at the University of Chicago was actually a half-scholarship toward tuition. He deemed that he would be unable to work during the time he was studying. He felt it would take all of his energy and thought processes to keep the grades necessary to maintain this scholarship. Both his mother and father, Russian immigrants, worked in a small tailor shop in New York and apparently were sacrificing considerably to send him to medical school.

It was terribly important to him to succeed in medicine to justify their long hours of work and their self-denials. Morris studied day and night and on weekends, without let-up. We could never get him to join us on a date, just sit around to play cards, or go to the movies. The only interruption from his studies was our occasional walks along the gardened Midway.

In class, when called upon to answer a question, he would jerkily project himself from his seat, look about with his vulnerable eyes, sweat profusely and develop a fine hand tremor. Then, with slight stutter he would answer the question. In the quiet environment of his room, there was no doubt that he mastered his material and could calmly discuss it, but when called upon by a professor, he seemed at total loss, appearing not to remember any of the things he had learned, or if he did remember, he was unable to present the information in its correct form. This became increasingly worrisome to Morris and especially to his dissecting partners in anatomy.

One day during a lecture in histology, he suddenly jumped from his seat, rushed down the aisle, and out the exit. We did not see him for the rest of the day. He came to classes the next day, smiling broadly and inappropriately, again his forehead wet with perspiration, but calmer than he had been for the week or two prior to the incident of his dramatic classroom departure. I invited him to join me at the Hillel House on campus. I thought it would be good for him to meet and socialize with the young undergraduate co-eds. He promised to call me on Friday night to set up the Hillel House meeting for Saturday. He did not call on Friday nor did he call Saturday morning. I phoned several times but there was no answer. He avoided the social meeting.

The following Monday we studied the anatomy of the heart. We saw the auricles, the so-called appendages that look like ears, the right and left atrium of the heart, the ventricles, the valves: tricuspid, pulmonary, mitral, and aortic; the differential thickness of the left and right myocardium (muscles of the heart), the large pulmonary vessel leading off from the right side of the heart to the lungs, and the large aorta emerging from the left side and starting its tortuous course throughout the entire body. We identified the return vessels, the large superior and inferior vena cava veins into the right atrium, and then the return of the four pulmonary veins from the lungs into the left atrium. It was fascinating to all of us.

I noticed Morris seriously measuring the various appendages and various ventricles of the heart. We all had learned that the apex of the heart, the conical part of the left ventricle, reached normally to the fifth interspace, between the ribs, approximately eight centimeters from the mid-sternal (breast bone) line. This was to be the gauge for the normal adult heart, and any deviation would either be a smaller heart or an enlarged heart. The next day was quiz day at the tableside of the cadaver, and our assistant in anatomy queried us thoroughly. Morris did indeed know his stuff. He was especially fascinated with the heart; he knew all of its dimensions and its positions. He deftly indicated the location of the apex of the heart in the fifth interspace, eight centimeters from the mid-sternal line. He seemed more cheerful that day, and when we all went out to lunch he even cracked a few jokes, unusual for Morris. It was a relief to see that the severe tension seemed to have eased. The next two days he did not appear at any classes, lectures, or labs. The following day he presented himself for a few hours in the morning, but after lunch did not return. After missing him on Wednesday and Thursday, we became apprehensive.

On Friday morning at 7:30 A.M., I went to his rooming house to see if he would attend classes that day. I knocked several times. No response. I thought perhaps he was in the bathroom down the hall. I checked, but it was empty. I returned to his room again and loudly banged on the door yelling, "Morris, it's me," but still receiving no response. I tried the door and found it unlocked. Upon opening it I stood ftozen in abject horror, for there I saw Morris, stretched out on the floor, naked to the waist. There was a black crayon circle on his body at the fifth interspace, eight and one-half centimeters from the mid-sternal line, and projecting into the middle of the circle was a large eight-inch butcher knife plunged into his left ventricle! There was clotted blood all over his chest, spreading down the left side of his abdomen. He had a relaxed smile on his face with eyes staring wide open. He apparently had been dead for at least twenty-four hours. The shock of seeing him thus brought an immediate sensation of nausea and I could not keep from vomiting. I forced myself to feel the pulse but, of course, there was none; he was already cold and rigor mortis had set in. I rushed to the phone and fearfully called the Dean's office.

Our group of three were deeply saddened and developed a tremendous sense of guilt. Why didn't we recognize that Morris was suicidal? What should we have done to prevent this great tragedy? We later learned that Morris had been talking to the Dean about his deep depression and had actually consulted a psychiatrist for the past several months. He had endured all of this quietly, without telling his friends. We also discovered that an older brother had committed suicide five years earlier by plunging from the fifth story of a building in the Bronx. The brother had been a brilliant student in the school of engineering at New York University. This was our first introduction to familial incidences of various diseases. I learned later when in active practice that there are as many as 25,000 suicides yearly in the USA, and that there is an extremely high incidence among physicians, and especially among psychiatrists.

Morris was apparently guilt-ridden and was losing his self-esteem as he realized that he was not learning at the rate of his competency. Though he was apparently looking for help, no one appreciated the depths of his grief. I learned then, what we all experience when someone close to us or dear to us dies, the lingering questions: was there something else we should have done or could have done?

For several weeks after this tragic episode, the three of us tried to cheer one another with practical jokes. At lunchtime we asked Sidney to reach into his pocket for some supposed notes, from which he withdrew a section of a cadaver's liver that we planted and that precluded him from completing his liverwurst sandwich we had suggested he order.

We then collaborated on a scheme to play a trick on another student, Carl Gray. It seems that Carl was quite proud of his very high IQ, which was indeed spectacular, ranging at 162. This was brought up frequently by him and, frankly, the rest of us were tired of listening to how bright he was. So, we concocted a scheme.

Carl was told that a call had come in, while he was in anatomy class, from the psychology department. They were using electroencephalogram studies to accumulate evidence among superior people for scientific publication. They had records of Carl's unusually high IQ and requested that he please be at the psychology department on the sixth floor promptly at 6:00 that evening. It was 5:30 when we told him of the concocted story. The psychology department was at the diametric opposite end of the campus and we knew that he would have to rush to get there on time, and as there was no elevator in the psychology building, he would have to run up the stairs. Further, what he didn't know was that the building only had five floors. There was no sixth floor! We sent him off on this errant chase and waited gleefully to see his dejected response when he returned. We wondered whether he would tell us truthfully that he had rushed to the building late, climbed the five floors, and probably found only a janitor to alert him to the fact that not only was there no sixth floor and that no one in the building had electroencephalograms. We never heard again of Carl's superior IQ.

*   *   *   *   *

My freshman year was a very busy year because, in addition to the usual scheduled subjects for first year medical students, I simultaneously enrolled in classes of comparative anatomy, histology, and psychology in order to complete my fourth year of pre-med. At the end of my first year of medical school I also was able to obtain my BS in anatomy and went through the customary elaborate convocation services with cap and gown at the end of that year. Between studying for my Bachelor of Science degree, completing my first year of medical school, tutoring Robert Wilson, working as a technician at Woodlawn Hospital in the evenings and in the labs of the various research areas, I was kept thoroughly busy. With the tragic loss of my friend, Morris, it was quite a sobering year. I was maturing.

My second year of medical school was a happier one. I enjoyed the subjects tremendously, and had a special situation offered me for which I am forever grateful. Sidney Smith, whose home was in Chicago, became a close friend and invited me to live with his family during the sophomore year. The Smiths lived in Hyde Park, in an apartment on the fourth floor at 5536 Cornell. There was no elevator, but I was extremely happy to ascend the four stories and reach into the warmth of that home and family. Sara Smith, Sidney's mother, was a delight. She was an attractive woman with luminous, pale skin, small uptilted nose, a constant smile, and oozed a maternally affectionate personality. She made me feel as if I were one of her sons. Phillip, Sidney's older brother, was an interior designer. He showed no resentment of the fact that his mother and Sidney, with the father's permission, had invited me to live with them.

The apartment was close to the Lake Michigan residential area that included beautiful apartments and hotels, each of which had its own swimming pool, gardens, tennis courts, bridal paths and a large common marina off Lakeshore Drive. A five minute walk to this plush area afforded great opportunity for relaxation. I hoped that, if I were to become a successful physician, I might live in a similar manner. I had my own room in the Smith's apartment and ate breakfast and dinner with the family, and Mrs. Smith did my laundry. The entire house was at my disposal. Knowing how poor I was, Mama Smith charged a minimal amount for my room and board. I am sure she lost money in this enterprise. Sidney and I studied together and walked the two miles to and from school daily. It was especially arduous during the cold winter. At times the temperature ranged from 20 to 30 degrees below zero, and we sloshed our way through deep snow until we reached the school, my newly grown mustache frozen with ice crystals.

The tranquility at the end of the second year was shattered by a terrible tragedy. Phillip, Sidney's brother, had taken his mother for a ride. Sarah loved rides and as they were driving down 55th Street in front of the dime theater, a car came careening across their path, crashed into their vehicle on Sarah's side, and threw her out of the car. She was bleeding profusely from a severe laceration in the neck. Phillip, who was unhurt rushed out of the car and not knowing the various pressure points for stopping hemorrhage in the neck, helplessly and tragically watched his mother bleed to death before help came. This was too ironical to accept. If only Sidney had been in the car, he would have known how to staunch this massive loss of blood, and she would have survived. It was a great loss to the Smith family, to their friends, and to me, for I felt like one of her children.

THE UNTOUCHABLES

In Chicago, the years 1935 through 1939 were the Al Capone era. Striving against the formidable organized crime mob were the "Untouchables," those federal agents who attempted to restore law and order. The "feds" must have earned their nickname because there were wild shoot-outs on the streets of Chicago with the bad guys falling down wounded or killed, and the good guys emerging untouched from sprays of machine gun fire.

My medical school years at the University of Chicago spanned that very era. But in my perspective the "Untouchables" were the faculty of the school. The great deities of medicine, they had all-encompassing knowledge and they were inspired teachers, brilliant researchers, excellent diagnosticians, and humanistic doctors. To me they were truly untouchable, as they were unforgettable.

*   *   *   *   *

Swedish born, Dr. Anton J. Carlson appeared the typical mad scientist. With necktie askew, wrinkled shirt, pants much too long and dragging after him, shoes that had forgotten their shine, rumpled

jacket, and unruly, uncombed rust-colored hair. He was affectionately
known as "Old A. J." He spoke with a slight lisp and constantly blew
his nose, adding voluminous excretions into an already too-dirty hand-
kerchief. On occasion he was known to use his lower right hand desk
drawer as a spittoon. Dr. Carlson was a very colorful figure and had
been at the university approximately ten years prior to my meeting
him in my freshman year in biochemistry. A passionate scholar, he had
done brilliant research work in the physiology of the gastrointestinal
tract.

He was best known in medical literature for his follow-up work
on Pavlov's famous canine experiments. Dr. Carison was one of the
first to recognize the effect of hydrochloric acid in the production of
peptic ulcer, and developed beautiful research programs to prove it. A
good deal of his research was carefully and skillfully done by studying
a patient who was shot in the abdomen and unfortunately the wound
did not heal. Since there had been no healing, there was a direct opening to the exterior from his stomach, a sort of artificial stoma. Dr.
Carlson recognized that there was a living laboratory in which he could
study the mucous membranes of the stomach. Using a small scope and
pipettes, he was able to obtain the various enzymes and hydrochloric
acid and mucous concentrations produced by the stomach under various conditions. This in effect represented a human equivalent of Pavlov's dog. He studied the color and texture of the mucous membrane of
the stomach as well as the productions of enzymes and peptides and hydrochloric acid under situations of stress and strain, happiness, lack of
sleep, and during pain. He also studied the effect of various pharmacological drugs on the upper intestinal tract through his stoma. His
early experiments proved that hydrochloric acid was an etiological
(causative) factor in the production of peptic ulcer, and antacids were
needed to promote healing. Thus were born the Gelusil, Maalox, and
Tagamet, et al., that made pharmacological industries and stockhold-
ers rich.

When we studied the microscopic appearance of urine in his class,
A. J. requested that we each analyze our own urine under the microscope. As he went from table to table peering into the various scopes
and checking the written analyses, he stopped abruptly at Helen's desk
as he peeked at her urine specimen. "Madam," he lisped out loud, "are
you married?" "No," she retorted, "Why do you ask?" "Because," he
answered, "the motile sperm in your specimen tells me you better get
married or use a better spermicidal jelly!" She was not alone in her as-

tonished, humiliated embarrassment. The tall freckled face student behind her bumped his urine specimen bottle which crashed on the tile floor as he awkwardly pretended to adjust his microscope, futilely attempting to hide his joint mortification.

One gray Monday morning, Carlson shuffled into the classroom late and irritable, looked at all of us scornfully, and then asked with his lisping shrill voice, "Who knows the theory of coagulation?" I had borrowed Howell's book on physiology from the library the night before, and knowing today's subject would deal with blood and its various properties, I read up on coagulation. Therefore with an eagerly, outstretched hand, I jumped up, prepared to show Dr. Carlson I knew my stuff. Old A. J. looked at me, sighed, and then said: "OK, Youngster! Come down to the blackboard and write out the formula!"

I approached the blackboard with assurance, took the chalk he handed me, and wrote out the complicated formula for coagulation, which I had memorized the night before from the physiology text book. I turned around to him, waiting for approval. Instead, he scratched his head and asked: "Sonny, what is your evidence for this theory?"

"This is the theory that I read presented by Dr. Howell in his book on physiology," I assured him confidently.

"I know that," he replied. "But what is *your* evidence that this theory is correct? Did you do the experiments to check Howell's theory? Have you checked it with any other physiologists? Have you talked to any hematologists to see if it works?" I stood before the class, partly humiliated and wholly enlightened. I learned more from A. J. Carlson in those few minutes than I learned through many years of exposure to other informed teachers. Dr. Carlson taught me that in medicine one does not take anything for granted. One must prove and recheck again and again before assuming that what is printed is correct. Throughout the years, I continued to remember A. J. Carlson and the lesson learned from this episode. Whenever I read poorly written articles in medical journals, or pursued research that could not be substantiated, or was dismayed to learn of research that had been fabricated, I thought of him. A. J. taught me to approach every problem in internal medicine critically, never to "shoot from the hip" with its resulting disastrous mistakes.

Another very important lesson A. J. taught his neophyte medical students was to be wary of confused conclusions drawn from research experiments. "Critically analyze," he would shriek at us, "think it through, don't accept a theory unless it unquestionably makes sense." Then he proceeded to tell the classical story of the researcher who conducted the following simple experiment with a simpleminded deduction:

A scientist placed a frog on his forearm at the junction of the elbow, with the palm facing upward. He quietly said to the frog "Jump!" and the frog jumped about four inches. Then in a voice twice as loud he yelled, "Jump!" This time the frog jumped eight inches. He placed the frog back again at the crease of the elbow and shouted very loudly, "Jump!" and the frightened frog jumped from the elbow down the entire length of the forearm to the floor. He then picked up the frog and tore off both hind legs. He placed the frog again at the starting point. Once again he said quietly, "Jump!" The frog did not move. Then he yelled, "Jump!" Again, the frog did not move. Finally he trumpeted loudly, "JUMP!" The frog still did not budge. "Gentlemen," he addressed his audience, "I have just proved that frogs hear with their hind legs!"

*   *   *   *   *

During the early part of the winter, anti-vivisectionists created quite a furor in Chicago, complaining in large newspaper headlines and constant radio accusations that the group at the Billings Hospital were mercilessly using animals for research and should be stopped. A. J. was called as one of the witnesses for the research group. The president of the anti-vivisectionist group sat on the witness chair and gave a long tirade against the Frankenstein-type physicians at Billings Hospital who were using animals to improve their skills, when it wasn't necessary to sacrifice these wonderful creatures that God put on our earth.

It was a chilly February morning and the courtroom was very cold. Dr. Carlson asked to interrogate this witness and was permitted to do so by the judge.

"Mrs. MacHenry," he said drolly as he scratched his head, "I noticed that you are quite cold this morning."

"Of course," she replied, "and I am dealing with a cold subject."

Dr. Carlson continued, "and I noticed that you are wearing your coat and you have a fur collar around your neck."

"Yes, it is very cold in this courtroom," she replied.

"Madam, may I asked what type of fur collar that is?"

"Squirrel," she answered.

Dr. Carlson stood up, walked over to her, and lisped in his Swedish accent, "Do you think it is more important for someone to kill a squirrel so that you could have a fur collar around your neck than to destroy an animal to save your neck?"

She became terribly embarrassed, flushed, said she did not want to speak anymore, and quickly departed the witness chair. There were no problems from the anti-vivisectionists for a number of years after that courtroom scene.

A recent paradoxical decision was made by a large state university research center. The foundation infected thirty-seven chimpanzees with AIDS and hepatitis viruses but decided it was unethical to kill the animals and instead set up a $1.7 million fund to provide them with a "retirement" home!

*   *   *   *   *

Dr. Dallas B. Phemister was chief of surgery at Billings Hospital during my years at the University of Chicago Medical School and for ten years thereafter. He was lean, tall, had penetrating, coal black inimical eyes, and heavy black eyebrows. His brow was always furrowed, as though he were critically observing everyone around him in addition to his patients. When he strode into a room, everyone was aware that Dr. Phemister was there. He looked, and was, dynamic. His surgical skill was legendary, the envy of everyone on the surgical service, but he was distant and unapproachable. His theory was that the "laying on of hands" only worked when one had on surgical gloves and used a scalpel, a hemostat, a retractor or surgical needles. As externs on his service, we feared him, respected him, but idolized him. In his remote fashion, he seemed to delight in the shock approach to teaching and was a master of theatrics.

Our surgical amphitheater consisted of concentric rows of seats looking down at the pit where Dr. Phemister presented the surgical patients. He would discuss the case in great detail and never tolerated questions from the students. If you interrupted him you were invariably asked to leave the surgical theater.

Charles Hartley, a young man who was a heavy smoker, was wheeled into the amphitheater one morning and his case history presented. Dr. Phemister discussed his diagnosis of Buerger's disease, an inflammatory disease of the walls of the arteries, veins, and nerves. By virtue of this inflammatory process, obliteration of the lumen (opening) of blood vessels occurred so that circulation was markedly impaired. The pathology of the blood vessels also was complicated by frequent episodes of bloodclotting within the lumen (thrombosis). Mr.

Hartley appeared to be in deep pain. His extremities all seemed atrophic and there were gangrenous ulcerations on his finger tips, as they had been deprived of normal circulation. His neck was scrawny, his face was drawn, he was slightly cyanotic, coughed constantly and indeed looked to be in an advanced state of malnutrition and dehydration, and seemed to be confused as to his whereabouts. After presentation of the case, the patient was wheeled out and the next case brought in.

The following week when we met for the session, the resident brought in a large tray with a number of gauze wrapped organs, which he carefully unfolded. Dr. Phemister strode into the room, pointed to the organs in the tray and said, "Gentlemen, may I reintroduce you again to Mr. Hartley who died last night." With that, he passed the tray around to the students. This, of course, was for shock effect. There followed a discussion of the full pathology of the disease and the advanced condition as seen in the pathological specimens. Although this was a real jolt to our sensibilities, the case was presented with full impact. I'm sure all the students remembered Buerger's disease for the rest of their medical careers and from then on promoted abstinence from tobacco.

Dr. Phemister had particular interest in bone disease and probably knew more about it than the orthopedic surgeons and pathologists. One day he discussed a condition known as aseptic necrosis of the hip. This was an area in which he was an expert, having spent considerable years of study and research on this problem. He presented the x-rays, discussed the clinical condition, and then made mention that a new enzyme, known as alkaline phosphatase, had recently been identified as a marker for various bone diseases. This, he said, was a tip-off for the diagnosis of aseptic necrosis (a destructive disease of the hip bone) wherein the newly discovered enzyme, alkaline phosphatase, was lowered.

Sitting next to me was a heavily-bearded, short, ruddy-faced, red-haired, older student, who jumped up from his seat, called down hoarsely with a Russian accent to Dr. Phemister in the pit. "Dr. Phemister, alkaline phosphatase in aseptic necrosis is *elevated,* not lowered!"

There was a deathly silence in the amphitheater and Dr. Phemister looked up at this student, aimed one of his piercing hostile looks, with the veins in his forehead protruding, and then turned to the class again. "Gentlemen, as I was saying, in aseptic necrosis, alkaline phosphatase, the new enzyme that we have recently learned about, is lowered!"

Up jumped the student again, waving his arms wildly, and again repeated hoarsely in his foreign accent, "Dr. Phemister, alkaline phosphatase is increased in aseptic necrosis!"

No one had ever questioned, let alone contradicted, Dr. Phemister, and it was apparent to all of us that this older student was doomed! Dr. Phemister asked the gentleman to sit down and proceeded to report that he had just returned from Galveston, Texas, where Dr. Bodansky, head of the department of physiological chemistry, had developed the enzyme studies and had indicated that alkaline phosphatase was indeed lowered in aseptic necrosis.

Again the student jumped up, braving the shocked glances of his fellow students. "But Dr. Phemister," he said, "I am Bodansky!" Taken aback, Dr. Phemister made an unprecedented apology and invited Dr. Bodansky to come down to the pit to lecture on alkaline phosphatase. It seems that Dr. Bodansky, who had his Ph.D. in biological chemistry, was teaching at the medical school in Galveston. A recent ruling made it necessary to have an M.D. degree to continue teaching in the medical school. He had come to the University of Chicago to sit in on the lectures, take clinical courses, and then take the comprehensive exams for his M.D. That was the reason for his presence in Dr. Phemister's course, and the great surgeon had not been informed that Bodansky would be at this session. We all enjoyed this interlude immensely. Imagine! Someone had corrected Dr. Phemister and survived!

*   *   *   *   *

One New Year's Eve, as a second year extern, I was assigned to Phemister's surgical service. Along with disgruntled nurses, technicians, interns, and residents, I had to spend New Year's Eve on the ward. At exactly ten minutes to midnight there was a great commotion at the elevator door. An unbelievable sight presented itself. An intern sat astride the horse that was used for producing the serum for meningitis, and he rode the horse off the elevator. Totally inebriated, he galloped up and down the corridors of the surgical ward, back and forth until the nurses, with the aid of the orderlies, quieted the intern down, took him off the horse, and put him into a side room to sober up. They then led the stallion back into the elevator, returned him to the fifth floor, and locked him back in his stall in the research lab. We all decided to keep very quiet about this incident. If Dr. Phemister were to discover what had happened there is no doubt that would have been the end of this young doctor's career.

The following morning on rounds Dr. Phemister, surrounded by his usual entourage of externs, interns, residents, and nurses, all bowing to him obsequiously, holding his charts, presenting one patient after another, arrived at the bedside of Mrs. Goldberg, who had had her gallbladder removed two days previously.

"How are you feeling, Mrs. Goldberg?" Dr. Phemister asked.

"Doctor," she answered, "I had a terrible nightmare last night. You won't believe it. All night long I kept dreaming that somebody was riding a horse up and down the corridors here, up and down, and it scared the life out of me!"

Dr. Phemister turned to the resident and said, "Dr. Jones, we're going to have to change her night medication. Stop the phenobarbital, it's giving her bad dreams. Let's try giving her chloral hydrate." With that he strode to the next bedside. The rest of us kept biting our lips to stifle our laughter. We truly enjoyed the scenario of Mrs. Goldberg's nightmare.

*   *   *   *   *

Dr. Huggins, the urologist, was an excellent lecturer. He was an attractive man, with thinning hair, steel blue eyes, hair turning gray, no facial wrinkles, about forty-five years of age, short, agile, moved very rapidly, had a razor-sharp mind, and arrived at diagnoses quickly, concisely, and correctly. There was no doubt in all our minds that we were dealing with a brilliant man. Indeed, several years later he won the Nobel Prize in medicine for his spectacular advances in treatment for cancer of the prostate. I worked in Dr. Huggins's lab, cleaning glassware and learning to assay hormone concentrations in urine. Following his intuition, he soon determined that the concentration of androgenic steroids (male hormones) in elderly men who had carcinoma of the prostate was very high. This was not so for those who merely had the enlarged prostate found in men who had reached fifty. He realized that if this high titer of steroids could be depressed, perhaps the growth and spread of the cancer could be retarded. Convinced of this theory, he started his approach to remove the testes (orchidectomy) in men who had advanced cancer of the prostate. Simultaneously, or independently with the orchidectomy, he proposed the administration of large doses of female estrogenic hormone. The theory was brilliant and results were spectacular in patients with intractable pain due to cancer of the prostate that metastasized (spread) to the bones, and in those with widespread metastases to the lungs. After orchidectomy and/or the use of large doses of female hormones, the pain of the various metastases would subside and the growths began to resolve rapidly. X-rays would reveal resolution of the bone pathology and the lungs would clear miraculously. This was one of the first early great advances against cancer. In addition to the Huggins' approach, in advanced carcinomas of the prostate, today various platinum chemical derivatives and radon seeds are also used.

Huggins would invite the clinical students on his service for 4:00 tea every afternoon. At that time we would crowd into his small office, occupy the few chairs, and the rest sprawled on the floor to listen to him discuss clinical cases in a calm, relaxed, informal, informative manner. One morning he presented himself on rounds with two black eyes, a swelling of the right ear, a large bruise on the left cheek, and he limped as he walked. It seems that at 3:00 A.M. the previous night he had heard a commotion in his downstairs library. Obtaining a flashlight, he stealthily climbed down the stairs and shone the light into the eyes of a housebreaker. Most of us would have run back up the stairs and locked the door. Dr. Huggins was accustomed to tackling problems. He tackled the burglar, brought him down to the floor, held him while his wife called the police, had him bound and ready for arrest within twenty minutes. Of course, he was bruised and showed all the marks of his heroic experience the night before. He was soundly criticized by all the members of the faculty, and was reminded that he was forty-five years old, and too important an individual to have exposed himself to such danger. But he laughed and said, "I did it, didn't I?" And so he said after getting his Nobel Prize after four years of intense research, "I did it, didn't I?"

He was not too happy to have female students in his classes, and frequently made them uncomfortable. He would ask them embarrassing questions, and insisted that they learn how to do rectal examinations on the males to become familiar with the feel of the prostate gland. He warned that they must lose all modesty for they were going to have to examine male patients.

One day, in the surgical amphitheater, he discussed the path of the gonococcus organism in the male. It starts at the meatus (opening) of the urethra at the very end of the penis, travels back through the urethra to the bladder and prostate gland, and then to the seminal vesicles. He asked one of the women students to come down as he was discussing the case, while the patient was lying on the examining table. He threw back the sheet, exposing the young man's genitalia, and asked the young lady to put on a surgical glove. He then told her to hold the penis and discuss the course of the gonococcus from the meatus backward. She blushed, was hesitant, but realized that she had better follow through or lose her position in the class. She gingerly lifted the penis, and started to discuss the gonococcus entering the meatus, the opening, and traveling down the shaft of the penis towards the bladder. Dr. Huggins, who had a terrific sense of humor, said to her, "Miss Baker, you don't have to hold it up to describe it anymore. Now it will stand up by itself." Which it did!

*   *   *   *   *

The chief of gastroenterology at the University of Chicago Clinics was an expert clinician. Dr. Waiter Palmer had a better rapport with patients than any teacher. He was a contemporary practitioner who excelled in the art of "laying on of the hands." He believed that it was of paramount importance to touch the patient to gain rapport. When he walked to the bedside, he came in with a broad smile, approached the patient, held his hand outstretched to shake hands. He then sat on the edge of the bed, smiled again, exuding warmth and interest, and called the patient by first name. He took detailed medical histories, dwelling not only on the patient's immediate complaints, but also eliciting information about the family, education, employment, and past medical history.

One of the more difficult diagnoses is that of "functional bowel distress" (spastic colon). This condition mimics any and all gastrointestinal complaints. Dr. Palmer was the pioneer who wrote extensively about this disorder and taught many gastroenterologists how to recognize this previously misunderstood clinical entity. He demonstrated the importance of studying the patient psychologically as well as physically and the necessity of determining their stresses and strains and their reactions to them.

The intestinal tract may react with nausea, vomiting, loose bowels, constipation or cramping when one is confronted with a disturbing situation. The degree and the intensity varying with the patient's threshold.

If the upper intestinal tract (stomach and duodenum) are the focus of the reactions, then a peptic ulcer may develop. If the lower bowel is the site that responds, then it is the "functional bowel syndrome" that occurs.

Diet, low residue foods, brans, rest, and antispasmodics do help the lower intestinal tract, but the elucidation of causative factors that produce this condition must be explored and their importance explained to the patient. When the problems were discussed freely, there often was a tremendous amelioration of symptoms.

On rare occasions, Palmer felt it necessary to refer the patients for psychological help. But, for the most part, his demeanor and approach to the case resulted in the patient's recognizing the problem followed by marked improvement.

* * * * *

One Monday evening the surgical resident was called to see Kevin Brown, an orthopedic resident, who presented some alarming abdominal symptoms.

Kevin was a strikingly handsome, tall, confident, extremely capable young doctor. He was also an exceptional tennis player, the star of the University's tennis league, and had won the men's singles competition that year. He and his partner, June Colmer, the wife of a prominent staff man, were to play in a doubles tournament the following day. The large gallery that came to applaud this twosome every time they played came not only to see championship quality tennis, but to ogle June, who was as lithe and lovely at twenty-nine and the mother of two children as she had been at nineteen, when she was a beauty queen.

Kevin, writhing in pain, was concerned that he would not be able to play in the tournament. I was on duty as an extern when Stanton Smith, the surgical resident, responded to Kevin's frantic call late that evening.

I accompanied him to the E.R. to meet Kevin. We found the ordinarily calm, confident resident agitated and in severe distress. He reported that he had suddenly developed unbearable, excruciating pain in the right upper quadrant of his abdomen. After questioning and examining Kevin, Stanton was at a loss for a clear-cut diagnosis. He had ruled out acute appendicitis, found the gallbladder normal, and found no discernable abdominal pathology except for a doughy, spastic, exceedingly tender bulge in the region of the large intestine. Stanton thought it might be in the pancreatic area, but with negative lab tests, no fever and the indiscrete bulge deep in the abdomen, he was uncertain of his diagnosis.

Since this was prior to the development of the CAT scan and MRI, routine flat and lateral x-rays of the abdomen were taken, which revealed diffuse, gaseous, spastic loops of bowel. Stanton very kindly pointed these out to me, the neophyte extern, and I was thrilled to be a part of this intriguing diagnostic workup.

However, in an afternote, the radiologist raised a red flag, reporting that he had noticed a lemon sized pancreatic cyst with a thin, calcified rim. But, all the routine lab and enzyme studies for the pancreas were normal, and there was no physical evidence for rupture, inflammation or hemorrhage in the bowel.

During the x-ray studies, Kevin, usually controlled and imperturbable, groaned with pain. His entire bowel was irritable and sensitive to the slightest touch. He was tremulous, perspiring freely and tearful. He needed help badly and Stanton, unable to make a definite diagnosis, concluded that a surgical exploratory procedure was indicated and surgery was scheduled for 7:00 A.M. the next morning.

Apparently, Kevin asked that Dr. Palmer be called in consultation, and although past midnight, Dr. Palmer arrived. He entered the room, smiled, shook Kevin's hand, and sat down on the edge of the bed. He listened intently to the history, reviewed the x-rays and lab reports, and turned reassuringly to Kevin and said, "When you started your internship here five years ago, routine x-rays of the chest and abdomen were routinely taken. I would like to review those earlier films."

He sent me, the lowly extern, to the film library for the old x-rays. When I rushed back, proudly clutching the films, Dr. Palmer put them on the view box, studied them intently, and then turned to Kevin and me.

"There it is," he said. "The *same* lemon size pancreatic cyst with its thin calcified lining, unchanged in the five years. There are no indications of rupture, hemorrhage or inflammation. It is a congenital cyst (present at birth) of no consequence."

Kevin was beginning to relax, and Dr. Stanton and I were fascinated with the Sherlock Holmes approach! Then skillfully, with gentle and experienced tactile palpations, Dr. Palmer proceeded to minutely examine the already relaxed abdomen while questioning Kevin. "Is the pain aggravated by sitting up? By lying down? Is it altered by turning to either side? Does it increase when you *take a deep breath,* or decrease when you exhale?" Kevin responded that none of the changes affected the discomfort. At this point Dr. Palmer concluded that an acute spastic colon (functional bowel distress) was responsible for the apparent emergency.

Stanton had not yet finished his evening rounds, and responding to still another emergency call, left the room. I remained unobtrusively in the corner, anxious to follow this interesting case to its conclusion.

Dr Palmer, still sitting on the edge of the bed, decided to have a quiet intimate talk with Kevin. They had forgotten that I was still in the room, and so I became an unwitting eavesdropper.

"Kevin," he said, "I don't think this irritable bowel syndrome was brought on by tension about tomorrow's tennis tournament. You know you and June will win. Something else is alarming you. Feel free to tell me what emotional turmoil has tied your gut in knots."

Eyes downcast, embarrassed and tearful, Kevin admitted that prior to the onset of his symptoms, he had suffered a terrible jolt. It seems that his relationship with June had progressed beyond the "love" of tennis to the real thing, at least on his part. They had been involved in a passionate affair for the past three months, and even though she was several years older than he, Kevin was sure she was the ideal woman for him.

That evening, after practicing, they had gone to a motel together. After wonderful lovemaking he pleaded with June to leave her husband and start a new life with him in Wisconsin, where he had been invited to join a very successful orthopedic group.

"She called me a silly, immature boy," he said sadly, eyes downcast. "She told me our affair was just to have fun, similar to our experience on the tennis court. She loved her husband, children, and her life as the wife of a popular doctor, and she wouldn't give that up for me. She called me a 'nobody'."

With the confession, Kevin smiled wanly at Dr. Palmer and said, "I guess you think I'm an immature fool."

"Not at all," soothed the understanding doctor. "You have had a traumatic experience. It's no wonder your colon is spastic."

"June told me she never wanted to see me again after tomorrow's tournament. I don't think I'll be able to play with her as a partner." "Son, you'll play just fine," reassured the doctor. He shook his head sympathetically, gave Kevin a fatherly pat on the shoulder. "Just add it up to life's experiences and go on! It won't be easy, but you'll get over her." With that he went to the phone and cancelled the scheduled exploratory surgery.

"I'm planning to come to see you play tomorrow," he said as he left the room, "and I expect you to win both the tennis tournament and the ability to put this episode with June behind you, as a 'no show' and get on with your life!"

This "untouchable" physician had perfected the technique of *touching* the patient physically and emotionally, and this was typical of the art that he left as a legacy to the students who came under his tutelage.

CALL ME DOCTOR

As second year medical students we were fascinated by preclinical study of pathology and histopathology. Whatever pathological diseases were studied, we students were convinced that we had developed that illness. When we studied anemia in hematology, we all thought we looked pale and started to examine one another's spleen, certain that it was enlarged. During our study of cirrhosis of the liver we all palpated our liver and suspected it was hard and sclerotic. Exposed to the study of Hodgkin's disease and lymphomas, all the medical students started to check their lymph nodes, axillary lymph (arm pit) nodes, and inguinal nodes (groins). We imagined they were enlarged, tender and growing. It was almost standard procedure that medical students developed neuroses at the first exposure to pathology. If we had headaches from too much studying, or from sinuses, we immediately concluded that we had a malignant tumor of the brain. If we awakened with backache, naturally we were sure we had ruptured an intervertebral disk. And if we had a lingering cough, there was no doubt in our minds that we were developing a carcinoma of the lung. If, after too heavy an Italian or Mexican meal, we had heartburn, of course we were certain that a large peptic ulcer was developing.

The stressful sophomore year was almost always the time for hypochondriasis. Every week at least five or six of the medical students would rush to the doctor in charge of the clinic for medical students with their complaints, always suspecting the worst. Dr. Isabelle Thompson, in charge of the student clinic, was rather an unsympathetic person. She was tall, masculine, homely, and noncommittal. Instead of reassuring the overly apprehensive medical students, her comment usually was, "You are too emotional and should not be studying medicine." If Morris Katz (the freshman who committed suicide) were alive during the second year, and she responded to his insecurities in her brusque, derogatory fashion, I'm sure he would have left the university immediately and given up the idea of studying medicine; however, she might have saved his life.

One night, during a winter storm, while studying heart disease in McCullough's pathology book, and reading the section about coronary occlusion, I was interrupted by a loud banging on my door. In came my friend Fred Kelly, another sophomore student, breathless and blue from the cold; heavily bundled with coat and hat, muffler, and thick gloves. "Cooper," he yelled apprehensively, "I just had a coronary occlusion. Please call an ambulance at once." I was unperturbed. Fred lived two blocks away on the third floor of a rooming house. Thus, he would have had to climb down three stories, rush two blocks through this blizzardy, snowy weather, and then climb the steep flight of steps to the second floor to my room to report to me, after all that exertion, that he had just had a heart attack! I reassured him that if he had a coronary attack, he would have called for help. He would not, I reminded him, have been able to rush out wildly, descend three flights, run two blocks, climbed rapidly up my staircase without collapsing in shock. It then occurred to me that Fred was also studying McCullough's pathology, and that he was also reviewing the section on diseases of the heart. Fred, a very nervous individual, probably felt some slight discomfort in his chest due either to muscular strain or poor posture while studying, or perhaps he had mild indigestion (since the food we ate in those days was not gourmet) and then, hypochondriac that he was, allowed his imagination to run away with him. The classical sophomore syndrome.

Since we now knew how to take blood pressures and listen to the heart, I suggested he strip to the waist. There I was, a sophomore medical student, assuming the role of a physician! I listened to his chest carefully. I told him to *take a deep breath*. His lungs were clear. The heart sounds seemed normal; I detected no murmurs; the beat was regular; and his blood pressure was a normal 120 systolic over 82 diastolic. So, I reassured him in my most "professional" manner, "Fred, you didn't have a coronary! You couldn't possibly have had a coronary! And if you still need total reassurance, we'll go over to the clinic and get an EKG." He calmed down and we sat and talked as I assumed the role of a psychiatrist. Finally relaxed, he smiled embarrassedly and admitted that he must have assumed he had the disease that he had been studying.

During this second year, I continued to tutor four times a week and worked nightly at the nearby Woodlawn Hospital as the lab technician, and fortunately also obtained a job as a lab assistant in anatomy. This position paid very well and occasionally allowed me the luxury of purchasing tickets for symphonies and concerts. I was enthusiastic about this anatomy assignment as it helped me to acquire expertise in a field I enjoyed. A voluptuous blonde freshman (one of the six females in the anatomy class I taught) insisted on calling me "Doctor Cooper" which pleased my ego. I was tempted to give her special after hours tutoring in the course, until I discovered that her fiance was the Associate Professor of Anatomy — the faculty member who hired me!

The sophomore year was pleasant. I had recovered from the depression occasioned by Morris Katz' suicide. No new insoluble problems appeared. My economic situation seemed under control and the generous living arrangement with the Smith family was working out beautifully. I met my financial commitments without calling on my parents, who could ill afford to help. Best of all, I was learning medicine and loved it.

*   *   *   *   *

The Chicago Lying-In Hospital was across the street from Billings Hospital (the University Clinics) and was devoted entirely to obstetrics and gynecology. It was a new building, staffed by two very prominent chiefs, Dr. Joseph DeLee, the editor of the obstetrics textbook, and Dr. H. Morris, a gifted gynecologist.

Dr. DeLee was an imposing figure, well over six feet tall, slim, handsome, gray haired. He sported a Van Dyke mustache and beard, resembling a groomed Mark Twain. He was a great educator, and particularly known for his pioneering obstetrical procedures in both normal and abnormal births. Every Thursday evening Dr. DeLee presented and discussed one of his obstetrical movies. Although they were presented primarily as educational films for the obstetrical medical students, the Thursday evening gathering soon became very popular with the undergraduates who came to enjoy the "exotic" pictures!

Dr. DeLee's quest was to one day stimulate the imagination of one of his medical students to find the cure for "toxemia of pregnancy," a serious and common problem with a high mortality. He would take each sophomore class outside the building, point to a blank cornerstone, and dramatically pronounce: "One day, one of my students will have his name engraved on this stone as the genius who solved the riddle of toxemia." As it turned out, toxemia was eventually eradicated, not by one physician but by the accrued knowledge of how to control hypertension.

Today the pathophysiological mechanism producing toxemia is relatively well understood. Toxemia is a complication of the last three months of pregnancy associated with the retention of a considerable amount of salt and fluid producing generalized swelling and severe hypertension. This apparently is brought on by the release of excess amounts of the chemical angiotensin which causes the accumulation of sodium and water in the system, and this produced the edema and elevated blood pressure. The diuretics of today and the drugs that inhibit the angiotensin production (Enalapril-Vasotec) are lifesaving. Dr. DeLee would have had to inscribe the cornerstone, "Evolution of Pharmacology."

In the third quarter of our second year, we were labeled "externs" at the clinics, and the faculty of Chicago Lying-In taught us how to deliver normal presentation and breech births (buttocks first) babies. To pass the course in obstetrics, each student had to complete ten normal deliveries in the hospital. My first patient presented herself in the outpatient department in the final stage of her last trimester, almost ready to deliver. Although an extern, and not officially a doctor yet, I was introduced to Mrs. Newman as Dr. Cooper, a member of the house staff. Mrs. Newman was told that if I were on duty the night she went into labor, I would be the "physician" who delivered her. I met her weekly for the last three weeks prior to her labor. She went into labor at night, as they usually do, and I, flushed with anxiety and excitement, delivered her healthy, crying eight-pound baby boy while the resident stood by to assist if necessary. It was an emotional experience to realize that I actually assisted in bringing a new life into this world, and forgetting it was 3:00 A.M. called my parents in Cleveland to share my thrill.

During this year I also worked as a shoe salesman on Saturdays, selling shoes off the rack on downtown Chicago's Wabash Avenue. I was a poor salesman indeed. My book showed the poorest results at the end of each day. The problem was, I was too honest. If the shoe didn't look good, or it didn't fit well, or was the wrong color, I would tell my customer the truth. I never learned to push the PMs (the accessories that we were asked to sell along with the shoes), a matching purse or gloves or a bottle of shoe polish. I never felt right in pushing them and concentrated on helping women find the best pair of shoes; a pair that looked good and fit well, and I did poorly at that.

I remember vividly my manager calling me after a particularly poor Saturday showing. He looked at my salesbook, and asked: "Aren't you a student at a University?" Yes, I am." "What are you studying," he inquired? "I'm studying to be a doctor." He looked at my book again and sadly shook his head and pronounced, "You'll never make it!"

One Saturday I was up front, ready to handle the next customer, and was horrified to see that it was Mrs. Newman awaiting service. This was the woman whose baby boy I had delivered less than a month earlier at Chicago Lying-In Hospital. She saw me and went into minor shock, as did I.

Very apprehensively she ventured: "I don't understand it. I don't understand it. Aren't you Dr. Cooper?" Thinking fast, I quickly reassured her: "I know what's concerning you, lady. I have a twin brother at the obstetrical hospital who is one of the staff obstetricians there."

She sighed with great relief. "Thank God. I thought a shoe clerk had delivered my baby!"

How much greater her distress would have been had she known I was not even a good shoe salesman.

HOME DELIVERIES

The Maxwell St. Clinic, a Chicago charity obstetric clinic, was located in a tough, low-income, depressed area ruled by the Mafia. An arrangement was made with the Chicago Lying-In Hospital whereby pregnant women came to the Maxwell Clinic as outpatients and were seen by the hospital externs at weekly intervals. When the mothers were ready to deliver, they were to call the hospital and we would proceed to their homes and deliver the baby there.

During the first three deliveries at home, the externs were accompanied by the obstetrics resident who taught us the procedures. The patient was "prepped" with soap and water and pubic hair was shaved. Newspapers were rolled in approximately six inch rolls, which were placed at the foot of the bed. The patients were instructed to push against them during contractions. A wire hanger draped with gauze was used to form a crude anesthesia mask, and ether was dripped to alleviate the patient's violent cramps. We had learned how to do rectal examinations to check the state of cervical dilation. The entire procedure often entailed remaining in the home for hours until delivery was completed.

We were taught how to determine if the pregnancy was in the normal presentation, or in the breech presentation. A breech makes for a difficult, complicated delivery. Often we could effect rotation and have a normal delivery. If unable to rotate, or experiencing a complication, the extern located the nearest phone booth and called the hospital to send the intern. (There were usually no phones in these poor homes.)

On occasion, the patient was brought by ambulance to the Chicago Lying-In Hospital. For obstetrical credit, each extern had to perform thirteen home deliveries. Many of Al Capone's lesser henchmen roamed the Maxwell area with knives and guns, robbing and attacking. When called, the extern went by taxi to the homes, wearing a white uniform. But the return was by street car. Immediately upon alighting from the taxi, by some radar known only to them, one of the henchmen of that neighborhood would saunter up with club in hand, demanding "protection money." We would immediately give him the two dollars we had prepared, and for that payment he would protect us for the rest of the night. There was some sort of reciprocal loyalty among those goons. While one was protecting, no other hood would bother us.

On my first solo delivery, at 2:00 A.M., I sprinted from the taxicab, two dollars in hand, and was promptly approached by one of the gang. I gave the large burly, slavic looking brute the money and quickly said, as instructed, "Don't hit me, I'm a doctor. Take care of me for the evening." And he did.

I entered the small, dark house. The living room was sparsely furnished with four cots for the children. The bedroom and kitchen were small and dark and the foul smelling bathroom had a rusty tub and leaking faucets. There was virtually no light in the gloomy house. One naked 60 watt bulb hung from a twisted wire cord in the bedroom. How I wished for a surgical floor lamp!

The husband was a middle-aged Italian, who had been drinking heavily and reeked from wine. In baggy pants, wine stained shirt, black suspenders, and bare-footed, he approached me menacingly and said, "I have a-now four girls, bring by you-a-doctors. And this-a-one better be a boy! Cause I'm-a-telling you, if this-a-one is not a boy, I'm-a-gonna kill-a you. I mean-a it!"

At first I thought he was kidding, but when he went into the kitchen and brought back a large bread knife, I began to take him seriously. I tried to tell him that at this time I had no way of knowing whether it was going to be a boy or a girl, that all I wanted to do was help his wife, Anna Maria, deliver a nice healthy baby. She was shy, diminutive, and quiet, although experiencing violent labor contractions.

"Whatever it is." I said to the husband, "God has decided ahead of time and sent me to help bring your baby."

"Doctor, I no gonna listen to you-a-baloney! This-a-time it better be a boy, or that's-a-last time you gonna bring a baby, God or no God!" It was then that I decided I certainly didn't want to deliver any more babies under any circumstance. Internal medicine was to be my field! I proceeded diligently with all of the preparatory steps I had learned. The newspaper rolled, water was put on the old wood-burning stove, the patient was prepped, the light was fixed in the best position possible, an anesthetic mask was made out of a wire coat hanger and a small porous towel, and a few drops of ether were dripped from time to time, as the patient went into active labor.

Since this was her fifth pregnancy, it went very rapidly and within an hour and a half with a muffled shriek she delivered. What a relief! After the head, chest and abdomen appeared, a little round sack with a small projection also appeared. The father was uproariously happy. Yelling and screaming, he banged me on the back, and weaved back into the kitchen to do some more drinking.

As instructed, I cleaned the woman, used the hemostats I brought, tied the umbilical cord, sterilized it, allowed the placenta to be delivered, and as instructed, wrapped the placenta in newspaper. I took off my bloody uniform and wrapped it separately in newspaper. I then gave the paper wrapped placenta to the father to burn in the wood stove.

I quickly procured the paper wrapped package with my uniform to return to the hospital for laundering. After shaking hands with Angelo, and anxious to be gone, I hurried to the nearest streetcar, accompanied by my early morning protector. I was fatigued and anxious to return to the hospital after the harrowing experience.

Upon return, I reported to the intern, and carefully unwrapped the package to put the dirty uniform in the laundry. But, I wasn't unwrapping the uniform, I was unwrapping the placenta, the afterbirth!

In my nervous haste and state of fear, I had wrapped the uniform and presented it to the father to burn, and brought back the placenta! For the rest of the term I was labeled "Cooper, the Placenta Kid"!

*   *   *   *   *

Visual retention is extremely important in anatomy, and the ability to memorize helps tremendously. Studying the beautiful dissecting atlases of Sabota and Spalteholtz was invaluable. At a later date an accomplished anatomical medical artist, Frank Netter, published a series of books with explicit, detailed, artistic renditions of anatomy and pathology.

Since they are all so complicated, everyone develops a system of memorization of the bones with their relationship to one another. The eight bones of the wrist gave particular trouble to students. I recognized this when I was a freshman in anatomy and had it re-emphasized to me again while I was teaching the freshman class that followed. The eight bones were as follows: navicular, triquetrum, lunatum, pisiform, multangular major and multangular minor, capitis and, finally, the hamatum.

Not only were these names difficult to retain, but their relationship to one another was confusing. I devised an acrostic scheme as a memory tool for the students. **Never Take Lucy's Pants, Mother Might Come Home.** (Thus, the bones were recalled by their first letters). I have been told that Cooper's acrostic is still used in the anatomy lab today.

* * * * *

The summer after my second year I returned to Cleveland to find employment for additional funds for the third year. Fortunately, my tuition scholarship continued for the entire four years. The depression was still smoldering and I was only able to find a morning job as a truck driver. My afternoons were free and I went to Cleveland's St. Vincent Catholic Charity Hospital to "volunteer" as an orderly/extern. I wanted to be exposed to as much clinical work possible, as this was a large busy charitable institution.

The work in the emergency room at St. Vincent's was exceptionally exciting. All day long different trauma cases presented themselves. There were knife and bullet wounds to be treated, fractures to set, burns to be attended to, and a profusion of acute medical and surgical emergencies. I had the opportunity to observe and help the interns and residents. Since Billings Hospital in Chicago did not have its own emergency service, the time spent at St. Vincent's that summer was extremely helpful in preparing me for emergency room duties at Mt. Sinai later on during my internship. More than that, my job at the hospital proved to be a God-send for my father!

During the depression my father had worked for the Metropolitan Life Insurance Company for ten years. He was forty-six years of age and did not have the most impressive sales record. It was the policy of the Metropolitan and other companies then to fire the less productive employees when they reached forty-five and, of course, Dad lost his job. We needed the income badly and he finally found employment at a local factory that manufactured pants.

Three weeks after the start of his employment there was a strike at the factory. My father, being a new employee, did not join the ranks of the strikers. He continued to work and found it increasingly more difficult to enter the factory. Strikers blocked the entrance gates, threw stones, and cursed employees who continued to work. The atmosphere became more hostile daily, and soon thugs were sent in by the union to prevent people from going to or returning from work.

One day, while my dad was at work, a large crowd of menacing strikers gathered outside the building armed with clubs, rocks, and glass bottles, shouting at the employees, the "scabs." "When you come out, we're going to beat the hell out of you, and you won't reach home alive!" Though the police were informed about this unruly gathering of thugs with their threats, they sent only one officer on a mount.

Naturally, he was unable to control the crowd by himself. It was obvious that the police department sided with the union strikers and would not do much for those trapped inside the building. The atmosphere became increasingly tense and hostile. After 6:00 P.M. none of the workers dared to leave the building for fear of their lives.

My mother called me at the St. Vincent Charity Hospital, tearfully describing the situation. I was the emergency extern on emergency service at that time and had made great friends with Carl, one of the ambulance drivers.

I devised a plan which I discussed with him and fortunately he was anxious to help. We were to drive rapidly to the factory site with the ambulance siren screaming and lights flaring, rush into the factory with a gurney announcing that there was a man inside who had had a heart attack and needed to be rushed to the hospital.

We put on white uniforms, hung stethoscopes around our necks, and borrowed a doctor's bag from one of the physicians. Tourniquets dangling from our white coats, we commandeered the ambulance, and with sirens blaring and lights flashing drove to the factory. As we approached the shouting masses of unruly thugs, they gave way to the ambulance.

We went from floor to floor trying to find my father, finally locating him on the third floor, sitting quietly behind a sewing machine. He was as fearful as the rest of the employees and shocked to see me. I told him to open his shirt and lie down on the gurney, explaining our plan. He did so, and we covered him almost entirely with a sheet.

We rushed out of the building, carrying the cot gingerly between the two of us, and pushed the gurney back into the ambulance. I stayed with Dad, Carl jumped into the front seat and, with the sirens blaring and lights flashing away, we returned to St. Vincent's Charity Hospital.

Mother called me that evening to tell me how happy she was that I was a "doctor," and able to save my father's life. I reminded her that I wasn't a doctor yet, but appreciated the compliment. The rest of the interns, orderlies and externs heard about the rescue mission and thought it was great. They got a real kick out of it, and even the administrator of the hospital did not chastise us for commandeering the ambulance without permission.

* * * * *

During the third year at the University of Chicago, externs took histories and performed physicals at the bedside of the hospital patients. We would make morning rounds with the clinicians in small groups and observe how the professors tackled the various problems.

The outpatient departments were especially interesting as we did the first histories and physicals on all patients who presented themselves to the various specialty clinics, always being introduced to the patient as "the doctor." When, as often was the case, we faced a difficult problem, we would call upon the help of the staff. The externs were scheduled to rotate through separate sections of the hospital. Medicine for a month, surgery a month, orthopedics a month, neurology a month, etc., thus changing from one outpatient department to another.

I recall a particularly amusing situation that occurred when I was in the orthopedic department and took the history and did the physical on Mrs. McMann, an elderly, obese, red-faced Irish woman who complained of muscular weakness, said she dropped things, bumped into chairs, and generally lacked coordination of movements. She had hand tremor and visual disturbance. As her condition was neurological in origin, I told her that she was in the wrong clinic, and I would refer her to the neurology department and schedule her to see the neurological *specialist* the following Monday. I did so, forgetting that on Friday I was to rotate to neurology.

To my chagrin, on Monday, of course my first patient was Mrs. McMann. Imagine our reactions when the hospital aid brought her into my examining room and said, "And now you're going to meet the neurological specialist."

I thought that I had better quickly allay her apprehension and distrust of the system, so I said, "Mrs. McMann, I came to the neurology department this morning to discuss your case with the attending neurologist. I'm interested in his impressions."

With that, I walked out of the room and called on one of the other junior medical students on the service to come and do the history and physical on the astonished Irish woman. I watched with amused interest as he performed our typical "student caliber" neurological exam.

Mrs. McMann then told me she was impressed with my dedicated attitude to my patient because I followed her case even in another department, and she promised to send me referrals!

Through the years of my practice I would often recall my student experience with Mrs. McMann. She taught me the intrinsic value of following the medical course of a patient, even when referred to other physicians.

FATHER'S CORONARY

The summer after my third year was both happy and troubled. The happy part was that I met Sally Tempkin, whom I later married. She was a junior at Western Reserve University in Cleveland, Ohio. She was pretty, cheerful, had an exceptionally extroverted personality, and was loved and admired by all her girlfriends, and by too many boyfriends.

My friends, who went to college in Cleveland, told me that she was one of the most popular girls at the university, an exceptional student on full tuition scholarship, editor of the university paper, and that she played the violin in the Cleveland Women's Orchestra. After seeing her picture in the campus yearbook, I knew I had to meet her.

My family lived upstairs in a modest two-story frame and brick house in a section called "Kinsman" on Cleveland's East Side. The area was populated by Italians, Greeks, Poles, Jews, and Blacks. For the most part the families were all first generation European immigrants.

This was not the proverbial melting pot, as no group attempted to become friendly with the other groups. The Italians stayed Italians, the Poles stayed with their group, the Jewish people had their own little section, and the Greeks avoided everyone. The Blacks were the most friendly, and they were, unfortunately, the poorest among all of us.

Sally and I were sitting on a swing on the downstairs porch at about 6:00 P.M. one evening when my father, Louis, aged forty-eight, came walking up the hill to the house. He did not have a car at that time, and used the streetcar to go back and forth to work. He was still employed in the pants factory that had had the strike several months earlier. As he approached the top of the hill coming toward our house, I noticed that he seemed somewhat pale and was breathing heavily. There was slight perspiration on his brow. As he climbed the steps to the porch he said, "I believe I've had some indigestion. I don't know what I ate, but it's not agreeing with me, I feel very tight in the chest and a little nauseated." I opened the door leading to the steps to the second floor where we lived, and started to ascend the steps with him slowly, holding him by the arm. We had taken about ten steps when he suddenly stopped, gasping as he complained of excruciating chest pain, binding and compressing him front to back. The pain then radiated under his breast bone into his neck, and spread along the inside of his left arm with increasingly intensity. The nausea became worse and he vomited twice. He began to sweat profusely, became extremely pale, and went into shock with rapid, shallow respirations. He had to hold on to me and the bannister to keep from falling down the steps.

It was apparent that he was suffering a coronary occlusion, and it was imperative to Sally and me that we get him to a hospital immediately. We did not have EMS at that time, nor was it easy to get ambulance service. Sally and I partially carried him down the steps, placed him gently in my cousin's borrowed car, and rushed him to the emergency room of the University Clinics Hospital in Cleveland. Since we had no insurance and very limited means, he was admitted to the charity ward. I called Dr. Harold Feil, who was the leading cardiologist in Cleveland at that time, explained that I was a medical student at the University of Chicago, and asked if he would attend my father. He very graciously agreed to help and came to the emergency room promptly. Dr. Feil was Chief of Cardiology at the University Hospital, a very much admired clinician. He was a friendly, fatherly type and took control of my father's case immediately. The x-ray of the chest showed some beginning fluid at the bases of the lungs, and the electrocardiogram showed evidence of an early coronary occlusion. The ST waves were markedly elevated in Leads II, III and AVF, suggestive of a posterior coronary occlusion, not quite as serious as an anterior occlusion, but all coronary occlusions have initially poor prognosis. Dad was admitted to the coronary care unit on the charity ward, under the personal care of Dr. Harold Feil, which was most unusual since most of the patients there were under the care of the residents of the hospital. For the three days during the acute episode, we were all extremely apprehensive. On the third day he was removed from the oxygen tent, the pain had subsided, his blood pressure had stabilized, his pulse rate was regular, there were no signs of cardiac failure, and the EKG seemed to improve. We felt the worst was over.

Late that afternoon a team of laborers presented themselves in the ward and began to remove a section of the wall just behind my father's bed. It seemed that they were going to change the wall to improve the plumbing. The deafening hammer blows and clanking of the metal wrenches were disastrously irritating to my father who became extremely restless and uncomfortable, and began again to suffer pain in the chest. I was at the bedside and realized that he was having an extension of his coronary, precipitated by the commotion behind his bed. The noise did not abate and Dad's condition deteriorated.

I realized that Dad had to be moved at once, and I ran to the admitting officer, a serious looking impersonal elderly female and explained the situation to her. I told her that I thought my father would succumb if he wasn't moved to a quieter area at once, and pleaded with her to move him into a semi-private room on one of the private wards. She agreed, and said she would move him but she had to have $200 cash deposit before the change could be contemplated. I had $3 in my pocket, and it was already 5:00 P.M. Where would I get $200 cash? I pleaded with her to move my father, explaining that it was dangerous for him to continue to be in that area, but she refused, was adamant and totally indifferent. "No money, no move." I explained I was a medical student and shocked at her immobile attitude when confronted with a medical emergency. Once again, "No money, no move."

It was then that I realized that there was a sordid side to medicine, a side very distasteful to me, a side of medicine that would disturb me throughout my medical career. The business side of medicine, wherein "the medical caduceus was replaced by the dollar sign!"

This was no time for further frustration, anguish and argument. I had to get $200. My father had a close friend, Isadore Cholfin, who was a relatively successful merchant, and I knew he would help me. Our families had known one another for twenty years. Sally and I drove rapidly to his home, explained the situation to him, and fortunately, he kept a certain amount of cash around the house, and he gave me the $200 without hesitation.

We fled back to the admitting officer, plunked the cash on the table, and my father was then moved to a semi-private room. The next morning he was much better and continued to improve thereafter. After the third week in the hospital, we took him home. Having obtained a loan from the Morris Plan Bank in Cleveland, we paid our obligations to the hospital. Dr. Feil had not charged for his professional services. He very graciously extended his professional courtesy. During my years of practice I never accepted a fee from a member of a doctor's family or religious order, as I felt honored and respected to be selected as their physician. This used to be the norm — not today!

Mt. Sinai — Too Many Commandments

The year 1939 was considered Hollywood's Golden Age. *Gone With The Wind, Goodby Mr. Chips, Mr. Smith Goes To Washington, Of Mice and Men* and *Wizard of Oz* were produced and made history. That was the year of my medical school graduation and the plunge into the Golden Age of Medicine.

During the last part of the senior year, students scramble for admittance to the various hospitals for their term of internship. I do not use the word "scramble" lightly. Obtaining a good internship at that time was most difiicult. I was accepted to Chicago's Michael Reese and at Mt. Sinai Hospital in Cleveland, Ohio. I preferred Cleveland, although Michael Reese was a better qualified teaching institute, but Mt. Sinai meant I would be close to Sally. I packed my few belongings into Sally's old Dodge, and off we went to Cleveland. I, to start my internship, and Sally to return to her teaching.

The Mt. Sinai Hospital was a 250 bed, red brick, five story, private hospital with a large charity ward. Although not affiliated with Western Reserve Medical School, Mt. Sinai's many well trained staff members were connected to the University clinics, and developed and implemented an excellent teaching program. Near the hospital, facing Euclid Avenue, were the renowned Cleveland Clinics, affiliated with the Western Reserve Medical School and the University clinics at Lakeside Hospital.

The Cleveland Clinic was noted at that time for its world famous chief of surgery, Dr. Crile, who was exceptionally gifted in thyroid surgery. More recently, the Cleveland Clinic has become one of the world's top cardiac centers, vying with Dr. Denton Cooley's group at the Houston Medical Center for the quality and quantity of cardiac bypass surgical procedures.

Mt. Sinai was noted for the series of shenanigans pulled on the medical interns. I would define "shenanigan" as an episode in which there is some good, but in the process, someone has been exploited.

Shenanigan #1: We learned the first day that we had to be on thirty-six hour call, followed by eight hours off. This spartan regime was to be interrupted by one day off every three weeks.

Shenanigan #2: Although there were only twelve interns selected for Mt. Sinai, our group was to cover the entire hospital — admitting all patients, medical and surgical, completing all the histories and physicals, assisting in all surgical procedures and postoperative care, handling the very active emergency room, and controlling intravenous therapies throughout the hospital.

Shenanigan #3: Interns were responsible not only for admissions of all patients, but for all lab work that needed to be performed when the technician left at 6:00 P.M. If one was on night duty, as was the case every other night, one had to do all the routine bloodcounts, the urinalyses, the chemistries, as well as the typing and cross-matching of blood for transfusion.

Shenanigan #4: Our salary was to be $10 per month, from which were deducted one percent for state tax and $1.80 for laundering our uniforms. We were to purchase our $8 uniforms, consisting of a white jacket, a white pullover shirt, and white pants, and we were instructed to wear a black belt. After several weeks at the hospital, we felt we had indeed earned a Black Belt! Shoes were to be black and shined.

Shenanigan #5: All meals while interning were free. That's when I realized the truth of the adage, "What you get for nothing, is worth nothing." Our breakfast was always the same, grapefruit, orange juice, cereal, milk, and coffee. On Sundays, the Jewish treat, scrambled eggs and salami. So far not too bad.

Lunch — boiled potatoes, turnips, tomatoes, rye bread, and salami. Salami — day in and day out — salami! Supper — same as those fed patients on their third postoperative day, namely, soft pureed foods consisting of minced chicken or liver with baby food spinach or pureed peas. We were convinced that the dietician accumulated all the unfinished food in the various wards, dumped it together, and then distributed it to the interns as stew.

In charge of the twelve interns were six hostile residents, each one more sadistic than the other. I would have liked to decimate them. They believed that cold indifference was the best way to get most of the work performed by the interns. Indeed, their method did work, as it was necessary to get their approval before we could receive our internship diplomas at the end of the year.

Between the strenuous work hours, the poor food, the overwork and the hostility, we felt that the hospital regularly received instruction from Auschwitz. We quickly learned that the best way to supplement our diet was to learn which patients were on high-caloric, high-nutrition diets. If they did not have any infectious processes, we would pick up their trays before the orderlies got them, and then polish off any unfinished food. Also, it was good to make friends with the rich patients on the third and fourth floor who always had special treats brought in: fruit, chocolates, and cakes which they generously invited the interns to enjoy.

I was concerned that these prolonged work hours — thirty-six on, eight off — and the disturbed sleep surely could lead to incompetency among the interns, certainly irritability, and, of course, rampant paranoia was created by the residents. Unquestionably, some of us did become a bit clumsy and depressed from time to time — experiencing a sort of "hospital jet lag."

Our chief resident was Dr. Allen Bard, a tall, well-built, good-looking young man with ruddy cheeks and a constant smile. We were aware that he was always plotting and planning to have fun at our expense. On our first day, he immediately lined up the twelve interns in the Emergency Room and handed each of us a "scrub suit." What we didn't know at that time was that the green scrub suits were imprinted "Mt. Sinai" on both shirt and pants, and were the property of the hospital. They were always available in the cabinets adjoining the entrance to the scrub room, and were laundered and sterilized by the hospital after each use. Dr. Bard told the naive initiates, "Gentlemen, I'm going to give each one of you your scrub suits for the year. They will cost you three dollars." He then collected the money from each intern. I had only one and a one-half dollars, and told him I would pay the rest after I received my first salary. Of course, later on we learned that this was Bard's peculiar sense of humor and a yearly trick on all new interns. No one got his money back, even when we learned that the scrub suits were hospital issue. Bard was chief resident of Mt. Sinai Hospital for three years, and performed his annual scrub suit ceremony on all new interns.

My first assignment was on the charity ward service, and I was also allowed to see Dr. Stanley Mortimer's private patients on medicine. I found this tall, lean, well-groomed, jocular physician likeable. Listening to his early morning clinic jokes complete with authentic accents were God-sent after our weary, exhausting night duties. Dr. Mortiner taught at the medical school, was connected with University clinics, and was a brilliant diagnostician. He had the keenest eyes of any practicing physician I've ever met. His diagnoses were precise, complete and correct. If a patient succumbed and went to autopsy, he would sit down prior to the autopsy and write out what the findings would be, and was invariably correct. I liked working with Dr. Mortimer, and when I'd completed my internship, he invited me to join his medical practice in Cleveland. I was greatly honored, but declined because I wanted to get more training before going into practice.

Although the food was terrible, doctors were allowed to invite friends or wives to join them at lunch, and Sally came on weekends. None of the interns knew that I was married, and thought that Sally was my fiancée. It would have been disastrous had the marriage been revealed, for Sally would have lost her job as a school teacher. With my $8.20 remaining after tax and laundry each month, we couldn't survive. So the secret remained.

Dr. Mortimer was a typical didactic internist. It was all medicine. He used to say, "You live medicine. You eat medicine. You sleep medicine. You talk medicine." He did just that, excepting when he told his jokes. I recall with wonder how Dr. Mortimer attended with complete detachment the autopsy of his own eighty-one-year-old mother. "Check the left hemisphere of the brain," he ordered the pathologist who was conducting the autopsy. "You'll find an old hemorrhage near the left middle cerebral artery." He was correct! "The gallbladder," he continued, "will be filled with eight faceted stones." Again, he was correct! "There will be a small adenocarcinoma of the pancreas," he added, "and metastatic tumor in the liver." The pathologist found them just as Dr. Mortimer, the cool, reserved scientist, had anticipated. I felt certain that I could never attend an autopsy on any member of my family and be so completely didactic, impersonal and unemotional.

With his marvelous sense of humor, he delighted in telling the story of the person who phoned the head nurse on the third pavilion to ask how Mr. Louis Stern in Room 306 was doing. "Quite well," she answered. "Does he have any fever?" "No." "When does the doctor intend to let Mr. Stern ambulate?" The nurse looked at her chart and replied, "He is scheduled to start walking in the morning." "Good, then he should be ready to go home soon?" "Yes, in three more days. By the way," she asked the caller, "whom shall I say is calling?" "It's me, Louis Stern, the patient in Room 306. Dr. Mortiner never tells me anything!"

Dr. Mortimer also delighted in telling the story of the heart attack patient, Mr. Stanley Levine who, at his six week checkup, was told by his physician that he had made a remarkable recovery. Cardiac behavior was excellent, his blood pressure was normal, and EKG improved. Mr. Levine immediately asked if it was safe to have sex and was told yes. His wife, still apprehensive, not completely believing Stanley's oral report, requested that he bring a letter from the doctor testifying unquestionably as to his improved status before she would permit sexual relations. Reluctantly, he approached his doctor to have him type a letter declaring it was safe for him to have sex. As the secretary was completing the letter, he had a sudden inspiration and had her change the address from "Dear Mrs. Levine: . . ." to "To Whom It May Concern: It is safe for Stanley to have sex."

*   *   *   *   *

Of the 250 patients in the Mt. Sinai, every morning at least fifty had venipunctures done either to draw blood for lab testing or to start intravenous therapies. Of course, the interns were assigned to do this; nurses and technicians didn't perform this function at that time. We became quite expert at intravenous probing, and learned that all veins are different. Some are mobile and difficult to penetrate; some are very tough and one has to be very careful not to puncture through them. Others are flaccid and collapse when the needle intrudes on the vein, and some are so small that one must reduce the size of the needle. We also learned the various sites from which to collect blood. The basic area is usually the antecubital veins, that is, the veins at the inside of the elbow. We also learned how to penetrate veins in the wrist, hands, scalp, neck areas, and groin. Blood was usually drawn at 7:00 A.M., when patients were sleepy, in pain, uncooperative, and irritable. In addition to the problems which occurred mechanically, we also had to learn how to handle the patients psychologically. We did the "scut work," the hospital earned the money.

I was barely twenty-three when I interned, thin and pale, and looked like a high school senior. I regrew my mustache, made sure a stethoscope was always around my neck, kept a reflex hammer in my pocket so patients could see it, a tourniquet swinging from the other pocket and, of course, a large name tag, "Dr. Elmer E. Cooper," blazing on the left size of my white coat. With all that, it was frequently embarrassing to walk down the hall or the wards and have a patient see me pass and hear that person call: "Hey, orderly, would you be kind enough to hand me a urinal?"

Although most of the patients at Mt. Sinai spoke English fluently, here and there we had Jewish patient who couldn't give us a good history without lapsing into the Yiddish dialect. Fortunately, one of our interns, an Irishman, Sean O'Hara, was born in Brooklyn, New York, He knew more Yiddish than the cantor who came to talk to us once a week. He had worked part-time in a pawn shop while growing up and went to medical school at New York University. Sean's father owned a bar which was frequented by the Jewish people in the neighborhood, and he often helped his father in the bar. O'Hara was indeed a paradox: freckle faced, sandy haired, blue eyed, and spoke with a slight Irish brogue; yet he could speak fluent Yiddish with an authentic accent. We learned that later in life he became an oil multimillionaire. I guess it was the pawn shop training!

Mt. Sinai was the first private hospital in Cleveland to accept a black intern. George Jones claimed that we were outrageously overworked, and that finally whites were doing slave labor. His many beautiful expressions often had us falling out of our seats with laughter. His best parody was his description of an American bigot complaining that when the African blacks arrived in the United States, they took away all the "slave jobs," leaving none for anyone else. We all liked George and considered him a clever and exceptionally broadminded person. Once recovered from the shock of having a black doctor, patients voiced how impressed by his ability and dedication they were. He married one of the black dieticians in the hospital and, on many occasions, she would sneak us a tray of goodies which she had baked especially for the intern staff — residents were excluded.

One lunchtime, after intolerably poor food, the intern staff rose in disgust and made the bold decision that once and for all we had to teach the administration and director that they couldn't work us the way they did and feed us in this poor fashion! We decided to strike! The plan was to walk out in unison, having arranged with the administrator's secretary to keep his office door open so he could see us marching out of the hospital. As we noisily trooped by the front of his office, he quickly arose from his desk and ran out to confront us. "What's all this about?" Dr. Woods asked. Our spokesman, Dr. O'Hara said, "We can't eat this trash anymore. We can't work on the food you're giving us. Were going to start eating outside in cafes and restaurants where we can have decent meals."

With surprisingly good judgment, Dr. Woods said, "Wait, I'm going to join you." He reached for his hat, joined our group, led us to nearby Clark's restaurant, and ordered steaks, salad and desert for all the boys. Then he discussed the situation freely and promised a new approach to our dietary situation. Beginning the following morning there was marked improvement in the food brought to our dining room. The salami was a thing of the past. We were now getting roast beef, steak, chicken and fish. Every meal was accompanied by a desert, and by the end of the year I had gained twenty pounds!

*   *   *   *   *

At 4:00 A.M. one morning, after returning from an extremely hard, unpleasant treatment of a comatose, incessantly vomiting, alcoholic, cirrhotic liver patient who had to have her stomach irrigated and intravenous liquids administered to correct her electrolytes (body fluids), I ran up to my small intern quarters, fell on my cot completely exhausted, hoping for a few hours of sleep. Almost immediately, the phone rang and I had to return to the emergency room. Lying on a cot was a young man, about twenty-four years of age, with a deathlike pallor, vomiting up copious amounts of fresh blood, tremulous and cyanotic. Totally incoherent, he was unable to give a definite history. It was apparent that he had lost massive amounts of blood. I was fearful that he would succumb immediately. The tiny, silent, competent emergency duty nurse, familiar with the problem, had already started intravenous therapies for the shock. She reported his pressure had dropped to 80 systolic over a low diastolic of 40. I quickly drew blood and rushed to the lab to type and crossmatch. I prepared five units of blood, rushed back to the ER and pumped the lifesaving fluid into his veins as fast as tolerated, and the blood pressure rose to normal. Then

I lavaged (washed out) his stomach with ice water and the hemorrhaging ceased.

Once he was out of danger, I had him admitted to the ward, and told the nurse that I would check on him later, as I was dreadfully tired. I dragged myself back up to my sleeping quarters and fell into a deep slumber from intense fatigue. The following morning at 8:00 A.M., approximately three hours after I attended this young man, I found him in bed number three on the medical ward. His color had returned, the blood transfusion was flowing nicely into his veins. He was now coherent, and when I saw him with his eyes open, he looked vaguely familiar. I hurried over to the chart. "This is impossible," I thought to myself. "This can't be. It just doesn't justify." The name on the chart said, "Jerry Sands, age 26, 3358 East 135th Street."

Of all the tough hoodlums who lived on my street, worse than the Italians who used to beat up the Jewish boys, worse than the Poles who kicked the smaller Jewish boys, worse than the Greeks who threw rocks, was Jerry Sands, the ornery Jewish boy. He was big for his age, and although he was several years older than me, took great delight in pummeling me whenever he saw me. Jerry was my arch-enemy during the fourth and fifth grades in elementary school! He would wait for me to leave class when the bell rang and try to catch and beat me! Many a black and blue eye, many a sore muscle, many a pulled ligament, did I suffer from the indignity of being mauled by this ruffian! My mother had talked to his mother. My father had talked to his father, but to no avail. He was intrinsically "bad boy" material.

What a paradox! Here he was. The same Jerry Sands who beat the hell out of me for two years, whose chasing improved my running speed so much that when I finally reached junior high I was able to make the track team.

Here was Jerry Sands looking so benign and peaceful, lying on these white sheets, color returning into lips and cheeks, and all because of Elmer Cooper — the beatee for two years who, thirteen years later, worked half the night restoring him to viability!

I walked over and shook his hand and said, "Jerry, do you remember me?" When I told him who I was his eyes shone with unshed tears. "Jerry, you are awfully lucky that you were in such extremis when brought into the ER, that I didn't bother to look at the name on the admitting chart, because had I known who you were, before I attacked your problem so aggressively, I wonder if — " I said only half jokingly "— I would not have mismatched your transfusions."

* * * * *

One of the problems we encountered at the hospital was infection of newborn male babies' circumcision wounds. It seemed that the Mohels (ritual circumcisers) did not use aseptic techniques. I was assigned the task of teaching a class of six Cleveland Mohels how to do aseptic "surgery." I brought them to the scrub room outside the surgical theaters and went through the regime of surgical preparation. I described the method of thorough surgical handwashing. I described the use of the hard bristle brush in the fingernail area. We discussed that this had to be done vigorously from the fingertips to the elbows for three minutes by the clock. I described how one held the hands so that there was drippage to the elbow, after immersing the hands in antiseptic fluids. I indicated the method of holding hands up for sterile towels. We then demonstrated, with the help of the surgical nurses, the technique of putting on sterile gowns, explaining that the nurse, who is already in surgical dress, ties the cords to the gowns. I explained how the hands entered into the stretched sterile rubber gloves, held by the nurses, one at a time, each finger in the correct part and making sure there was no contamination. No touching of any other object. Right hand, then left hand. Then both hands crossed in front of the sterile gown with a sterile towel over them until the infant was ready.

Looking over my shoulder, as I demonstrated, I noticed and overheard the Mohels talking agitatedly among themselves. The eldest, an imposing looking man, with a fine well trimmed long beard was continuously ringing his hands and woefully repeating "Oy vez mir, oy vez mir, I'll never learn the technique." The youngest, clean shaven and athletic appearing, kidded the one next to him exclaiming, "These fancy doctors will soon request that the shokets (orthodox person certified by a rabbi to slaughter animals as prescribed by Jewish law) scrub their hands by the clock and put on sterile gown and gloves before they cut the heads off the chickens. This brought on a heavy laugh and they all relaxed. Then they practiced the aseptic method over and over and when I felt comfortable with their technique, I signed a document indicating each was ready to continue with the circumcisions.

I decided, however, to watch the first few. Mohel Schwartz was the first one to perform a circumcision under surgical technique and I observed quietly over his shoulder. He brushed his hands and nails vigorously, held them correctly, dipped into the aseptic solutions, dried with sterile towels, placed his hands correctly into the sterile gloves, had his gown put on meticulously, without any evidence of contamination, held his hands in front of his chest draped with a sterile towel, and then the baby was brought forward. He walked towards the baby, dropped the sterile towel, held both of his hands to his face and "ptchew! ptchew!" He spit into each hand, as he rubbed them together gleefully and said, "OK, I'm ready to do the first circumcision!"

I was amused, but frustrated. After all the education and drilling of the past four days it seemed that they had "missed the boat" on antisepsis. I quickly stopped him from proceeding with the circumcision, and explained to him that the "ptchew, ptchew," meant saliva and bacteria on his gloves. He understood, was embarrassed and promised not to do it anymore. Schwartz repeated the entire surgical technique without the "ptchew, ptchew," and performed a beautiful job on the baby boy!

Although circumcision was first introduced as a biblical covenant (Genesis 17), in actuality there are many hygienic conditions to recommend its use. The removal of the prepuce (foreskin) results in less infection of the smegma (cheesy sebaceous secretion) that accumulates, which is considered by many scientists to be a carcinogen. There have been reports in the medical literature that wives of circumcised husbands have a lower incidence of cancer of the cervix.

*   *   *   *   *

The Chief of Obstetrics and Gynecology at Mt. Sinai, Dr. Martin Garfield, was indeed a comical character. He was very short, about five feet, two inches tall, and when he did his gynecological surgery it was necessary for him to stand on a small flat stool in order to peer into the abdomen. For his deliveries, he always sat on a high stool. However, he didn't do all of the deliveries for which he was credited, as I discovered when I became an intern on his service. The resident on the service told me that I probably would be doing all the normal deliveries, and Dr. Garfield would get the recognition. I was told that I was to follow the course of labor, and just about the time the patient was to deliver, I was to alert Dr. Garfield, who would come to the hospital about the time I completed the delivery. He would then walk into the delivery room and ask the attending intern if it was a boy or a girl. Once he determined the correct sex and weight, he would don the surgical gown, put on a cap and a mask, and rumple up the front of the surgical suit, smear it with a bit of the delivery fluids and rush out to the waiting room to announce proudly to the expectant father, "I have just delivered you a beautiful eight pound, perfect boy/girl! " I discovered that this had gone on for many years and none of the interns or residents wanted to voice any criticism because they were delighted with the opportunity to gain the obstetrical skill.

What would happen, I wondered, if one day one of the interns, unhappy with him, and having delivered a boy, would announce that it was a girl? Dr. Garfield would be in a real dilemma, after announcing the wrong sex. Or perhaps, if twins were delivered, and he was not told, he would rush out to announce "I have delivered a girl!" Fortunately for Dr. Garfield, none of us had the courage to "blow his cover," although I was sorely tempted to do so. For years afterward I heard he continued this practice and, as far as society was concerned, had the unearned reputation of being an excellent obstetrician who delivered more babies than anyone else at the Mt. Sinai Hospital.

One evening I called him to come to the hospital because there was a complication in a delivery that he asked me to do. He came, resplendent in his tuxedo on the way, with his wife, to attend the symphony at Cleveland's Severance Hall. He told his wife they would stop at the hospital and asked her to remain in the waiting room until he evaluated the situation. He left her sitting quietly, reading one of the old magazines in the outer room, walked into the labor area, discussed the case with me and the resident, felt confident that we could handle it, proceeded to the parking lot and drove to the symphony. He had completely "forgotten" that he had left Mrs. Garfield in the waiting room at the hospital. After being seated on his regular seat, fourth row center, the usual occupant of the seat on his left noted that the adjacent seat was empty, and asked: "Where is your wife? Is she ill?" Abashed, he realized he had forgotten her and left her in the waiting room at the hospital! He abruptly left the hall, jumped into his car and drove wildly back to the hospital, went to the back elevator, rushed into the scrub room, put on a scrub suit, smeared some stuff on it, as he was prone to do, walked out into the waiting room and said, "Sylvia, everything is under control. I'll put my clothes on now, and we'll see if we can get back to the symphony in time to hear the last half." Once again Dr. Garfield got away with it! The residents and staff had a hearty laugh when the true story got around and whenever he made rounds one of us would venture boldly to kid him — "Hey, doc, where's Mrs. Garfield?"

*   *   *   *   *

The medical service was the largest service at Mt. Sinai and was combined with the charity ward and, therefore, had the greatest number of nurses on duty. Nurses were young, pretty and very active. The Mt. Sinai Nursing School was attached to the hospital and graduated some of the brightest, best-trained nurses at that time. The nurses were well aware of how hard the interns worked and how tired we were, and how often we became depressed contending with the unreasonable patient load.

In addition to the nurses, there were twelve nurses' aids working in the medical department. They did some of the menial labor, cleaning of patients, handling of bed pans and urinals, and delivering food trays to patients. They also were responsible for the morning baths and evening rubdowns. Although they did not have nurses' training, they were extremely efficient in their duties and, especially important to us, was their respect shown to the interns. The registered nurses, on the contrary, categorized the interns as hospital employees and often just called us by our first names, or "Hey, Doc!"

One of the nurse's aids, Lucy Green, was particularly appreciative of our overworked status. She felt it was her duty to ease the lives of the overworked, tense, depressed interns. Whether she "did it" in the storeroom, the basement, the linen closet, or the interns' quarters, Lucy knew how to effectively relax and overcome the intern's depressions. She took on the entire intern staff, but steadfastly refused to entertain the residents. As she explained, "They don't work as hard and aren't so depressed; and besides, they had all of their experiences as interns and there is no need for them to be greedy! Mt. Sinai didn't realize how valuable Lucy was to the decorum and the peace of the intern staff. Dr. Louis Fried, the jocular intern from Detroit, was so enamored of Lucy's attention that he approached the hospital administrator to inquire, "How does one flunk internship, so I can spend another year here?"

Lucy had one annoying habit during her relaxation sessions. She would constantly munch on a juicy delicious apple, taking large bites, audibly snapping into the apple with her incisors and allowing the juices to drip all over her face. One of the young psychiatrists who enjoyed Lucy's favors when he was a Mt. Sinai intern discussed this unusual behavior by explaining that there is a definite association between oral and vaginal expressions.

*   *   *   *   *

Among the doctors on our staff were two brothers, the Grant Brothers, who were supremely gifted and popular. The elder Grant was an abdominal surgeon, and his brother did OB/GYN. On one of the rare occasions when Sally had the courage to have lunch with us in the doctor's dining room, Dr. Grant, the eldest, told me that he was going to do an emergency hysterectomy, and would like me to scrub with him. Of course, I was delighted. He then turned to Sally and asked, "Have you ever watched a surgical procedure?" When she replied, "No, and I'm not sure that I would like to," he coerced her, saying, "You must expose yourself to all the environs of a doctor's life." She agreed.

We all went to the surgical scrub room. Dr. Grant and I went through aseptic-prophylactic preparations for surgery, and Sally was given a cap, mask and sterile gown to stand by. When we entered Surgical Room A the patient was already under the effects of the anesthetic, correctly draped, and all signs were "go." Dr. Grant was notorious for his speed and, in fact, was known as Speedy Grant. He prided himself on the fact that he could do a hysterectomy faster than anyone else at Mt. Sinai. He always timed his procedures, hoping each time to knock off another minute or two. When we all gathered about the operating table, he glanced at the clock and announced, "It is now 2:15." With that, he made his first incision, cutting through the abdomen in the lower pelvic area. As the knife went through the skin, subcutaneous fatty tissue and muscle, there was free bleeding with blood all over the abdomen. Dr. Grant was busy tying and coagulating the endpoints. Just then we heard a soft thud as Sally quietly slid to the floor in a semi-faint, having been overcome by the odor of the anesthetic and observing all the blood. The attending nurse quickly ran to her aid, lifting her as she regained her composure. Sally smiled weakly and said, "I think perhaps I'd better wait outside until you gentlemen are finished." When we were reassured that she was OK, the nurse let her out quietly.

Dr. Grant looked at the clock again and said, "I've wasted two minutes." Speedy Grant went to work again, cutting vessels, cutting through the broad ligaments, removing the uterus, cauterizing the stump, and quickly closed the abdomen. He turned around and said, "Well, 18 minutes and 30 seconds. That's not bad." Of course, it wasn't bad. It was an exceptionally speedy hysterectomy. The only problem was that in his haste he had tied off both ureters. The next morning, when the patient was unable to void, it was necessary to re-

turn her to the operating room and Dr. Grant had to remove the liga-
tures from the ureters. He meekly said, "Well, at least I didn't leave a
sponge or hemostat in the abdomen." I believe that thereafter Dr.
Grant spent most of his time peering into the abdomen and less time
peering at the clock on the wall!

The second brother, Dr. Joe Grant, was a very accomplished violinist. He had a chair in the Cleveland symphony, an esteemed position. He was known to sneak into the basement of the morgue and play
his violin for hours at a time in the quiet solitude of that room. Of
course, when he finished, there was no applause from the audience,
just dead silence.

One of the world's most renowned violinists, Isaac Stern, was a
good friend of Dr. Grant, and it was not unusual for Dr. Grant to
board a plane early in the morning and fly to New York to meet with
the great musician. The two of them would play for hours at a time,
sometimes throughout the entire night, enjoying one another's music.
Then, Dr. Grant would take the morning plane back to Cleveland.
Occasionally, the violinist flew to Cleveland to meet with Dr. Grant,
and the two of them would fiddle in the quiet of the morgue.

*   *   *   *   *

Dr. Mortimer asked me to see one of his patients in the private
pavilion on the fifth floor of the hospital. He told me this man was
having severe functional bowel distress and hypertension, only partially controlled. He suggested I do a work-up and report back to him.
Before I entered the room, I stopped at the nurses' desk to get his chart
to see what had been done to date. As I read the name on the chart:
Nathan Gold, occupation Knitwear company owner, I had vivid flash-
backs and memories.

This was the same Nathan Gold at whose knitwear company I had
worked briefly after graduating from high school. It was he who had
fired me after the altercation with his nephew. Gold was reported to
be, even during the Depression, the youngest millionaire in Cleveland.
He was quite snobbish, and indifferent to his employees. He wasn't
even sure of my name. I recall once timidly knocking on the door of his
private office after begging the secretary for permission. When he
thundered, "Enter," I entered hat in hand, stood three feet from the
desk where he sat chomping on a foul cigar. There sat a short, rotund
man with wide shoulders and a very short neck, thick glasses, and early
baldness.

"Mr. Gold," I said, "I am one of your truck drivers."

"Yes, I know. I know," although I'm sure he didn't know. "Get on with it. What do you want?"

What I really wanted was to punch him in the face at that moment, and to tell him that he wasn't a very nice person. But I needed the job badly. "Sir, what I want is to report the following: When I back up through the long alley from your loading dock on the main street, there are brick walls on either side, with barely one foot leeway on each side of the truck. It would be a lot safer for me to back out without the risk of banging my head against the brick wall. Would you OK the purchase of a side door rear-view mirror for the truck, sir?"

The answer was abrupt, "If I thought the truck needed a side rear-vision mirror, I would have bought one and had it attached. We have had the truck for three years and no one has ever hurt himself backing out of the alley. When I want your advice, I'll ask for it. Don't bother me anymore. I'm busy." And that was it!

It was seven years later when I entered his hospital room. There he was, looking quite a few years older. There was the same short, stubby, fat man with the wide neck, wheezing as he chomped on his foul cigar. He was now completely bald, had a deeply furrowed brow; and skin sagged on both sides of his mouth, and he was very pale. He was surrounded by three friends who were sitting around, all smoking cigars and discussing business. I introduced myself as the intern for Dr. Mortimer, and after shaking hands said, "I don't know whether you remember me. I'm Elmer Cooper, and I was your truck driver seven years ago."

"Of course, I remember you, Elmer," he lied. "How are you? It's good to see you." Then he introduced me to his friends, and he said, "You see this boy? I helped put him through medical school." What he conveniently forgot was not only did I not get the rear-vision mirror, but after the fistfight with his nephew, I was fired. I made sure that I told his friends that I only worked for him for about four months, twelve hours daily, and my salary was $13 a week. "He wouldn't even let me have a rear-view mirror," I complained. They all laughed heartily, and all agreed in unison: "That's why Nate became the youngest millionaire in Cleveland." After a few more pleasantries I asked his friends to please leave the room and went about my medical business, smiling to myself, thinking: "These people never do change."

As I conducted my examination I found myself regretting that

Dr. Mortimer had not asked me to do a rectal exam, to check Mr. Gold's prostate or, better yet, do a proctoscopic exam. I had hoped Mr. Gold needed a rear-vision look at his hemorrhoids, direct invasion by a large oversized instrument.

*   *   *   *   *

It was expedient economically for Sally and me to remain secretly married while I completed my internship. Tallying my hospital salary, I calculated that I was earning less than twenty cents an hour. Where was the minimum wage when we needed it? Sally's salary was $104 per month and barely sufficed to pay for her car, personal expenses, and allowed a saving of about $15 per month.

Finding time to get together was most difficult for Sally and me. I worked thirty-six hours on, and eight hours off during that year. That meant that approximately every third night I could conceivably spend the evening with her. The entire staff knew Sally and assumed she was my fiancée. On my nights off I would sneak down the back stairway at midnight and meet Sally, who was waiting in the parking lot behind the emergency room. Fortunately, her home was only fifteen minutes from the hospital. When we got to her mother's house, there was invariably a large meal prepared for us as she was well aware that, although Mt. Sinai was a Jewish hospital, the interns did not get the proverbial "Jewish Mother's cooking."

Sally's best friend, Mildred, lived downstairs in the two-story house that her folks rented. A fascinating girl, she played the piano like a concert artist, and was very knowledgeable in art and literature. She also taught school, but could have been a good detective. When we finally told her we were married, no longer needing to keep it a secret after my internship, Mildred told us that she knew we were married right along. "How did you find out?" I asked. Her bedroom was directly beneath Sally's room and Mildred claimed that when she heard my shoes drop to the floor she knew they were much too heavy to be Sally's shoes. In those day, if my shoes came off, it meant we were married!

One winter evening I followed my usual routine of sneaking down the back steps and meeting Sally in the parking lot. I had to be back on duty at 7:00 A.M. and Sally thought best to return me to the hospital while it was still dark, at 6:00 A.M. In our haste neither one of us got dressed. We were both still in pajamas and bathrobes. As we drove into the dark parking lot, by sheer coincidence, Dr. Lester, the

intern on duty in the emergency room, was outside smoking a cigarette. He saw Sally's car coming up the hill and watched while I
jumped out of the car, clad in pajamas and robe, and noticed that Sally
was also in nightclothes. Lester was chagrined. He knew and respected
Sally very much and felt he was a close friend to the two of us, but
never thought that I would spend the night with my fiancée, and
couldn't reconcile it. For the rest of the internship, whenever Sally
came to visit me for lunch, Lester managed to turn his head and not
speak to her. Sally and I both found this very troublesome but we were
not at liberty to let him know we were married.

A few years later, while I was attending a convention in New
York where Lester was practicing, I called him and told him, that the
time he caught us in our nightclothes we had already been married
well over a year. "Thank God," Lester said. "I just couldn't believe
Sally was that kind of girl." It's different now.

*   *   *   *   *

The thirty-six hours of continuous difficult work with the desperate need for sleep concerned all the interns. We worried that this
would interfere with our competency. Often we went about our morning duties in a state akin to jet lag. The hospital didn't seem to understand this or, if they did, overlooked the problem.

One evening at about 11:00 P.M., Dr. Morris Feld and I were busy
in the lab performing routine lab work for the newly admitted patients
who were scheduled for surgery in the morning. We also had the responsibility of doing the lab work for patients who developed various
problems during the night. Neither one of us had slept in over thirty
hours; so, we were quite irritable, and righteously disgruntled.

As Dr. Feld wearily reached for the diluting fluid for his hemo-
cytometer (the chamber into which cells are suspended and counted
under the microscope) he fumbled and the bottle came crashing down
on the hard concrete floor. We were both so fatigued, all we could do
was laugh. About that time I reached for some of the reagents to do the
urinalysis and the bottle slipped right through my tired hands, drop-
ping to the floor on the other side. Again, we found it very funny and
had to giggle. It tickled our senses so much that we felt it was time we
left a message for the hospital administration.

With one shove, Dr. Feld threw all the bottles off the top shelf
onto the floor, clattering, breaking and spilling all over the place. Not
to be outdone, I did the same thing with all the reagents and bottles

and glassware on the second shelf. The third shelf was stacked with various forms and manuals for completing lab work, and it took no time for us to deposit all of them into the wastebasket, making sure the sheets were crumpled and soaked by the various reagents.

Aware that the lab was in complete disarray, we stealthily crept out of the lab and went to see our patients. We giggled constantly, like two silly kindergarteners, but this was the release we needed at that time, and we hoped that we had left a loud and clear message to the hospital. The disagreeable fumes from the sulfides of the reagents and sulfuric acid quickly spread through the upper floor and a security guard approached the lab to determine the cause and discovered the havoc.

The next day at lunch our administrator, Dr. Woods, made an important announcement. "Gentlemen, this morning we had an emergency meeting of the Directors of the Hospital, and we have decided to employ three full-time lab technicians to assume duty from 9:00 P.M. to 6:00 A.M., so the interns will not have to do night lab work. Feld and I both had difficulty keeping straight faces.

When the rest of the interns and residents found out what had happened and who had perpetuated the destruction, we were heartily congratulated. We were now heroes. For years after the incident, interns who came to Mt. Sinai and heard the story would send us notes of gratitude.

Military — "You're in the Army Now"

My internship was drawing to a close. Sally and I were both aware that we couldn't live on her meager school teacher salary and the poor earnings of a three-year medical residency. The average salary was between $75 and $100 monthly. We decided that I had to defer my continued training. At the suggestion of Dr. Bernes, a practicing internist at Mt. Sinai, I applied to the Arizona C.C.C. Camps to become a "camp doctor" and was accepted.

A law had been enacted to set up Civilian Conservation Corps Camps (C.C.C.) throughout the Southwest. These were projected to give opportunities to poor young boys and pay them as they performed outdoor work. Among the more popular jobs offered were those in the forest areas. I was to receive the same pay as a Second Lieutenant in the Army, $3,280 per year. Since living expenses would be minimal, we planned on saving enough to enable me to start a residency program at a later date.

My first task was to develop a hospital for the Williams, Arizona, lumber camp, approximately sixty miles from the Grand Canyon. This is undoubtedly one of the most spectacularly beautiful mountain areas in the United States. We arrived in Williams the early part of July and found the scenery absolutely awe inspiring. Highway 66 led directly into a street in Williams about a half mile long. There was the usual drug store, auto repair, garage, grocery, barber and general store of a typical small western town. A small movie house was showing a John Wayne film. How appropriate, we thought. Where were the saloon and gun slingers? The drug store sold beer, and that was it!

Sally remarked, "I guess this is the outskirts of Williams." When I told her that this was "it," the main street of the town, she was dumbfounded, but we both agreed that the small town experience would be a great adventure for a couple of big city dwellers, and we looked forward to our temporary stay.

Housing, however, was a difficult problem. There were no apartments or rooming houses in this town of 2,000 residents. Even if there were a hotel, we could not possibly afford it. Sally and I spent the greater part of the day looking, without success. Toward sunset, wearily, we drove across the railroad track and saw what looked like a large, one story rooming house. Sally remained in the car while I went to make inquiries.

After I used the heavy, tarnished brass knocker a few time, a large buxom woman in her early thirties appeared and drawled, "What I can I do for you fella?"

I noticed that she was in a bedraggled bathrobe and seemed to be somewhat exposed above. I told her that I was looking for a room for my wife and myself, and asked if perhaps there were rooms for rent in her rooming house? During this exchange, two young ladies came to the door, dressed only in a bra and panties, and peering over her shoulder invited me in. Suddenly it dawned on me that in this rooming house, the rooms were available, but only for thirty minutes or so, and I had better make my exit in a hurry! I thanked her very much and asked her for a referral to rooming houses. The "Madam" referred me to a house on Clinton Street and I went to the parked car to tell Sally of my experience. We laughed and laughed, which did much for us as this "virginal adventure" improved our faltering spirits.

We found the address on Clinton Street and the owner rented us her upper apartment. It was fairly priced, cheerful, and overlooked the magnificent mountains. We carried in our few belonging, happy to have found such a nice place. Our new landlady was very helpful, and said she was proud to have the new Camp Doctor as a tenant.

The next morning, as directed, I followed the tortuous, winding, narrow, unpaved rock road through the mountains to the campsite about eighteen miles north of Williams. I met the Captain in charge of the camp, and we took an immediate dislike to one another. He had a rapacious warthog look, and the malevolent eyes of a sadist. I was escorted to my personal quarters by one of the civilian boys, age nineteen, who was assigned to me as my orderly. We went to the building that was to be the new hospital and I began organizational work; figuring out how many beds would be necessary, what medications and equipment I would need, and I then started filling out procurement papers, ordering furniture, etc.

Within a month we had a nice small hospital of twenty-five beds with an active outpatient department. I enjoyed the work there tremendously, as the camp was situated high on a beautiful mountain with large pine trees, surrounding two small, crystal clear cold lakes. There were 500 young men in the camp. They were all from very poor families in Philadelphia and the Bronx. When I told them I had lived in the lower South side of Philadelphia at one time during my youth and enjoyed pretzels with mustard and dill pickles, I became "one of the boys," and they were quite comfortable with their camp doctor.

I was "one of the boys" with everyone at the camp except Captain Dick, who turned out to be a racial supremacist. He loathed Jews, Italians, Mexicans, and Blacks. He carried a policemen's billy club, which he brandished freely, terrorizing the boys. We didn't get along. He exuded hostility and argued with me on every occasion; interrupted me while I was lecturing and tried as often as he could to insult me. Finally, one day he challenged me to a fist fight behind the hospital. It was becoming easier and easier to want this demonic creature destroyed.

I wasn't sure how I would come out in a fist fight with a six foot plus pugnacious army captain, but I knew very well that once it was learned there was physical contest between the Captain and the Doctor at the camp, I, "new guy on the block," would be discharged, and I sorely needed this job. I was in the position of a ship trying to remain in my harbor, while a storm brewed about me.

Sally suggested that the best way to handle the Captain Dick problem was to talk to Major Tway, the senior officer in charge of Arizona camps who resided in Phoenix. We had established earlier an excellent rapport with him and knew he was a fair and honorable man. I called him, described the situation, and asked for advice. Major Tway listened thoughtfully to the problem. He said he had surmised Dick was an uncooperative, difficult person. There were rumors that he had caused trouble previously with a Mexican-American doctor who controlled a hospital near Tucson. The following week, lo and behold, the Captain received new orders. He was transferred to Alaska! I remained in Williams!

Once my hospital was organized and I felt quite comfortable with it, Major Tway asked me if I would leave it to set up another camp hospital near Nogales, on the border between Arizona and Mexico. I was reluctant to leave the glorious Williams' area, but moving to set up a new hospital for the C.C.C. would mean a promotion and a raise in salary, and this was welcome. The boys in the Nogales camp worked a nearby copper mine.

Nogales, Arizona, is divided into two towns: one on the Arizona side, the other Nogales, Sonora, on the Mexican side. The Mexican town was exciting, colorful, noisy, primitive, and inexpensive; the Arizona Nogales was a bustling, busy border town with many merchant stores.

When we arrived that afternoon, we were surprised to see a cafe with the sign "Border Delicatessen." Sally and I had not had delicatessen food for nearly five months. Surely this couldn't be the same type of deli that we were used to in Cleveland or Chicago.

We were greeted by the proprietor, a small, plump, charming middle-aged woman with a New York accent, who introduced herself as Mrs. Lasky. She did indeed have the real thing. We ate heartily of blintzes, lox and corned beef, and washed it down with authentic matzo ball soup. We established an immediate rapport with her and learned she had come to Arizona with her tubercular husband and two daughters some fifteen years previously. As she plied us with her wonderful food, she regaled us with stories of the town. Her daughter, Helen, and her husband, Zellie, whose family owned the local department stores, lived nearby and she thought we should all meet. With that, she phoned Helen who came to the restaurant right away, and we were introduced to a lovely blonde, smiling, friendly young woman who established an immediate friendship with us. She then called her husband, Zellie, to come meet us. Tall, lean, ruddy, bright looking, and handsome, Zellie had just come in from solo flying. On Thursdays, he left the store to fly his airplane. He was friendly and gracious, and upon learning that we needed a place to live told us they had an apartment behind their home and offered to rent it to us. His house was only fifteen miles from the campsite where I was to establish the new hospital.

Nogales had a very active social life. Their family was well known. Zellie had four brothers, several sisters, and many cousins, all involved in business in this small town. They were, without exception, cordial and amicable. There were parties, outings or gatherings almost nightly, and Sally and I felt fortunate to be included in their activities.

We were invited to attend a party Helen and Zellie were giving the following Saturday, and during my unpacking Zellie noted a green suit I had bought in Cleveland after finishing my internship. It was a bilious green with a red stripe in it. I bought it because it was on sale. Zellie took one look at the suit and said, attempting to keep a straight face, "You know, Al, this suit just isn't you." Helen agreed, and Sally said, "I told you so, Al!"

Zellie asked me to bring my suit and meet him at his department store the next morning. When the green suit and I arrived, he said, "I'm going to put this into the stock, and I'm sure we'll sell it. We can replace this with another suit that will look better on you." With that, he took me to the better suit department, helped me select a suit much more expensive than the one I had "traded in." He also told me that inasmuch as he paid wholesale prices, I could select a sport jacket, a pair of trousers, and a sweater, and Sally could have a new skirt and blouse as part of the trade. We were both overwhelmed by this graciousness, and appreciated what he was trying to do for us.

The following Monday after dinner, which we often ate together, he started to laugh and told us about a funny incident that occurred at the store. "You remember that green suit with the red stripe," he said, "that bilious looking suit? Well, I sold it to a customer from across the border, who was delighted with the suit. Two days later, a young man came into the store, asked for me, told me he saw the suit I had sold to his brother and liked it so much he would like one just like it." We laughed until our bellies hurt.

While we were enjoying Nogales and I was busy organizing the new camp hospital there, it was becoming apparent that world affairs were not good. We heard radio reports of what was occurring in Europe, although, as yet, we did not know what Hitler was doing in the concentration camps. The war clouds seemed to be gathering closer and closer to the USA. I suggested to Sally that I felt that I should join the Army at this time, before the USA got actively involved. I would be insured a good residency post if I volunteered before being called, and we certainly needed the money, as I would start as a First Lieutenant. If I had a three-year internal medicine military residency, I could then go into practice, finally ready — so, volunteer I did! Since war had not been declared, I was allowed to designate my areas of medical interest, I selected internal medicine, as I planned to practice that specialty after my training. I requested a three year residency in medicine at the Walter Reed Hospital in Washington, D.C.

One month later, my orders came in: First Lieutenant, subject to physical exam, assigned to Fort Sill, Lawton, Oklahoma, Field Artillery with the 45th National Guard. What a shocking surprise this was! No Internal Medicine, no Walter Reed Hospital, no Washington, D.C., but Fort Sill, Lawton, Oklahoma in Field Artillery!

Numerous telephone calls, telegrams, letters, etc., were all to no avail. "Buddy, you're in the Army now." And that was that.

Although we had not yet entered the war, the situation looked ominous, and all the 45th Division of the National Guard from Louisiana, Arizona, and Texas were called to Fort Sill for further preparatory training. It strained the resources of the small town of Lawton, with a population of approximately 11,000, trying desperately to accommodate 36,000 to 40,000 recruits and officers with families. It was impossible to find housing and many had to find lodging in one of the neighboring small towns and commute twenty miles or more daily to the post. The soldiers were put up in tents, and I was in charge of a tent hospital with fifty-seven cots, a wooden floor surrounded by muddy grounds, with a separate latrine. This was truly Hollywood's "M*A*S*H."

One of my nurses invited Sally and me to live with her in her own home. She was married and had a ten-year-old boy. Her husband was a funeral director for Lawton and we got along famously. Sally taught them how to enjoy gefilte fish and chicken soup, and they in turn showed us how honey baked ham and venison were prepared.

About two months after my assignment to Fort Sill a severe pneumonia epidemic occurred. Almost every other recruit had pneumonia, and I must have had a bad case of the flu, since I was running a high temperature myself. With no medical replacements, I had to continue to administer to my soldiers. Our nurse-landlord and her husband,

Janet and Hank Clair, decided to take their two week vacation, to go deer hunting. Off they went in a hurry, leaving us a note. Two days later I received a telegram ordering me to transfer to Brooke General Hospital at Fort Sam Houston in San Antonio, Texas. I was to report there the following day at 4:00 P.M. We hastily packed our few belonging, left a note and our newly purchased victrola as a gift for the Clairs, apologizing for not being able to say goodbye in person, and left money for the rent.

The following morning at 6:00 A.M., in near blizzard weather, we packed the car, cleaned the ice off the windshield, warmed up the car, and off we drove with our maps to find San Antonio, Texas.

About eight hours later we drove into San Antonio and down a street called "San Pedro." The sun shone though it was December 20th. Poinsettias bloomed at doorways. As we passed an area known as San Pedro Park, we saw people playing tennis in white shirts and shorts. We had just left Fort Sill, with 20 degree temperature, a pneumonia epidemic, icy winds and ice-encrusted roads. This wonderful green land called "San Antonio, Texas," inspired me to say, "Sally, if I ever get out of this Army alive, this is where we're going to settle." Which is what we did!

After the Pearl Harbor incident I was busy doing cardiology examinations at Brooke General Hospital, and listening to the recruit's chests as they took their deep breaths. After being stationed there for six months, I began to develop a severe form of asthma. My superior officer, Major Ben Sweet, was an allergist and interested in my asthmatic problem. He thought it was due to infection and attempted to overcome the infection through the respiratory tract by using a new experimental research development, an aerosol sulfanilamide.

What Dr. Sweet and I didn't know was that I was developing an additional allergy to the sulfanilamide vapor. Although breathing the aerosol insufflations probably was killing the bacteria, the allergic reactions to the drug was markedly aggravating the asthma. I became progressively worse and finally was told that I had to be discharged from the Army. I was furious at this! I had no source of income and I had gone to great lengths to join the Army prior to the war, and enjoyed my post at Fort Sam Houston. I protested vehemently, but to no avail. This time, "Buddy, you're out of the Army." I went back to civilian clothes, suffering from asthma, broke, and still needing a medical residency program.

Residency — This is a Surgeon?

Honorably discharged from the Army and experiencing a winter in San Antonio without ice and snow, I made the decision to apply for a medical residency in Texas. There was a war time shortage of residents. So I applied to the Green, County Hospital in San Antonio, and received an appointment. I surmised the hospital would have a large patient load and present a wealth of pathological cases to study. As it served a largely Hispanic population, I was assured of treating many diabetic and cardiovascular patients, since these patients have an inordinate incidence of these diseases. Also, as the attending staff physicians rarely came to the county hospital, and as there were ample interns to do the scut work, it would be a great opportunity for residents to study and treat the patients.

As I recalled my own difficult internship and how badly we had been manipulated by the residents, I felt kindly toward my group of fourteen interns. I didn't sell them hospital issue scrub suits like the senior resident, Bard, did to us during our internship at Cleveland's Mt. Sinai, and I was always available to help.

There was a very active emergency service with knife wounds, fractures, bullet injuries, and auto accidents. It was necessary to learn some Spanish in order to get a decent history and physical, and I learned to say, "Donde le duele" — where do you hurt?, and *"Respire profundo" — take a deep breath.* The rest of my examination was pantomime and mimic — a la Marcel Marceau! The nurses were young, cute and available, and the unattached interns and residents were constantly on the prowl but, of course as I told Sally, they all knew I was a happily married man!

One Friday afternoon, I received a phone call from the surgical resident asking me to cover for him as he wanted to visit his girlfriend in Galveston over the weekend. I reminded him that I was on the medical service and had done very little surgery, and what I had done was under close supervision at the Mt. Sinai. He reassured me that all was quiet on the surgical front. None of his patients had any undue complications and his interns could handle any emergency that presented itself. Reluctantly, I agreed to cover for him.

Naturally, I was awakened at 2:00 A.M. on Saturday morning by the surgical intern who told me that he had a patient with an intractable uterine hemorrhage that he could not handle. He had consulted with two other surgical interns and they all agreed that the patient needed an emergency hysterectomy. I suggested they call the staff physician, and they reminded me that if the staff man came and found the surgical resident absent, he would be discharged and his career ruined. As I had allowed the resident to sign out to me, I felt a sense of responsibility *not* to call the staff man; but, my first priority was to help the hemorrhaging patient.

I asked the surgical intern to bring one of the newer surgical gynecological books and I said, "Let's all sit down; let's read; and let's plan how to cut and sew!"

Preparation for the surgical procedure was like reading directions for assembling a chest of drawers from Sears "Do It Yourself" catalogue. After the patient was properly anesthetized, we read and cut and sewed, from A to B, to C, to D, and all went well. At completion, I *took a deep breath* in relief. Then, for an encore, I removed her appendix, as it is common practice to remove the useless vestige. The surgical interns observed the operation apprehensively and applauded when the patient left the O.R., and bathed in nervous perspiration, I applauded the anesthesiologist.

Twenty-five years later, Alicia Zuniga came to see me concerning diabetes and heart failure. I took a detailed history and learned that she had had a hysterectomy and appendectomy in the past, and had relatively decent diabetic control through the years. She had developed advanced coronary artery disease and had an enlarged heart and hypertension. During the physical exam, I commented favorably on the small, fine, linear scar in her abdomen and asked, "Who did your surgery?" She bolted upright on the examining table and answered, "You did!" I was sure she was mistaken! "Mrs. Zuniga, I think you must be wrong. As you know, I don't do surgery. I do internal medicine and cardiology." She was adamant. "No, you are the one who did my surgery." Once again I tried to correct the error. "Mrs. Zuniga, there are a lot of Dr. Cooper's in San Antonio. There was a surgeon named Dr. Kuper with a 'K' Perhaps he was the one." "No, Dr. Cooper, you did it. My hysterectomy was done at the Robert B. Green and YOU were the surgeon."

Then it all came back to me in a flash — the massive uterine hemorrhage in the middle of the night, the "by-the-book" cutting and sewing. How thankful I was that all went well that stressful night when the "amateur surgeon" covered for the real surgical resident twenty-five years ago; and how lucky that I complimented Mrs. Zuniga's neat incision!

* * * * *

I was invited to make rounds with Dr. Henry, one of the astute internists at the nearby Santa Rosa Hospital where he was Chief of Medicine. We stopped at the x-ray department as he wanted to review a film with the radiologist. Looking over his shoulder I noticed that it was an x-ray of a very unusual gallbladder filled with many faceted stones lying in an unusual position.

I remarked, "Isn't that a coincidence! Just last week I saw a patient at the Green Hospital who had exactly the same type of gallbladder (known as a phyrigium), and coincidentally, had the same number of gallstones in the same position!"

Then I noticed the name on the x-ray — "Mrs. Louis Golder." I began to smile. It seems that Mrs. Golder was concurrently seeing Dr. Henry as a private patient and attending my charity clinic at the Robert B. Green, and comparing our diagnoses and treatments. We both agreed that in addition to her gallbladder disease she had a low threshold of pain and a high degree of hypochondriasis and paranoia. We decided that Dr. Henry would phone her and tell her he'd met with me, that we had discussed her case, agreed on her diagnosis, and that she should select just "one" of us in one of the hospitals to continue with her treatment. She chose the older doctor!

In my last month of residency I learned that Dr. Henry had an overly-active, enlarged thyroid removed. I believe too much was removed because he became somewhat hypothyroid (low thyroid function). He moved sluggishly and his thinking lagged, he gained weight, and his exophthalmus (protrusion of the eyeballs) receded.

It was at that time that I became interested in cholesterol metabolism and recognized there was a reverse reciprocal relationship between cholesterol and thyroid activity. As the thyroid activity increased, the cholesterol decreased, and vice versa. I was concerned early on about the adverse effect of cholesterol deposits in the formation of atherosclerotic plaques in the blood vessels. When I suggested to the doctor that he seemed somewhat hypothyroid, he freely admitted that he was; but he was content with his condition. "I've lost my irritability," he said. "I move slower. Things don't bother me. I'm a much happier man, I enjoy my diminished sense of urgency."

I cautioned him that there was a penalty for his happiness in the resulting elevated serum cholesterol. His cholesterol was over the 350 milligrams mark. The normal range is 150 to 200 milligrams, and his concentration was dangerously high. I suggested timidly to this well versed diagnostician that he start taking small doses of thyroid to become euthyroid, that is, to normalize his thyroid, and this would lower his cholesterol to a satisfactory safe level. He was much too content with his new status in life as mildly hypothyroid, and rejected the suggestion. I was concerned about his hypercholesterolemia (excess cholesterol) and the ensuing developing atherosclerosis with its deleterious effects on his blood vessels, and implored him to take thyroid, but he refused.

Several years later I noticed him walking slowly down the Santa Rosa Hospital corridor, and observed him as he stopped and placed a nitroglycerine tablet under his tongue. Dr. Henry was revealing evidence of atherosclerotic blocking of his coronary vessels. He had angina pectoris!

Two months later he developed classical intermittent claudication. This is a syndrome in which one interrupts walking because of leg pain due to insufficient circulation in the lower extremities caused by cholesterol atherosclerosis in the leg blood vessels. This condition did not respond to vasodilators. Surgical by-pass, angioplasty, and laser treatments had not yet been developed. Within the year, he had a minor stroke and developed hemiparesis (partial paralysis on the left side). Eight months later, he had two successive coronary occlusions and succumbed in cardiac arrest despite repeated electric shock applications. I believe these complications could have been retarded or perhaps avoided had he heeded the warnings of his dangerously high cholesterol; but, this was not yet the dawning of the Age of Cholesterol.

My First Hat — Practicing Medicine

The Black Bag — House Calls — The Office

The time had come. I was ready and eager to accept the challenges of medical practice. Having made many professional and social contacts in San Antonio, we decided to remain there. We found the city charming, with a beautiful winding river coursing through the downtown area. The Hispanic atmosphere was warm, colorful, intriguing and exciting.

At last I was ready personally to accept the responsibility of diagnosing and treating internal medical problems manifested in all of its forms — acute, chronic or degenerative. I felt prepared to contend with disabilities, congenital or acquired. I anticipated helping people beset by problems of depression and anxiety, brought on by organic disease, or the complications of aging, substance abuse or venereal disease. I would have to relieve with tact and skill the suffering people bring upon themselves as a result of social maladjustments and behavioral misconduct. Iatrogenic disease (caused by drugs, physicians' errors or hospital infections) would have to be contended with. And finally, I would have to face the ultimate test for a physician: the death of a patient whose life I had struggled to save and lost and then how to help to console the grieving family.

I mused to myself, "these will be windmills that this new Dr.

79

The Black Bag

Cooper of LaMancha will have to attack with his medical lance. I was ready!

In addition to the stethoscope, the symbol of the physician at that time was the black "doctor's bag." This satchel-shaped bag, with drawers for various medications, housed the portable emergency equipment that the practicing MD carried on house calls. I had already located the black bag of my dreams. It cost $28 and it was beautiful: grainy black leather, not too shiny, and boasted a pull-down flap which had four small drawers for vials and bottles, plus a long, narrow drawer for syringes.

It was prominently displayed in the window of the Physicians and Surgeons Supply Company at the corner of Broadway and Houston Streets. For months, as a resident, I had admired it in the window — peering longingly at its many wonders. Occasionally, I had mustered up sufficient courage to enter the premises and examine it. Now at last, that coveted black bag, with all that it symbolized, became mine.

Along with the black bag I purchased supplies that I felt would be needed for various house calls and emergencies. First, I bought my own stethoscope. Those I had used previously were borrowed and inferior. Then I bought the portable sphygmomanometer for taking blood pressures. Next came the Welch-Allen otoscope and ophthalmoscope. These were interchangeable to the hand-held battery powered light. Thus, one could examine eyes, ears, nose and throat with this one versatile instrument. It also had a tongue depressor attachment. In addition, I purchased a tuning fork for testing vibratory sense and a hard rubber reflex hammer for neurological examinations.

After selecting with great deliberation these basic instruments which would be kept inside the bag, I was ready for the exciting choice of the necessary supplies to keep in its various compartments. Insulin for diabetics; glucose for those who took too much insulin or were in diabetic shock; needles, syringes for the various injectables; ampules of digitalis for cardiac failure; morphine and demerol for pain; calcium gluconate for tetany; injectable mercu-hydrium for diuresis; atropine for spasms; tranquilizers in tablet and injectable form; luminal for sedation; vitamin K for overdoses of anticoagulants; injectable quinidine for irregularity of the heart and nitroglycerine for angina; adrenaline for asthma and severe allergic conditions; nitroprusside for elevated blood pressure, ephedrine for shock; and dilantin for attacks of epilepsy.

In addition, I stocked my wonderful bag with tourniquets to handle excessive bleeding and help prepare a vein for intravenous injection. Also included, of course, were alcohol, iodine, bandages and a couple of ace bandages. With this copious pharmacopeia I carried the Merk's Manual, a small reference book carried by all doctors, to help them quickly recall which drug to use for each condition.

Holding the black bag in my right hand, I felt equipped to take on the medical challenges of the world. If, on a house call, I was presented with a problem beyond the capabilities of the accessories I carried in this bag, I would immediately call the admitting office and send the patient to the hospital.

My black doctor's bag has been replaced today by the Brown Bag. The Brown Bag is a beautiful wood sculpture of my original black bag, carved in all its timeworn intimate detail in a deep, rich Mexican mahogany, even including a wooden replica of my stethoscope draped over the top of the bag. This prized sculpture was done by my good friend and patient Naomi Seigmann, an eminent Mexican sculptor who works in many different media.

On my retirement, Sally sent Naomi my old battered, dusty black bag as a model. The wooden sculpture, standing proudly on our piano as a poignant reminder of my earliest days in practice, is so like the old leather bag that people are drawn to finger it, to try to probe its contents. It never fails to amaze its admirers with its life-like illusion.

While waiting to find a site for my office, I volunteered to make house calls for some of the well-established practicing physicians. I welcomed these house calls, not only for the remuneration, but because they gave me an opportunity to see the patient in his environment, and to study the relation of the patient with the family. One can determine whether domestic factors, or stress, or diet, or bad health habits contribute to the complaints. Is the patient a hypochondriac and do family members placate him and help exaggerate the illness? Or, is the patient stoic and belittles the problem while the family pleads with him to tell how often the attacks occur and their true severity? All this information is invaluable in coming to a diagnosis.

Dr. Henry signed out to me the first weekend I started my practice, and at 1:00 A.M., I had my first emergency telephone call. I was asked to see Mrs. Lintz. Her husband, in a marked foreign accent, complained wildly on the telephone that his wife was in terrific pain and needed a doctor immediately. I entered the house, and at first was not sure who was the patient. The husband was walking rapidly from room to room, yelling, "We need help! We need help! We need relief" When I first approached him, believing he was the patient, he pointed to his wife, an obese elderly woman, less than five feet tall, with straggly gray hair, bent over, holding her abdomen, grimacing with pain and yelling, "I kent stand it! I kent do it! I kent stand it! Vot am I going to do?"

Here indeed was a challenge. Who was going to give me a history? Should I try to get it from the husband or from the wailing woman who was apparently in acute distress? The husband kept repeating: "She needs help! She can't do it! She can't do it" I was beginning to get some sort of clue. I went over to Mrs. Lintz, convinced her to sit down, and said patiently, "What is your problem, Mrs. Lintz?" She said in a thick Russian accent: "I kent do it. I kent do it. I tried all night, but I kent. It's hurting me terrible." She pointed to her abdomen. I asked her to lie down on the bed and went over her abdomen very carefully and found the bladder was distended up to her umbilicus (belly button). Her chest was clear; heart rate normal; and the blood pressure was only slightly elevated. She was sweating profusely. She would repeatedly jump up saying, "I kent do it. I kent. It hurts. It hurts," and pointed this time to her pelvic region. It dawned on me that she was trying to tell me that she couldn't urinate and this could explain her bladder distension. I asked her how many hours had passed since she had urinated. She told me she had been unable to "pish" all day long, and every time she tried to "pish," she couldn't "pish!"

Imagine my chagrin when I recalled stocking every injectable, every medication, all the instruments in my new black bag, and it had never occurred to me that I would need a catheter to relieve a urethral obstruction. What an embarrassing situation! The new doctor appears on the scene, confident and bold, and quickly makes a diagnosis, and hasn't the equipment to handle the problem. I was certain that after this fiasco I would never get another referral from Dr. Henry. A possible solution occurred to me. I told Mr. Lintz to fill the bathtub with hot water, and we placed her in the tub. I told her to "urinate in the tub." She kept repeating. "What d'ya mean? I should pish in the water?" I said, "Yes, pish in the water." Fortunately, her spasm alleviated itself in the hot water, and out flowed a thin yellow stream, and she emptied her bladder with a great sigh of relief. I was redeemed!

I met Mrs. Lintz at the hospital early the next morning and had an x-ray taken of her abdomen, a flatplate, or KUB (kidney-ureter-bladder) film. As suspected, a large stone (calculus) was lying in the bladder pressing against the opening. I referred her to a urologist who crushed the stone with an instrument and removed the particles. Of course, I was her hero. Within a few days she called all her friends to tell them about the bright new doctor and told them they should certainly become his patients. "He doesn't give shots and besides, he only charged me three dollars and spent almost two hours the night I couldn't pish!"

The next day I purchased three different sized catheters and placed them in one of the drawers of my black bag. For the next forty years I never had a similar case.

*   *   *   *   *

Early one morning I was asked to make a house call to see a young girl who lived in one of the better neighborhoods in San Antonio. Her father was a successful, well-established executive, heading a large electrical contracting business.

I was greeted on arrival at a very nice, two-story large brick home, by a dignified man in his early forties, who thanked me for coming so soon after the call. I didn't tell him it was my only call for the day, and the office had no appointments scheduled.

The patient was a small, friendly, frightened young lady in her mid-teens. The complaint was fever, nausea, vomiting and abdominal cramping of two day's duration. This was the first attack of this disorder and there were no other complaints or findings referable to any other systems. The physical findings, as anticipated, were confined to the abdomen and classical for an acute appendicitis. I reported the results of my examination and told the father his daughter had acute appendicitis and needed immediate surgery to preclude a possible rupture.

He accepted my decision and after consulting with his wife, said, "OK, doctor, go ahead and operate." I explained that I did not do surgery, I did internal medicine, which was my specialty, and since I was new in this area, and didn't know all the doctors, if he would refer me to some of the local surgeons, I would call one to do the surgery. He gave me the name of a general practitioner who did surgery.

I called him, he presented himself at the house, repeated my physical exam, found a characteristic localized tenderness at McBurney's point (right lower quadrant of the abdomen), with the rebound pain and said, "Yes, your doctor is right, she does have acute appendicitis and I will admit her to the Physicians and Surgeons Hospital, and we'll operate this afternoon at 5:30 P.M.

Then he turned to me and said, "Would you like to assist me?" I thanked the doctor, and told him that I did internal medicine and cardiology and did not do any surgery. With that, the father of the child put his arm around me and suggested patronizingly, "Maybe you should go ahead and help the doctor operate. Then you will learn how to do an appendectomy." How would I explain to the people in San Antonio what an internist is?"

PHARMACIST, GIVE THEM AN ASPIRIN

Dr. Sidney Kalis, San Antonio's leading pediatrician, moved into a large suite of offices across the hall from my small office. He had a huge practice, and was very well respected in the city. Sidney told me about a small drugstore in the market area, the popular, old, well known Guadalupana Drugstore. The pharmacist there, Jose Gonzales, who had equipped a small physician's office in a room behind the drugstore, was looking for a physician who would come each evening to practice in this office. The equipment and the office were to be rent free. Patients would generally come into the drugstore and if they had a medical problem they were referred to the back room to see the doctor. My only obligation was to make sure each patient who came to see me received a written prescription, even if it was just aspirin, and was referred back to the pharmacy. I was to charge $2 per visit. The druggist would supply everything needed for the practice; bandages, needles, syringes, hemostats, tourniquets, antiseptics, all would be available. As new patients were few and far between at my own downtown Moore Building office, and the only other income was derived from the night and weekend calls, I readily accepted the proposition. I practiced there for two to three hours each evening and on weekends, attending six to ten patients at each meeting. The $12 to $20 earned at Guadalupana sustained us in those lean days.

The drugstore was bright and cheerful and there was always a good deal of exciting activity. Jose had a large parrot in a cage who constantly shrieked, "Guadalupana Drugstore, come on in!" I learned a good deal of Spanish and made quite a few friends. Some of the patients I encountered there remained with me through the years. What delighted me most in this pharmacy was Jose's display of beautiful antique porcelain apothecary jars which he had been collecting for twenty years from almost every country in the world. I was fascinated with their history and developed an intense interest in them, and decided that as soon as I could afford it, I would start collecting them. Today, I have a collection of well over 300 porcelain apothecary jars that occupy two entire walls in my living room.

Guadalupana Pharmacy was just two blocks from the famous Matamoras Street, San Antonio's red light district. In the forties prostitution was legal in San Antonio. The girls were required to have monthly tests for syphilis and weekly studies for gonorrhea. Every night I had the unpleasant task of taking several vaginal smears for gonorrhea. The fee was $2. Once a month I did venipunctures and sent the blood to the state lab for Wassermann syphilis tests. For this I charged $3. The girls were very young and proud of their profession. They did not need a guard (pimp) to protect them, since prostitution was legal in the Alamo city. The "ladies" exposed their wares in the open doors and windows of their "Houses" to potential clients and sightseers who drove along gaping at the "wares" so openly displayed. Some girls had their own public relations staff, in the persons of their little brothers, who would parade down the streets asking, "You wanna sleep with my sister? It only costs you three bucks and she's beautiful." If refused, the enterprising little entrepreneurs volunteered to wash your car for fifty cents.

Talkative Felipa with heavy makeup, tight purple pants, and a low cut revealing blouse, was not as self-conscious around me as the other "Ladies." Always last in line for her tests, she managed to linger on in the office to talk. Each week she would regale me with episodes of her family history. Her father left the house when she was six. Her mother, a severe diabetic, worked part-time in a local tortilla factory. She had three younger sisters, and one small brother. There was never enough food, and they wore discarded clothes until she started her "profession." Although a fifth grade dropout, she planned on returning to school and graduating and then studying to become a nurse, a specialist in "Crud Sickness" (her term for venereal diseases) she said "cause I know all about them infections, and I want to succeed in life."

What a paradox. Jose Gonzales told me at a later date that he heard Felipa did indeed come up a few notches. She became a madam, running a fancy "House" of her own. So apparently she did succeed, even if in her own fashion!

Several years later, long after I had given up the evening drug-store practice, prostitution was outlawed and all the brothels were closed, and the Best Little Whorehouses in Texas were gone!

*   *   *   *   *

The equipment for my downtown office came from the Physicians and Surgeons Supply, across the street from the New Moore Building. I met Mr. Pierce, the friendly owner, and explained to him that I had no money, but I anticipated a great future, and I proposed that he let me have equipment on credit. I needed an examining table with stir-rups, standing spotlights, blood pressure equipment, needles, scales, syringes, and even a basal metabolic rate machine to evaluate for thy-roid disorders, another less expensive examining table, a diathermy machine, blood pressure equipment, and the numerous odds and ends needed to start practice. The very pleasant Mr. Pierce agreed, and the equipment was delivered within two days. All I still needed was fur-niture for a reception room, some throw rugs in the various rooms, desk and chairs for myself and the receptionist.

I recalled that on my first house call for the grateful Mrs. Zintz, who finally "pished" in the tub, her husband told me he was in the fur-niture business. I boldly approached him in his Commerce Street store, explained my situation, and asked him for credit on an inexpensive sofa, three chairs, a rug, a second-hand oak desk and swivel chair and a side chair for the desk. I also selected a desk and chair for Sally, who had left her job selling stockings at a downtown department store at $3 a day, to be my first receptionist. Mr. Zintz agreed, patted me on the back and assured me that I would succeed in San Antonio. He didn't know how my knees shook and my stomach flip-flopped, worrying about the future.

My training at Mt. Sinai Hospital in Cleveland, also taught me to be an acceptable medical lab technician. I decided to equip a small laboratory and do my own minor lab work. I could do complete blood counts, urinalysis, blood sugars, BUN (measurements for retention of urinary products) studies for liver proteins, uric acid for gout, protein analysis for metabolic disorders, sedimentation rates for infections, etc. I also had x-ray and Duoroscopic training at Boston's Peter Bent Brigham Hospital and convinced Charles Moss, of San Antonio's General Electric X-Ray Department to install a complete combination x-ray and fluoroscope in my office without down payment. Mr. Moss was generous and also equipped me with electrocardiographic equipment. I had the Moore Building carpenter build a small dark room, and Charlie helped me put in developing and fixing fluid tanks. I was prepared.

Sally assumed the position as receptionist/nurse combination for the office. She sat at a desk in the outer room, which was both the business office and reception room. My consultation room and the reception area were separated only by a thin paneled wall. We communicated by using a buzzer system which indicated that the other should pick up the phone. Initially, I had one examining room containing an examining table and floor lamp, and I used the same ophthalmoscope, otoscope, stethoscope, reflex hammer, and blood pressure apparatus that I carried in my black bag. Adjacent to this room, we built a small lead lined room for fluoroscopy and x-ray. There was a small narrow hall between my suite and the fire escape, and I convinced Mr. Jacobs the building manager, to allow me to convert that into a lab, agreeing to keep the doors unlocked at all times so as to abide by the fire laws.

We were finally ready. All we needed was patients! To develop more exposure and contacts, I joined both the Temple and Synagogue. I volunteered to give Red Cross First Aid courses at all the churches in town. Cardiopulmonary Resuscitation classes were not yet in vogue. I offered my medical services at numerous church charity clinics.

The days rolled by slowly and the office patients were sparse. I was beginning to get a bit depressed and anxious. I recall having lunch with Sally at the Manhattan Restaurant on Houston Street after a particularly depressing few days when only one patient came in with a mild respiratory infection, and the ensuing apprehension I developed about our financial situation. I ordered a bowl of soup and experienced for the first time, cardiospasm from anxiety. I was so tense, anxious and worried, I couldn't swallow my soup. I became an expert in cardiospasm (nervous tightening of the lower esophageal sphincter), having had frequent personal episodes of the condition. There was a reverse reciprocal relationship between the cardiospasm attacks and the improvement of the practice. When I had more patients and finally could cope financially, the spasms left.

My wife has always had a good sense of humor. To overcome some of the long dull days in the office she would pull all sorts of stunts. One day a very attractive young lady about nineteen-years-old came to consult me. In discussing her case with Sally as she waited to see me, she mentioned that she was about ten pounds underweight and wanted to put on some weight as she was entering another beauty contest. It seems she had previously won the Junior Beauty Contest at the nearby Lackland Air Force Base.

Sally cheerfully said to the new patient, "Doctor Cooper is excellent when it comes to putting weight on people. He actually, in the last several months, put twelve pounds on me, so when you see him, you tell him you want him to put twelve pounds on you the way he did for me."

When the young lady was brought into my office, I was pleased to see such an attractive girl. She was a tall, willowy brunette with a very pleasing figure, beautiful white teeth, and a fetching dimple when she smiled. After obtaining a history and doing a physical, I found that her big problem was that she wanted to put on ten pounds. She said, "I would like you to put weight on me just exactly as you did for the girl at the receptionist desk."

At that, I quickly buzzed Sally at the front desk and said: "Are you sure?" She answered, "No! No! No! I was only kidding." Sally was four months pregnant and had gained exactly twelve pounds.

The patient's physical was negative with the exception of a mild anemia. I placed her on a high caloric nutritious diet, told her to eat four meals daily and to discontinue smoking, and promised she would start to gain promptly. Her anemia turned out to be a microcytic hypochromic type which is often associated with iron deficiency in a female with heavy menstrual cycles. I wrote a prescription for Feosol, an absorbable iron preparation with no side effects and told her to take the tablet three times daily, and to return for a repeat blood count in three weeks.

When she returned as directed, I promptly took her to the lab and repeated the blood count. Enthusiastically, I exclaimed that the medication did exactly what I anticipated it would.

"The Feosol restored your low blood count to above normal!"

"But, Doctor," she said, "you didn't allow me a chance to explain it to you — I lost the prescription the day you gave it to me and was embarrassed to call for another."

Thinking quickly I countered, "Of course, it was your high caloric diet that overcame your anemia."

"But, Doctor, I also lost the copy of the diet, and incidentally, haven't gained an ounce since my first visit." What an embarrassing situation!

Thereafter, whenever a patient returned for a repeat visit, after the customary greeting, I would inquire almost immediately, "Did you follow my instructions?" — medicine, diet or whatever the orders were. In this manner I covered all bases to prevent such a repetition.

An Epidemic Averted

In the early days of my practice in the downtown building many patients were referred to me by the tenants, and from the surrounding office buildings and retail stores. I called them my "neighborhood downtown" practice. I was consulted by a nurse, Miss Collins, who worked for one of the surgeons on the sixth floor. Her complaint evolved around a watery mucus diarrhea that had been present for almost a month. She complained of intermittent diarrhea, foul smelling loose watery stools with mucus, and occasionally with blood. There was no fever and no other specific complaints. She was tiny, about five feet-two, attractive, but quite nervous with a fine tremor of the hand, jerked her head constantly and sweated freely. Her routine lab and physical were negative with the exception of some slight tenderness in the liver area, and definite evidence of distension of the abdomen.

During the course of the interview she made note that she didn't like the doctor she worked for, that he was an ultra-perfectionist and that she was very uncomfortable whenever he was around her. She also admitted that she was having problems with her boyfriend. She had been going steady for three years and he just wouldn't ask the question for which she was waiting.

Recognizing that this was a highly anxious female, my first impression was that we were dealing with 'functional bowel distress,' the so-called spastic colon. I suggested to her at that time that she try a low residue, nonlaxative diet. I gave her antispasmodics and mild tranquilizers. After intense questioning about her relations with her boyfriend and her work arrangements with the doctor, I suggested that probably they were the etiological factors causing her tense, spastic nervous bowel condition. She seemed quite relieved because she was concerned that perhaps she had some serious medical disorder. I suggested a return visit in a week for re-evaluation.

She returned in one week complaining that she felt worse. She did seem to be somewhat dehydrated on this examination. I realized that perhaps I should reconsider the seriousness of the condition and suggested a proctoscopic examination. I had just bought my first shiny metal straight-tube proctoscope with a light bulb at one end. I was now ready to do rectal and lower colon examination which I knew would be quite helpful in evaluating bowel disorders. I sent her home and told her to cleanse the bowel and to return in the morning for the proctoscopic examination.

The following morning the scope was entered slowly and carefully, but it was quite painful to the patient. I noticed with alarm that the mucus membrane of the bowel was blood-tinged, and as I cleaned away some of these areas, there were many small bottle shaped ulcers seen in the rectum and the lower colon. The intervening mucosa was completely normal. I took a swab and wiped some of the material from the ulcer and placed it on a slide and studied it under the microscope. Initially I thought I saw an occasional cyst of the "Entamoeba histolytica" and perhaps some of the live trophozoites. The preparations were not ideal for evaluation because of the great amount of mucus in the specimens.

I suggested she return in the morning after taking an early morning laxative and that we would study four or five of her fresh stools with saline to look for active trophozoites of the Entamoeba histolytica and to make some iodine stains for cysts of the amoeba. She returned in the morning quite apprehensive, and I sat her in a room close to a lavatory, and as she produced each specimen, the nurse brought them to me in the laboratory while they were warm. I studied them in saline under the microscope and made and stained some slides. Among the stool specimens, three were heavily infested with the trophozoites of amoeba and in two slides, the cysts were well defined. She had amoebic colitis and it was necessary for me to immediately start therapy. We were then using "diodoquin" and "chloroquine." By the fifth day the spasm, tenderness, diarrhea and abdominal distention were gone, and the smiling patient came to see me to express gratitude. I checked her stools the following morning and the patient was cured. She was told not to leave the doctor as she had a very good job, and to make peace with her boyfriend. Neither of them was responsible for her medical condition. I was wrong.

*   *   *   *   *

Mrs. Potter, the wife of the podiatrist who was on the fourth floor of the New Moore Building, came to see me because of abdominal cramps, diarrhea, bloating and blood in her stools for three weeks. There was also nausea and vomiting and a low grade fever. She had considerable pain in the right upper quadrant of the abdomen in the region of the liver. Examination disclosed definite enlargement of the liver with severe tenderness. Her colon was markedly distended. I thought perhaps that she was a patient with spastic colon, but she didn't have that type of personality. Actually she was quite tough! She worked with her husband and ran the entire office and ran her husband, and was a difficult person to get along with. If anyone were to have a spastic colon, it would have been the husband who had to cater to all her peculiar whims.

Because of the enlarged, tender liver, I made some enzyme studies for hepatitis, and found evidence of inflammation. Was it bacterial, viral, or parasitic? The x-ray of the abdomen showed an enlarged liver and the right lobe of the liver was not its normal rounded convex contour, but revealed upward peaking projection into the diaphragm. The diagnosis was "abscess of the liver."

This was a second occasion to use my shiny new metal proctoscope and after proper preparation, she returned for examination. Unbelievable! She had the same tiny water bottle ulcers that were seen in the rectal and colon areas of the nurse examined two weeks previously. Swabs were taken from the ulcer and slides were made, and there they were! The trophozoites and the cysts of amoebic colitis. Inasmuch as the liver was so badly involved and suggested hepatitis or liver abscess, complement fixation tests (serum study), were sent to Austin with a request for a "stat," that is, an immediate, response. Within forty-eight hours they called to say it was highly positive. This patient not only had an amoebic colitis, she had an amoebic abscess of the liver. She was treated with diodoquin and injections of emetine. In ten days she was back at work, once again ordering her husband all over the office, but happy to be there. The podiatrist said he was pleased to have her back bossing him around.

*   *   *   *   *

Two days later, the elevator operator of the New Moore Building asked me if he could come to the office after work as he was not feeling well. Jose was normally a very cheerful young man who greeted everyone upon entering the manually controlled elevator, and knew everyone by name. He was constantly telling jokes and stories. I had never heard him complain and was surprised that he thought he was sick.

His physical examination, history, laboratory studies and the x-ray of the abdomen all led to the suspicion of another possible case of amoebic colitis. The third use of the new proctoscope revealed the same ulcerated condition of the rectum and colon. The swabs, the slides, the complement fixation tests, all confirmed another case of amoebic colitis. At that time I was beginning to think that perhaps my proctoscope was a carrier, but of course, it was sterilized constantly and this was an impossible contention.

*   *   *   *   *

When Joe Gross, a salesman in Zale's Jewelry on the ground floor of the New Moore Building came to see me one Thursday afternoon with griping diarrhea, abdominal distension, fever, watery stool and blood, I began to suspect the worst and once again had this patient prepared for proctoscopic examination, repeated the tests and confirmed another case of amoebic colitis.

I called the pathologists of the two hospitals downtown and asked them whether we were experiencing an epidemic of amoebic colitis in San Antonio. I told them about my four cases in succession. Neither pathologist had seen an acute case of amoebic colitis for the past month. I was concerned about the possibility of a so-called "Typhoid Mary" type: that is a carrier who was spreading the infection. I then called two internist friends who had offices near the hospital, approximately three miles from my office. Neither one of them had seen a case. It then occurred to me to call Dr. Allen who had his office next to the post office downtown, and yes, he had seen two cases in the past month. There must be a downtown carrier of amoebic colitis, I excitedly concluded!

*   *   *   *   *

It was Friday afternoon at 3:00 P.M. and I had not had my lunch yet, and I was starving! I usually ate at one of the downtown restaurants but it was too late. I remembered that there was a small diner in my office building on the first floor known as "Manuel's Diner." Manuel was famous for his so-called "make-it-yourself" sandwich. He had a very busy small dining room and people stood in line to get his famous sandwich which cost only $1.50. The ingredients for the sandwiches were prepared daily. He piled cut roast beef slices on one plate; beside it was a platter of sliced ham; next to that stood a large plate of sliced cheese; then came a large glass container of pickles; another large bowl contained olives; and finally a wide dish overflowed with lettuce and tomatoes; all lined up in linear fashion on a large narrow counter. Each customer would choose two slices of bread, and make his own sandwich in a buffet style. They had a few forks available, but the customers would pick the meat up with their hands and slap it between the slices of bread, piling up the ham, beef, cheese and vegetables to make a really "poor-boy" sandwich. All for a dollar and a half!

I was late for the big lunch crowd and sat at a small table directly opposite where Manuel was busy getting food ready for the evening meal. He was about forty-two-years-old, swarthy, with thick black curly hair, bushy eyebrows, acneic skin, a wide nose, walrus mustache, and enjoyed picking his nose through the grizzly hairs of his mustache. Maria, his short, fat thirty-five-year-old wife with pendulous breasts, wore a dark brown dress covered by a dirty gray apron, that probably was white — a long time ago. She was friendly and smiled and laughed easily. She wiped the dishes and utensils with a dirty, brown torn rag before placing them on the counter. "Eat good," was her frequent greeting to the customers, "plenty more." I noticed that Manuel had one of the circular manual meat-cutters and as he sliced the beef, he caught each slice with his open hand and slapped it onto a plate. I also noticed that his hands weren't very clean. After five minutes of slicing beef, which he piled on a plate, he put the ham on the circular cutter, manually using his blade in a similar fashion, and as the slices came off the cutting edge, he would catch them once again with his bare hand and slap them on another plate. So he did with the cheese as he prepared three large plates full of stacked slices of ham, beef and cheese. I then noticed that he had two wide-mouthed two gallon glass containers of olives and pickles, and he would put his hands into the olive jar coming out with a scoopful of olives which he would put on another plate. Likewise, he would put his hand into the pickle jar and pull out pickles and slice them onto a platter. About this time I stopped eating the sandwich I had prepared for myself.

I had seen enough! I left the diner in a hurry and paid for my sandwich, left a small tip and quickly went to the elevator to talk to the elevator operator. "Jose, where do you eat your lunch?" I inquired. "Oh," he said, "I always eat it at Manuel's because he lets me fix two sandwiches for the price of one because he knows I don't have too much money." "Thank you," I said. "Why did you ask?" I said, "I'll get back to you in a couple of days."

I ascended the elevator, couldn't wait to get to my office, ran to the phone and called the nurse who first came to me with the amoebic colitis. "Miss Collins," I asked, "where do you eat your lunch?" She said, "Oh, occasionally at one of the large restaurants, but when we're really busy I just run downstairs and have one of those famous "make-it-yourself, sandwiches." I said, "At Manuel's?" She said, "Yes, have you tried it? They're great! Why do you ask?" I replied, "I'll get back to you shortly."

When the doctor's wife told me that she also on occasion — when they were running overtime, ran downstairs and prepared herself a "make-it-yourself" sandwich, I knew I was on pretty sure ground. I called Joe Gross at Zale's Jewelry and Joe also said, "Oh, I eat at Manuel's. He makes the best roast beef sandwich in town."

With all this cohesive information, I returned to Manuel's Restaurant and called him aside into a corner. "Manuel," I said, "I think we have a serious problem." He was very apprehensive, sweated profusely and said, "What's the problem? I don't understand." I said, "Sit down, I want to ask you a few medical questions." "Oh," he said, "I'm strong as a bull. Strong as an ox. I'm never sick." I asked him, "Have you had diarrhea recently or in the recent past?" "No," he says. "I have normal movements. I'm strong as an ox," he repeated again. "Doctor, are you looking for business?" he asked. I said, "In a sense, yes." Then I asked him, "Have you been to Mexico recently?" He said, "No, I never go to Mexico. I live on the West Side. As a matter of fact, I've never been out of San Antonio."

I told Manuel about the four cases of amoebic colitis and reported to him that each one of these patients had eaten in his restaurant and it was very important to test him, his wife, the dishwasher, and the busboy for the possibility that one of them might be a carrier of an amoebic infection. A carrier is an individual who will have the cysts and trophozoites in the intestinal tract, but not necessarily be sick with it. This was the case with "Typhoid Mary," who produced an epidemic of typhoid in Chicago. She carried the typhoid bacilli in the gallbladder and excreted it in the stool, but she was not sick with typhoid herself. She was a carrier, just as I suspected someone in the restaurant was.

I suggested that Manuel report to the office the following morning prepared for a proctoscopic examination and to have stool studies. He was loaded with cysts and trophozoites in great profusion. His wife was also examined and was normal, as were the helper and the dishwasher. I suggested that Manuel bring in his children and any relatives that had had close contact with him for further studies. Two of his four children were found to be infested with the amoeba, and one had had diarrhea for the past three weeks.

I talked to Manuel and suggested that he close the restaurant for two weeks while we treated him and every member of his family and intimate friends. When his stools were negative and he no longer passed the cysts and trophozoites, he could go back into the restaurant business. He reluctantly agreed and I called the City Health Department, and they closed the restaurant. He placed a sign on the front window saying "Closed for Repairs." "Will reopen in approximately two to three weeks."

Manuel took his therapy and all the members of his family, close friends and associates all took diodoquin. All had repeat stool examinations in two weeks and all were negative!

He was allowed to reopen his restaurant (colon now repaired) with the promise that once a week he would have studies done to make sure there were no recurrences. This was continued for a period of one month and all specimens were clear.

So Chicago had its "Typhoid Mary" and San Antonio its "Amoebic Colitis Manuel." When he reopened the restaurant the place was sparkling clean, and Manuel was wearing plastic gloves as he handled the food. Maria changed aprons daily and used paper towels for wiping dishes and counters.

MY MOTHER — THE SHILL

After father's coronary, my family moved to San Antonio to live with us. He was unable to work because of his cardiac condition, but mother was brimful of energy. Each morning she would send brother Harold off to school and tidy up the little house. She would then prepare father's lunch, bid him farewell, hop on the bus and come to sit in the reception room at my downtown office. These were the most delightful days of her life. Since there were so few patients in the office, she felt that if she sat quietly looking at a magazine, she would pretend she was a patient and whenever a patient did wander in, the office would not look so empty. The patient would be reassured that the doctor, although new, must be all right since he had several other patients.

This was a good idea in theory, but my mother was much too energetic and imaginative to just sit quietly reading a magazine, minding her own business. Whenever a patient came in and sat down, she would start a conversation. Unashamedly, she would inquire as to what the problem was. If the patient said, for example, that he had a painful arthritic condition, my mother would exclaim, "That's exactly what my problem was. I had the most painful arthritis of the hips. It went on for years. But that doctor in there is brilliant. Within days he correctly diagnosed my arthritis, gave the correct medication, and since then I've been free of pain, and I can walk, run and even jump."

And, right there in the office she was likely to demonstrate her prowess! From the next patient she might learn that the problem was a very bad cough that had gone on for several days. Mother would promptly report, "I had one of the worst coughs that anyone could have. It lingered for weeks. But that doctor in there, the one you're going to see, is positively brilliant. He quickly made the correct diagnosis of a bronchial problem, gave me the correct medicine, and within two days, the cough was gone and I have never felt better."

One patient brought to mother's attention that she was having problems with her intestinal area, that she had severe nausea, diarrhea and cramps that went on for weeks. Immediately my mother had an answer. "I used to have the worse spastic colon that anyone could have. I suffered for years and I went from doctor to doctor with no relief. But that new doctor, the one you're going to see, is an expert in gastrointestinal diseases. He examined me, took a few x-rays, and in no time discovered the problem. He gave me medicine, corrected my diet, and within one week I had an absolutely normal gastrointestinal tract. It was several months since and I've never had any trouble."

None of the patients knew that this cherubic little white-haired smiling woman on the sofa was my mother, nor did they know that the secretary/receptionist at the desk was my wife. These little vignettes played out in the reception room amused Sally enormously, and she would report them to me in great detail. I continued to caution my mother not to do it, but this was one of her great joys in life and I could not stop her. I was constantly fearful that the next patient who came in would be a man complaining of severe prostate trouble, and I could just hear my mother commiserating with him, "I used to have severe prostate trouble for years until that doctor in there corrected it and cleared me of all my prostate trouble!"

Mother liked to tell my friends that she always knew I would be a doctor when I grew up. For proof she proudly described an incident that occurred when I was four years old. Our next door neighbor in Cleveland had a little girl my age, and one day while I was eating a large chocolate cookie, the little girl asked for some. I broke the cookie in half, mother says, and gave her half. The little girl quickly gobbled it up. Later that afternoon, little Nancy was out in the backyard eating candy and when I asked her for some she refused. I reminded her that I had shared my cookie, but she still refused. With that, I put my finger down the back of her throat and forced her to vomit up the candy and return any residual cookie that might be left in her tummy. Mother said it was then that she knew I would be a gastroenterologist. My own interpretation of these events is different. I think it was the beginning of my determination never to let anyone take advantage of me.

There was another clue that convinced my mother that I would grow up to be doctor. In those day, during the depression, it was common for families to take boarders to help pay the rent. Our boarder was Dr. Brodie, an osteopath who had lost his license for performing abortions. Dr. Brodie became a close friend of my father's. They met when they were both selling life insurance for Metropolitan Life. Dr. Brodie resided in our back room, ate supper with us, and introduced us to various forms of health foods we had never seen such as buckwheat, blackstrap molasses, brewer's yeast, day old bread, and honey and molasses. I was especially fond of sneaking up into his room when everyone was gone and thumbing through his various medical books, particularly his book on gynecology. I was probably nine or ten at the time. On page 315 there was a drawing of the female genitalia which I found quite fascinating. After memorizing all the parts, I soon began to brag to my boyfriends in the neighborhood about my prize possession. Stealthily, I would sneak them upstairs and we would all peer wide-eyed at the amazing drawing on page 315. It soon reached the point that if we dropped the book accidentally, it would automatically open to page 315. Mother caught us at this one day, and she told my dad she was sure I was going to be a gynecologist.

Mother had the mistaken impression during our youth that thinness promoted susceptibility to tuberculosis. She didn't understand that tuberculosis was a cachectic disease and once infected, the patient became thin. So to prevent her children from developing tuberculosis she decided to fatten us. We had massive amounts of butter, milk, cream, and eggs forced upon us daily. Each meal had mashed potatoes saturated with butter, chicken fat, and egg yolk. In addition, for years she compelled us to drink two miserable tasting glasses of her specialty "The Google Moggle." This consisted of eight ounces of milk with cream, sugar, four eggs, and honey!

Mother was right, none of us contracted tuberculosis. But unwittingly, through the years, she promoted cholesterol deposition in our blood vessels.

INVASION OF THE FUNGUS

As a medical student, one is intrigued and stimulated by rare, bizarre, and serious clinical disorders; as a beginning practicing physician, however, one is excited but apprehensive when contending with the very unusual. One might practice for years without being exposed to a fascinating and rare illness. Then the next patient may present an unusual, extraordinary, uncommon disease. Early in my practice, as I was augmenting my meager income by seeing patients at night in the little office behind the Guadalupana drugstore in the Mexican Market, I did not anticipate any profound medical conditions. The complaints were for the most part the usual respiratory infections, the occasional acute venereal disease, the migraines and spastic colons; however, one night I was confronted with a bizarre type of skin infection in the forearm of a thin, forty-year-old Polish widow from a nearby farm in Lytle, Texas. Her husband had been dead for four years and she managed her small thirty-acre vegetable farm without help. She tilled the soil, planted and harvested, working from early morning until late night. But for all her hard work, she was hard pressed financially, as she had had several bad crops in the past two years.

She did not recall scratching or injuring her arm prior to the ensuing infection. She had not been bitten by any insect or rodent. The lesion on her right forearm was necrotic and exuded foul-smelling pus. The area was swollen and spread to the size of a small saucer. The lymph nodes under the right arm were markedly enlarged, tender, and also draining pus. This tiny Mrs. Gracie Moxa, her skin weather beaten and dry, looked far older than her years. She had stringy, disheveled hair, crooked yellow-stained teeth, was poorly dressed and wore torn men's shoes. She was feeling chilly and had an elevated temperature. I told her she probably had a serious infection in her system and should be hospitalized. She replied, "Doctor, I'm sorry. I can't afford to go to the hospital. I have no insurance. Please help me." I felt for this sick but gallant little lady, and asked her to come to my downtown office in the Moore Building at 10:00 A.M. the next day, and that I would study her in great detail in an attempt to make a diagnosis without hospitalizing her.

The next morning she came in complaining of a terrible night, coughing incessantly and bringing up pus in her sputum. Her temperature was 102 degrees and she was chilling more than the previous evening, but now was also experiencing joint and muscle pain. She reported that she had been sick for well over a week prior to seeing me but had continued working as she had three children to support, ages six to twelve, none of whom were old enough or big enough to help with farm chores. I was intrigued by the diagnostic problem and felt concern for this poor woman. I was determined to help her, but learned very little from her additional history.

The physical exam, however, was quite spectacular in the array of unusual findings. Mrs. Moxa had a large infected ulcer in the lower gum that also exuded pus. Her throat was violently red and inflamed. She had large inflamed lymph nodes in her neck draining the infection of her mouth and throat. Her lungs were full of rales and when she *took a deep breath* she had pleuritic pain on both sides of her chest. Her white blood count was markedly elevated. Urinalysis was normal, there was no evidence of diabetes. A chest x-ray, taken in my office, was quite revealing. There was widespread soft infiltrations in both lungs. While she was in the office, she coughed violently and brought up a good deal of greenish foul smelling sputum. Since I did not have a lab technician, I collected the sputum, placed it on a slide, stained it and studied it under the microscope, expecting to find it full of staphylococcus organisms. This would easily explain her medical problem. I was amazed at what I saw under the microscope. There were no staphylococci, no streptococci, or any other recognizable bacteria. Instead, the slide was loaded with yeast-like organisms with double contour walls, and all with considerable "budding," that is, the appearance of a crown of small beads attached to the cellwall. Her spleen was enlarged and she had enlarged painful lymph nodes throughout her body. By this time her temperature was 103 degrees. I also placed under the microscope some of the infected material from the ulcer on her lower gum, which also was loaded with the characteristic yeast-like organism with budding. I then scraped material from the infection in the forearm and

found that it too was loaded with pus cells and the double-walled con-
toured yeast organism with the budding.

I recalled learning in medical school about a rare fungus infection
which occurs primarily in Mississippi and Ohio River valleys, known
as Blastomycosis. I remembered that this particular yeast resided in
soil, and could on rare occasion infest people exposed to soil. It was difficult to believe I was on the threshold of diagnosing an extremely rare
disease so early in my practice. Everything seemed to fit the diagnosis.
A female farmer developed the infection in the lungs through inhalation of organisms from the soil. This produced the extensive pulmonary infections and the localized lesions in the gums and arms. Microscopic examination of material from all these areas, as well as the
sputum analysis, revealed the classic double-contoured budding yeast
cells of Blastomycosis. I had read about it, seen specimens of it, but
had never encountered the active disease in medical school, internship,
or in residencies. I knew I had to make the diagnosis promptly and
start early treatment, as this disease becomes rapidly widespread, affecting lung, liver, spleen, intestinal tract and the brain, and has a
ninety-two percent mortality rate. I took cultures of the material from
the various infected sites and smeared them on both blood agar and Sa-
baraud media and took them to the bacteriologist at the Santa Rosa
Medical Center. The pathologist called me excitedly two days later to
tell me there was a luxuriant growth of the particularly pathogenic organism characteristic of the yeast of Blastomycosis. He said the Sabar-
aud's, which is one of the more positive culture media for growth,
would take two weeks to a month for final confirmation. I could not
afford to allow that much time to elapse without starting treatment,
because the patient would succumb to the disease by the time the diagnosis was one hundred percent confirmed by culture. When Mrs.
Moxa returned two days later for interpretation of the intradermal skin
test I had injected, it was also strongly positive for Blastomycosis.
Therefore, I felt I was on secure ground and suggested hospitalization,
and promised to get her into the charity ward. It was essential that she
start her intravenous treatment immediately with the antifungal agent
Amphotericin B.

The case was so rare and spectacular that I presented it at the
Thursday medical conference at the Santa Rosa. This was my initiation
into case presentation before the medical staff. It was well-received and
many of the doctors went to the ward to see this unusual case, as they
had never see an "active" case of Blastomycosis. Mrs. Moxa's treatment

was continued for a period of twelve days. I spoke with the hospital administrator, Sister Moran, who was very understanding, and allowed the patient to be treated as a teaching case. Thus she was not charged for her hospital stay. Mrs. Moxa recovered fully; the lungs cleared, the spleen and lymph nodes receded to normal, and the skin and mouth infections resolved with minimal scarring. For years after this, Mrs. Moxa continued to bring me goodies from her harvest which I enjoyed thoroughly — tomatoes, cucumbers, lettuce — and the spinach which I never had the heart to tell her was not my favorite. I never saw another case of Blastomycosis.

THE SISTERS

When I first met Dr. Potts he was in his early seventies, an old time general family practitioner. He continued to do some general surgery, deliver babies, and set fractures. However, his knowledge of medicine was a disaster. This was not due to his advanced age, but probably due to the fact that he had never really learned much medicine in the first place. His was a "mail order" degree. He wore baggy pants and suspenders, shuffled when he walked, had a weather-lined tanned face covered with heavily pigmented keratosis, and huge trembling hands with distended veins and dirty fingernails. His speech was slightly slurred and because he dragged his left leg somewhat, I suspected he had had a small stroke earlier.

Dr. Potts was continuously asking the younger men for advice on how to handle his patients in the hospital. When he discussed a case with me and asked whether he should use dextrose or glucose, both synonymous for the same solution, I realized that it was dangerous for him to continue to practice.

One day he told me he wanted to turn over two very interesting cases for my medical care. They were sisters who lived on the south side of San Antonio, about fifteen miles from my home. One had residuals of rheumatic heart disease, and the other was severely hypertensive. They were two maiden ladies who lived alone in a small frame house, and tended a small garden in front and behind their little home. He said they were too sick to come to the office and would need to have housecalls. He usually charged them $3 for a housecall, but since I was an internist I could charge them $5. Of course, that meant taking care of both of them for the same price.

On my first visit to the house, I found the two little old ladies sit-

ting on the swing awaiting my visit. The house was old and in sad
need of repair. The painting had chipped and the iron gate was rusty.
The old wicker furniture on the porch had faded and splintered. The
inside of the house was cluttered with old furniture, old photographs
and considerable dust all over. Five cats roamed throughout the house,
and here and there were saucers of milk, most of which had curdled.

Dutifully I took care of the little old sisters, making my housecalls weekly for the period of two years. Grace's hypertension was
under control, but she was rapidly developing signs and symptoms of
Alzheimer's disease. Hatty's cardiac failure was a bit more resistant to
therapy, because she was very uncooperative, and it was especially difficult to treat her because she was stone deaf. I finally decided to write
out all instructions.

We became quite friendly after a number of our weekly visits, and
soon they began serving me milk and cookies. My milk was put in a
glass and was fresh, unlike that set out for the cats. They had one living relative, a nephew who was a lawyer doing general practice on the
south side. He periodically requested a medical report on his old aunts.
Their bills were paid by this attorney. Every month I would get a
check for $20. After the second year of treatment, it became apparent
that these two women were totally incompetent and needed to be
placed in a nursing home. I notified their nephew, who promptly
placed them in a well run, but moderately priced facility. From that
time on they were under the care of the physician who handled all of
the home's patients.

I went to see them one time at the nursing home out of concern,
interest and friendship. They were well taken care of, and at first were
not sure of who I was. Then they began to reminisce about the milk
and cookies and I felt better. Six months later I read an article in our
local newspaper that the sisters had both died within one week of one
another and left their "five million dollar estate" to be distributed to
the medical research and medical foundations by their surviving
nephew.

A five million dollar estate! I had been charging $5 a visit to take
care of both of the little old ladies! The gasoline and medication I gave
them free each visit cost me about $7. I computed that it cost me $200
to take care of these two little old ladies over the period of two years.
However, I did enjoy the free milk and cookies, and, until they became confused, the ladies were a delight. However, I wish there had
been some small contribution for a "Cooper Medical Foundation"!

NIGHTCALLS

I always prided myself on being instantly alert when awakened by the sleep-penetrating piercing phone ringing at night. Along with the incessant shrill ringing phone shattering my deep sleep was my concomitant frightful forceful palpitation. It started to effect me initially as an intern on night duty and never ceased or decreased through the many year of practice. Always the quick wide awake "Hello," but always also the thrusting, pounding, rapid heart beat. Certainly the outpouring of my adrenaline through the years did me no good, but it helped the caller, as I was immediately alert and ready! Ready to allay someone's fears, or ready to advise some patient, a nurse, an intern, or to order more Demerol, or increase the Quinidine or start the oxygen, or get the following lab work or initiate the Lidocaine drip, etc. Whatever the order, "call me back in thirty minutes to report" — and of course impossible to fall asleep awaiting the results. But more likely, "Yes, I'll come down to the hospital to see the patient, I'll be in there in fifteen minutes. In the meantime, get the x-ray of the chest, or the EKG or start the transfusion, or have the blood counts ready, or I'll meet you in the emergency room in twenty minutes." Although there are always E.R. doctors on duty twenty-four hours a day, somehow I could not leave my patient to their care. They were my patients and the shepherd had to take care of his flock at night as well. Of course, I appreciated the life sustaining emergency methods done by the E.R. staff until I arrived.

How many relieved smiles greeted me from the patients upon my night arrival at the hospital when they saw me come in response to their need for help.

When the phone rang at night, it would also invariably awaken Sally, and she would start with her routine of questions. "What's wrong? Who's in trouble? Do you have to go to the E.R., or the coronary care unit or to the wards? Be sure to take a sweater, it's cold in the early mornings; or, take your raincoat it may rain. Drink some orange juice and please don't drive too fast. Don't stay at the hospital too long — you have to get up again soon to make rounds. I'm sorry you have to go, sure you can't handle it on the phone? etc."

So I would quickly put some clothes over my pajamas, switch on the kitchen light, drink my juice and dash to the dark garage, while stifling a few yawns. The motor started, and down the dark, lonely, quiet streets at 40, then 60, then 70 miles an hour I drove, cheating at

the red lights and pulling rapidly and carelessly into the hospital parking area. Lights off, door locked, I hurried through the dimly lit lobby
directly to the patient's side. When all was quiet and controlled and
the patient's condition settled, again the lonely trip home through the
streets of the awakening city to my garage and finally wearily up the
steps to undress again to opt for an hour or two of sleep. Sally, reawak-
ened, queried me again about the case. She wanted all the details, but
fell asleep as I answered.

The Hat Fits — Intriguing Early Cases

In the forties, a virulent epidemic of the highly contagious measles (rubeola) hit San Antonio, spreading like wild fire through the
city, attacking children and also infecting the ranks of the raw recruits
at Fort Sam Houston military base.

Today's widespread active childhood immunizations have led us
to forget the earlier severe epidemics of contagious diseases with their
high morbidity and mortality.

When Mrs. John Patton called me one morning to see her four-
teen-year-old only child, Jennifer, who had fever and a rash, I assumed
it was to be just another case of the rampant measles. Her husband,
John, had a large shoe store downtown on Houston Street. He was
amiable and talkative and knew all the downtown merchants. As a new
physician, I needed to make a good impression and I knew that the
garrulous father was in a position to promote me favorably among his
many friends. So I eagerly made the house call bright and early that
morning, thinking this case would be a snap.

Up the steps I ran with my little black bag, to be greeted by a
tearful mother who said, "I'm scared. Jennifer is really terribly ill."
Before I saw the child, the mother gave me Jennifer's classical history
of measles. It had started four days previously with a fever, a slight
cough; the eyes became inflamed and sensitive to light (photophobia);
then she had a runny nose with intense sneezing and constant tearing,
followed in a couple of days by a harsh, brassy cough. These symptoms
preceded the onset of a rash which she said started behind the ears and
then spread over the face and then finally over the entire body. She described it as initially being a faint red rash which would disappear on
pressure. Later it became a deeper red followed by small hemorrhages
into the red, elevated spots.

I went into the dark room (the patient couldn't tolerate light) to examine Jennifer and she indeed had the classical picture of a severe case of measles. Her tonsils were congested, the hard palate had the typical red spots and the mucous membranes of her cheeks were covered with the classical red, irregular spots with blue-white centers (Koplik's) which are diagnostic of measles and found in no other condition. What concerned me greatly was the "deep" redness of the skin spots plus the beginning "hemorrhages" into these areas. There were chest signs of early pneumonia, so I prescribed a sulfonamide, told the mother to push fluids and to start measures to reduce the temperature. I would return to see the patient in the morning. As the disease lasts only a few days after the onset of rash, I calmly reassured the mother that Jennifer would be well in a couple of days.

But going down the steps on the way to my car, I did not feel as confident as I acted. I asked myself a bit fearfully, could this case be developing into one of the "rare" severe cases of measles known as the "Black Measles," with a mortality of over 70 percent? In those complicated cases, the hemorrhage phase increases and patients bleed freely from mucous membranes of the mouth, throat and intestinal tract, as well as bleeding freely into the rash areas. This changes the red spots to a reddish black — hence, the name "Black Measles." Then I dismissed this troublesome worry as the typical usual anxiety gnawing at the apprehensive new physician.

At 9:00 that night I had a frantic call from Mrs. Patton, "Doctor, please come at once! Jennifer is much worse! Her temperature is 104 and she is hemorrhaging from the mouth. She is delirious and her rash is getting much redder and she is bleeding freely into the skin, and I'm afraid she's dying! Please come at once!" My suspicion was confirmed. Jennifer had the rare dreaded disease, "Black Measles" and I was fearful that I might lose her.

Although late at night, the house was crowded with family and friends, all waiting for me as I rushed up the steps, not quite as light-heartedly as earlier that day. As I re-examined the terribly sick child, I could hear my old professor exclaiming "pray that you don't have to attend a black measles case, as there is no treatment and they often have fatal hemorrhages!" I was praying!

I called the Pattons into a quiet adjoining room away from the crowds and explained the precarious situation and then divulged a plan that had occurred to me during the harrowing examination. "With your permission and prayers," I said, "I am going to try an experimental approach to save your child's life. It may not work, but it is harmless and seems logical to me. There is, as you know, a widespread measles epidemic among the young soldiers at the post. I am proposing that I obtain serum from the convalescent soldiers and administer it to Jennifer. The serum of the convalescents will have high titers of immune bodies which we need badly to fight this malignant virus." It seemed sensible to the family, grasping for any hope, and they sent me on with their prayers and blessings.

I called Colonel Franks, my friend at the military post, and explained Jennifer's deteriorating condition and my convalescent serum theory. Fortunately, he agreed to cooperate and together, late that night, we drew 10 cc of blood from each of the eight convalescent volunteers and separated the serum, which was pooled under aseptic conditions, and ended up with 26 cc of the concentrated immune serum! I rushed back at 2:00 A.M. to the dark little house on Maple Street and with one final check on family permission, I gave Jennifer 10 cc of the serum in each buttock and 3 cc in each arm and went home with my personal prayer for Jennifer.

The following morning at 7:00, I called the Pattons who exclaimed, "Her temperature is still up but the bleeding has stopped." At 10:00 A.M., I dragged up the steps to check my "experimental" patient and found some slight fading of the rash. Her temperature had dropped to 102 and she was alert enough to complain of sore buttocks.

The following morning, thirty hours after the trial injections, the temperature was 99, the bleeding had stopped completely, the rash was fading, and the child had stopped coughing and complained of being hungry. The happy parents greeted me, offered me breakfast, and although I had had my morning orange juice and coffee at home, I was delighted to sit with them and enjoy the bacon and homemade bread toast. But especially, I enjoyed Jennifer's improved condition. I knew she was going to recover!

Was it the serum, or was it her own normal spontaneous immune process, overcoming the crisis? I knew it was the serum and I didn't restrain the shoe store owner from lauding me all over Houston Street as the smartest doctor in town. I needed all the praise I could muster to help build my new practice.

One day I told John Patton about my miserable experience eight years previously, while at medical school, selling shoes at Allen's Shoe Store on Wabash Avenue in Chicago. My manager looked at my poor salesbook, shook his head sadly when I told him I was a medical student, and he told me, "You're never going to make it." After repeating the story to John, I said, "Do me a favor and call Mr. Harris at Allen's if he's still at the Chicago store, tell him he was wrong. *"I made it!"*

*   *   *   *   *

From the standpoint of overall reduction in morbidity, i.e., illness, and mortality rates, the greatest impact of drug therapy has been in the field of infectious diseases. Tremendous saving of life and limb have followed the introduction of chemotherapy. This started with the introduction of the sulfonamides during the mid-1930s, and continued with the widespread use of penicillin G. in the mid-1940s. Later, when bacteria developed resistance to penicillin, and people began to develop allergic responses, more antibiotics were sought and developed. Broad spectrum antibiotics were developed, i.e., streptomycin, chloromycetin, cephalosporins, the antituberculosis drug isoniazid, and intramuscular streptomycin. Then ethambutol and rifampin, followed by the antifungal agents. Many micro-organisms are being assaulted by new antibacterials. There have been recent developments in the area of antiviral agents, but AIDS still poses a formidable problem.

*   *   *   *   *

Shortly after my experience with the black measles, I was called to see a twelve-year-old boy who had an abrupt onset of illness with chills, high fever, nausea and vomiting. He had been ill for the past two days, and the family was understandably quite apprehensive as they told me that Charles never complained and rarely even had a sore throat. From the history, I was able to elicit the fact that he had played soccer four days prior to the onset and was kicked violently against the shinbone (the tibia). Since then, there had been spasms of the muscles around the area of injury, with swelling, redness, and warmth of the affected limb. His mother said he was very protective of this area and did not want to move the limb readily. All the physical findings revolved about the injured leg. The tissues overlying the involved bone injury were swollen, warm, red, and because of the distension of the swelling, quite shiny. All the muscles of the right lower extremity were tight and the patient was reluctant to move the leg. It was extremely tender on palpation. I also elicited in the history that he had had a large boil on his buttock in the past several weeks which had been treated by hot packs and manual drainage with some subsidence of the inflamed affected area.

I told the fearful family that I was concerned about the condition of this boy, as all the symptoms and the findings pointed towards "osteomyelitis." This disorder occurs commonly in children and involves the onset of bacterial infection in a bone that has been subject to injury. Inasmuch as he had had a carbuncle prior to the onset of this condition, it was quite possible, I explained, that the staphylococcus organism of the boil had entered the bloodstream, producing bacteremia. When the bone was injured in the trauma of the soccer game, the bacteria unfortunately settled in the bone and set up a local infection. The boy was hospitalized and treatment was started with hot packs, elevation, drainage, and use of the only antibacterial agent available in the early '40s, sulfonamides. I was very concerned about this boy because of the high mortality in osteomyelitis.

Charles was the only son of the very prominent Olson family. The Olsons had a large tire industry in San Antonio and owned a number of auto supply stores. They had a very comfortable relationship in the community, and were well-known at their church, partly because of their philanthropic activities. I was aware that the family would be somewhat uncomfortable with a young physician who, although he came well-recommended, was still new to them. I expected and tolerated a considerable amount of careful scrutiny as I discussed the condition of the boy and my proposal for his treatment. We used antipyretics to reduce the temperature, and after forty-eight hours it was apparent that the sulfonamides were not acting in an antibacterial fashion for the staphylococcic infection. Blood cultures came back positive for staph infection and the patient had a very high white count, which made the prognosis quite doubtful. On the fourth day of hospitalization, I detected a faint cardiac murmur and recognized that he now had the additional complication of a bacterial vegetation super-imposed on the valves of the heart. Of course, this was the staph organism. From the valvular infection, the staph could spread to every organ in the body: to the brain, to the liver, the kidney, the spleen, and to the lung. It was apparent that the high doses of sulfonamides were accomplishing nothing, I felt that this child was doomed.

A surgeon was consulted in an attempt to open widely the abscess of the bone in the leg to drain the infected area, but the procedure was of no avail. Aware of the family's severe apprehension and my frustration and worry, I called in consultation one of the leading internists in San Antonio. He concurred in both the diagnosis and treatment, and also reported a dreary prognostication. Understandably, the child became increasingly cantankerous, suffering from pain and high fever, and the many medical and surgical procedures, and I spent the nights at his bedside trying to assuage his pain.

On the fifth morning, I called the infectious disease specialists at my alma mater, the University of Chicago, described the case and asked if they had any additional thoughts. Dr. Allen Rogers, in charge of bacteriology, told me that there was a Dr. Alexander Fleming in London who was working on a new antibacterial, known as penicillin notatum, developed from a fungus. But none of it was available yet for clinical use in this country. I pleaded with Dr. Rogers to call the Guy Hospital in London and talk to Dr. Fleming to see if we could obtain experimentally, as a research project, a number of grams of the precious penicillin. Dr. Rogers said he would try to get the antibiotic in the attempt to see if this new agent would help. He called me back the following morning to say that he spoke to Dr. Fleming, but the material was not available for loan because the research was experimental and not enough was known about the drug's efficacy, its toxicity, or dosage. Dr. Fleming hesitated to allow any of it to leave his lab at this time. I then consulted the bacteriology departments at Harvard, the University of Pennsylvania, the University of Wisconsin, and at Ohio State University and reported the seriousness of the case to the various professors. It was futile. No one had penicillin, and no one had any other antibacterial other than newer derivatives of sulfonamides which had already proved to have no antibacterial activity against Charles' staph organism.

By the seventh day of hospitalization, the child was critically ill, semicomatose, with evidence of heart failure, violent headaches, and loss of vision. He had developed a staph brain abscess. An x-ray of the chest revealed multiple small abscesses spread through both lungs. The parents were beside themselves with grief, as was their attending physician. Our only accomplishment at this time was to keep Charles as comfortable as possible and he expired on the ninth morning of his hospitalization.

Having spent most of the days and many of the nights attending Charles, I became quite close to the Olson family, and grieved with them as though I had lost a member of my own family. They were understanding and appreciative of all the efforts that had been extended in behalf of their only son. The boy was buried one overcast drizzly morning and there was a large attendance at his funeral. The reverend's sermon brought most of the attendants to tears and it was difficult to comfort the family. The reverend, however, noted that all of the latest measures available had been tried, and complimented the intense medical approach in the attempt to save this boy's life. He was unaware of our futile attempts to obtain the experimental penicillin.

Four days after the funeral, I received an urgent call from the University of Chicago. Dr. Rogers had obtained, through diligent pleading with Dr. Fleming, 20 grams of penicillin notatum. He was preparing to fly the medicine to San Antonio with suggestions as to preparation of its use, experimentally. I told Dr. Rogers that unfortunately, we were too late; and decided not to tell the family how close they had come to a possible cure. It would only have added to their total state of grief and frustration.

It is ironic that today we take all of these new antibacterials with their widespread availability and efficacy for granted.

*   *   *   *   *

He told me that when he was eight-years-old he was quite mischievous, and that he had earned money from the kids in the neighborhood because he was able to do something that none of them could do. He learned early on that he could put a lighted match to the fingers and palm of his right hand and it would not burn him. He did not feel the heat. He also discovered that he could put pin pricks into the skin of his right hand and even put a safety pin through the soft skin without feeling pain. Soon his friend "Fatty," who was also eight-years-old, and who had a materialistic streak, became his business manager. He would gather eight or ten children to view this trick, and charge them each ten cents to see Arnold place a lighted match to his hand without hesitancy and complacently stick pins and safety pins into his hand. Arnold maintained, at that time, he had the sensation of touch in his hand, but not those of pain or temperature. Soon his right hand had considerable scarring and bruising because of his boyish chauvinistic exploits. He noticed that as he got older, the same loss of pain and temperature sensation progressed to involve the right wrist and forearm and gradually ascended to the right shoulder. The left side was completely normal. As he grew older, he recognized that he had developed a left-sided twisting of his upper thoracic spine, a typical scoliosis, brought on by virtue of the fact that paravertebral muscles were much stronger on the left side than on the right. When he was ten-years-old, his teacher noticed that the eyelid of his right eye drooped and referred him to the school doctor, who labelled his eye condition as

Horner's syndrome, but the doctor failed to determine the mechanism causing the neurological deformities.

Gradually, Arnold developed increasing weakness in the right hand and right arm and by the time he was fifteen-years of age, the right upper extremity was three inches shorter than the left and the hand had undergone considerable anatomical changes. The interosseous muscles, that is the muscles between the bones of the hand, had atrophied severely and he lost the little fat pads of the thenar (thumb side) and the hypothenar (little finger side). Soon the hand began to resemble the simian hand of the monkey family and, as the fingers curled, it became claw-like.

He developed considerable shyness because of this deformity and no longer used his defect as a carnival exploitation. He mingled with very few friends, but "Fatty" was still his best friend, and made light of the deformity. In actuality, Arnold knew he was quite good looking, but as he was constantly trying to hide the right arm, he avoided female social companionship and did not have many dates. He became intensely interested in boating and sailing at beautiful Canyon Lake, just thirty miles north of San Antonio. By the time he was seventeen, he was an expert at handling the sixteen to twenty foot skiffs and organized the San Antonio Sail Club. He was able to compensate marvelously with his left hand and learned to write adeptly with it. He was so skilled in single handling the sails that he soon became renowned for winning most of the races, despite his one arm handicap.

Whenever he used his right hand to winch in the sheets (winding ropes), he had the sensation that he was pulling them but did not feel the heat of the friction or any pain, should they rub off the superficial skin. The defects had continued to increase, leaving the right upper extremity virtually useless and the scoliosis of the spine quite unattractive.

He came into my office at twenty-eight-years of age complaining bitterly, "Doctor, I need help! I love sailing. It's my life and I find it increasingly difficult to handle yachting as these medical problems continue to progress. Please help me! I have no other pleasurable outlets!"

As he entered the examining room and stripped to put on his examining gown, I noticed his marked thinness, his twisted upper thoracic spine, and the impaired development of the right shoulder, arm, and hand with the typical claw-like appearance. I also noted that he had a spastic gait, as the muscles of the lower extremities were stiff and the movements of the legs were upward and outward. The spasticity was similar to that seen in the spastic paralysis of cerebral palsy (congenital birth defects). But his spasticity had only occurred in the past three years. It was obvious from looking at the lower motor neuron damages expressed by the changes in his hand and the upper motor neuron defects of his spastic walk, that he definitely had "spinal cord" disturbance that affected both upper and lower motor neurons.

This exciting puzzling neurological case was truly an enigma. Certainly it was not poliomyelitis that comes on acutely and affects primarily anterior motor neurons with resultant paralysis, and when these anterior motor cells are destroyed, there is atrophic paralysis occurring immediately at the time of the acute infection. Also there would be no sensory changes. I didn't believe I was contending with a case of multiple sclerosis, which is a patchy type of neurological disorder with remissions and exacerbations, as the various parts of the spinal cord are affected. I recalled from earlier training at medical school that multiple sclerosis had a certain characteristic triad, the so called "Charcot Triad," named after a physician who first recognized and accurately described multiple sclerosis. The triad consists of a characteristic nystagmus (involuntary rapid movement of the eyeballs), a classical stuttering speech; and finally a characteristic intention tremor. Also, Arnold did not have diplopia (double vision) that is seen in multiple sclerosis. And his abdominal reflexes were present, which is most *uncommon* in multiple sclerosis. Finally, I did a spinal tap and it did not reveal the marked increased gamma globulin (protein) characteristic of multiple sclerosis, so I dismissed this as a working diagnosis for Arnold's predicament.

What was particularly impressive in Arnold's case was the differentiation between the loss of pain and temperature sensation with the retention of touch!

This case brought to mind a classical case that I had seen as a medical student. I have seen only two others subsequently, in my forty years of medical practice. These cases are extremely rare. Arnold had classical *"syringomyelia"* (a cyst of the spinal cord), a congenital anomaly due to failure of closure of the embryonic tube. As the years ensued, the cyst enlarged and produced increasing damage as it expanded its volume within the spinal cord. It destroys the posterior columns of pain and temperature and spares the touch columns because the touch columns cross at slightly different levels. Also, the damage due to the destruction by the cyst would catch the crossing pyramidal tracts and therefore cause spastic paralysis of the limbs. The atrophic paralysis, due to anterior motor cell destruction, produced the claw hand and the twisted scoliosis of the spine.

Having found the answer to this intriguing intricate neurological puzzle, I immediately checked the available literature on syringomyelia. The problem was, there was no conclusive treatment! The disease, predominantly a male disorder, is slowly progressive and ends fatally before age fifty. My frustration centered about what to tell Arnold and his apprehensive family, who consulted the sophisticated new Yankee doctor from the great halls of the University of Chicago.

I returned to the medical library and perused the literature extensively to see if there were any new research findings on treatment for syringomyelia. I then learned that Dr. Bernard Alperts, an eminent professor in neurology at Jefferson Medical School in Philadelphia, considered a specialist in spinal cord diseases, had just published a new book entitled *Clinical Neuroloy* that devoted considerable attention to his research in syringomyelia. His suggestion was that the spinal cord should be irradiated by x-ray at the determined damaged levels to slow, stem, or stop the progression of the disease by fibrosis produced by the irradiation. Having no other answers, I took Arnold and family to Philadelphia to see Dr. Alperts, who confirmed the diagnosis and treated Arnold with his radiation theory.

Today Arnold is sixty-eight-years of age. He sails very skillfully, although he pulls the sails awkwardly. He owns a twenty-eight-foot sailboat and is presently president emeritus of the San Antonio Sail Club. There has been absolutely no progression of his disease in the past forty years since the x-ray treatment. Was this a spontaneous remission of the disease? I doubt it, as this is not the usual history of syringomyelia. The x-ray treatment must have produced the remission and I gladly accepted the satisfaction and compliments for the resolution of his disease process.

Treatment today is still undecided and unsatisfactory. Surgeons attempt to decompress the syrinx (cyst) for temporary alleviation of symptoms, and shunts have been tried to decompress pressure in the canal with unpredictable results. If a definite tumor is present, the surgical attack is warranted. But on the whole, treatment is unsatisfactory despite today's earlier and better diagnoses by the new MRI scanners. I'm convinced that the early irradiation given to Arnold at age twenty-eight fibrosed the walls of the canal and stopped the progression of his disabling disease which had, prior to the x-ray treatment, been spreading so rapidly he would have been destroyed before he reached fifty!

*   *   *   *   *

A tall, lanky, rangy cowboy was referred to me from West Texas.
He was about twenty-eight-years-old, slouched down into the chair of
my consultation room, failed to remove his rumpled stained cowboy
hat which sat firmly on his head, pulled down over his furrowed brow.
He wore a dirty, sweaty cowboy shirt with a bola tie, blue jeans held
up by a wide leather belt with a beautifully engraved silver buckle and
aged, dusty cowboy boots with permanently upturned toes. This cowboy was clearly very sick. He was coughing incessantly and bringing
up copious amounts of frothy mucous sputum.

Obtaining a history was difficult, as he spoke in a slow drawl and
never looked at me while I was questioning him. He seemed to be
transfixed by his boots and lifted his head occasionally when he had a
severe paroxysm of coughing. He was a hardworking, range-riding
cowboy who worked six days a week from early morning until late at
night rounding up cattle and branding them. He was unmarried and
spent his Sundays with his cowboy buddy looking for Indian artifacts.
In addition to his severe cough, he was markedly short of breath, unable to *take a deep breath* without severe pain. He said he had lost weight
during the past two weeks, was weak, had headaches, and had been
bedridden for ten days. His physical findings were quite interesting.
He had what appeared to be a large caked canker sore on his lower lip
and a series of smaller ones (aphthous ulcers) throughout his mouth.
The lesion on his lower lip was about half the size of a dime. It had a
large, ugly scab, and was slightly purulent. He was running a temperature of 102 degrees, had enlarged lymph nodes under his axilla and in
his groin. His liver and spleen were enlarged and tender. His chest was
full of sibilant rales throughout both lungs. X-ray of the chest showed
widespread pulmonary infiltrates of various sizes from pea-size to that
of small lemons. They were uncalcified, soft lesions. This case indeed
presented a diagnostic challenge. His white blood cell count was not
especially helpful; it was neither high nor low. Bacteriological smears
and cultures were taken especially for TB and fungus. Fungus seemed
a good possibility initially, inasmuch as the enlarged lymph nodes,
spleen, and liver indicated that somehow or other the etiological agent
had invaded his reticuloendothelial system since lymph glands, spleen
and liver are members of that structural system.

Although the disease caused by the fungus histoplasma capsulatum is found mostly in the Mississippi River Valley and its tributaries,
there were some strong clinical clues pointing to histoplasmosis as his

diagnosis. An initial skin test for that fungus was slightly positive. With this new evidence, I carefully cultured some material from the scab of his lower lip, placed it on Sabaroud's medium, and had it cultured for histoplasmosis. I also sent serum to Austin for complement fixation tests, with special emphasis on studies for histoplasmosis. This disease, produced by a yeast-like cell, can be very serious. When it is as widespread and advanced as it was in this patient, the possibility of a lethal outcome had to be considered. There was no evidence of meningitis at this time, but this is often a later complication. We ruled out TB, Hodgkin's disease, and brucellosis (caused by drinking unpasteurized milk from unvaccinated cows).

When the complement fixation test came back strongly positive for histoplasmosis and a confirmed positive culture growth of the material from his lip revealed the characteristic yeast-like cells, a bone marrow biopsy was taken for final confirmation. Present in the bone marrow cells was a luxuriant growth of the characteristic histoplasma capsulatum yeast cells. How did this cowboy pick up a disease which is characteristic of the Mississippi and Ohio River Valleys while riding the ranges of West Texas? I then recalled that in his history he had told me that on Sundays he went searching for Indian artifacts with his cowboy buddy. With this clue, I questioned him again, "Is it possible that while looking for artifacts, you entered a bat cave?" He responded immediately, "Yeah. I find lots of Indian arrowheads in caves, and I explored such a cave about two weeks before I got sick." He said the cave was about ten feet above a flat area and his buddy would go up into the cave, shovel the soil contents from the bottom of the cave into a pail, and then would lower the soil filled pail to my patient, waiting below, who would rummage through the soil by forcing it through a fine sieve. Thus, in the process of sifting the soil, he inhaled the histoplasma spores which apparently dropped into the soil from infected bats. Interestingly enough, his symptom-free buddy, who handed him the buckets of soil, did not sift it and therefore did not inhale any of the spores.

Having confirmed the diagnosis and having finally elicited the essential information from the reluctant history-giver, we immediately started the therapy which consisted of intravenous injections of amphotericin-B for a period of ten days. This drug is given extremely slowly and the patient has to lie quietly while receiving it in a darkened room as light would change its chemical formula. By the fifth day the patient was afebrile. The cough had ceased. The lesion on his lip began to heal, and the mouth lesions began to disappear. The chest lesions were resolving. And in one week, he was totally out of danger. This case reminded me of my early experience with another life-threatening fungus, blastomycosis, that had infected the poor widowed farmer.

My cowboy patient left the hospital on Friday morning. He was determined to get back to West Texas as soon as he could, so that on Sunday he could take up where he had left off! I couldn't believe it! He wanted to go right back to sifting soil to look for arrowheads. Initially, I had him promise to wear a double surgical mask, and then I coerced him into promising to quit this dangerous hobby. "All right Doc," he said, but I doubted he would heed the warning.

*   *   *   *   *

Poliomyelitis is like a devastating tornado, sweeping through a community and leaving in its wake the dead and the maimed. In 1948, San Antonio suffered one of its worst polio epidemics. No prophylactic vaccine had as yet been developed. There was no antiviral agent to control the disease, and antibacterials were ineffective. There had always been sporadic cases in Mexico, and a few isolated cases on the west side of San Antonio, an area of poor sanitation, drainage and sewage problems. This virulent disease spreads indiscriminately, hitting here and there without rhyme or reason. There were cases in the wealthy suburbs, in the middle-class sections, as well as in the poverty areas. The disease had no respect for rich or poor, young or old, weak or strong.

Two general practitioners who attended several cases of polio were stricken with the disease and succumbed to it within one week of the onset of their illness. Three hospital nurses were infected and died, and two lab technicians developed the disease. One was left with residual leg paralysis and the other died. There was no way of aborting the disease once it manifested itself. Sanitation measures were put into effect as the virus remains viable in water and sewage for months. Insecticide spraying the streets and alleys had no appreciable effect. High contagious disease quarantine procedures were practiced in each hospital and special contagious floors were used solely for the care of these patients.

The disease would start insidiously with an ordinary sore throat (pharyngitis). Then the patient would suffer malaise associated with fever and chills, followed within a few days by generalized muscular weakness, a prelude to spotty paralysis involving the extremities. There was also a severe form of poliomyelitis known as "Bulbar polio" which was extremely alarming and almost always fatal. The virus apparently entered the gastrointestinal tract, spread from one person to another through the handling of excreta, from stool to mouth (fecal-oral). Carriers (those immune to the virus but carrying the infection) were unknowingly transmitters of the disease. Invading the GI tract with minimal symptoms after starting in the pharynx as a sore throat, the disease would then ascend various spinal nerves and localize in the spinal cord or brain or cranial nerves, infecting the various cells and destroying them as they invaded, with the resultant paralysis. In Bulbar polio, the nerves that were affected were concerned with eye movements, swallowing and respiration. When these nerves were destroyed, the patient was unable to breathe automatically and was placed into the Iron Lung. A patient placed in the Iron Lung usually had additional problems: loss of control of the urinary tract and bowel, and paralysis of the muscles of the abdominal wall. The patient was barely able to talk and only in a hoarse whisper, if at all. Most of his contact with the environment was by blinking of the eyelids in response to questions; once for yes, twice for no. Eye movements (the eyeball itself) were paralyzed. Most of the time the patient was in and out of coma because of the severe anoxia to the brain. Bulbar polio was a horrible experience for both patient, family, and the attending physician, as well as for the dedicated staff, who bravely allowed themselves to be exposed, protecting themselves as well as possible.

The nurses who attended patients on the polio ward were indeed heroic. They constantly exposed themselves, despite the fact that the most perfect techniques of isolation and contagious approach were instituted. We learned that actually, the time of greatest contagiousness of polio was before actual symptoms presented themselves. Therefore, they probably were not in quite as much danger as we had thought initially.

Along with other physicians, I saw more than my share of polio cases. The son of my lawyer developed the typical symptoms of sore throat, pain and spasms of the muscles. When hospitalized, the spinal tap made the diagnosis, for there were the characteristic increased lymphocytes, the white cells that increase in an attempt to fight the virus. The pressure of the spinal fluid was increased, as well as the build-up of protein content. However, this young boy did very well, with only slight residual weakness in one leg.

The daughter of one of my closest friends, Francis George, developed pharyngitis, fever, stiff, neck, and weakness in both extremities in twenty-four hours. We were quite concerned about her prognosis because of the rapidity of the onset. Fortunately, it was an abortive type of case and within ten days all symptoms subsided without residuals. But only few who developed the infection were so fortunate.

Barry Smith, nineteen-years-old, strong, alert, handsome, and the only son of his elderly parents, was a college student when he developed the typical symptoms — sore throat, fever, chills, stiff neck and muscular aches. Then came the spasms of the muscles of his extremities. I hospitalized him on the polio ward at the Santa Rosa. His disease progressed relentlessly and within forty-eight hours it was necessary to thrust him into an Iron Lung. He was unable to swallow, unable to talk, unable to breathe. The muscles of his upper and lower extremities had already shown signs of paralysis. I spent three of the most terrifying days of my life attending this fine young man day and night beside the Iron Lung, but to no avail. On the fourth morning, while his parents were praying in the hospital chapel, he succumbed to the dreadful disease.

As the epidemic continued to spread, many mothers gathered their children and attempted to escape the ravages of the epidemic by traveling to other parts of the country. By train, by bus, by plane, by car, they carried them away from the disease-infested city. While in many cases this did prevent the onset of the disease in their family, others developed the dreaded illness en route to their destinations and returned to San Antonio for treatment.

My mother called me one morning during the epidemic to tell me that my young brother, Harold, who was a junior in high school, was very sick with a sore throat. I was devastated and anticipated the worst. I rushed to their apartment, ascended the steps quickly and found Harold lying in bed with high fever, generalized malaise, sweating and extremely weak. His breathing was normal. He was able to talk, and Mother said she had fed him liquid that morning so I knew he could swallow. I suggested that he give me a urine sample and on his way to the bathroom he collapsed. Already, severe muscular weakness of the extremities had set in. My mother and I knew our worst fears were realized: Harold had poliomyelitis!

The British Journal, *Lancet,* had just published a fascinating article which I studied. It described the unique methods of an English nursing nun, Sister Kenny, for treating acute cases of polio to ameliorate symptoms and possibly abate some of the spread of paralysis. I studied the procedures described in the article carefully. Harold was hospitalized at the Santa Rosa Contagious Disease Ward, and I immediately began instituting the "Kenny treatment." Sister Kenny's treatment was based on the use of hot pack treatments. We had to improvise. I bought a used washing machine that had a wringer attached. We set up two electric plates and placed a large tub on them, filled with water and kept at the boiling point constantly. Large towels were placed in the hot water and then rung out through the wringer and wrapped around the upper and lower extremities, as well as upon the abdomen. This was continued for five days and nights without let-up.

Harold was intelligent and knew his diagnosis. He questioned how far along his spinal cord the virus would extend, as he was fearful of the ultimate disability. Fortunately, the paralysis seemed to be confined to the lower extremities, predominantly the right leg.

Eighty miles northeast of San Antonio, in the small town of Gonzales, there was an institution with twenty beds known as the Warm Springs Foundation. This hospital had been set up for rehabilitation of patients who'd had strokes or various congenital paralyses or serious nerve injuries. They had hot baths, jaccuzis, a swimming pool and an excellent physiotherapy department. I knew all the referring doctors in Gonzales and also had treated patients from that area, including the mayor and other notables. I called the Foundation and requested that they treat my brother and other convalescing polio cases. They agreed to accept a total of twenty patients in a special ward which was to be set aside for polio patients. Their attitude was excellent. They agreed to use the "Kenny treatment" after being educated in this new technique. They continued with the pools, warm baths, and physiotherapy. Harold remained there for one month, during which time I traveled the eighty miles three times a week to check on his progress. After a month, we confirmed that the paralysis was only confined to the right lower leg, resulting in a slight residual foot-drop. But he was ambulatory and able to use all his muscles, weak as they were. But the nerves were intact.

Shortly after that, Dr. Jonas Salk developed the polio vaccine for infantile paralysis. He was at the University of Pittsburgh and had spent considerable time developing a vaccine for influenza. His theory was to use attenuated (weakened) virus of the polio strain and allow the body to develop antibodies. The Lederle Laboratories and Merck, Sharp & Dohme worked day and night to produce massive doses of this vaccine, which was sent to various areas where the polio epidemic was flourishing.

A month prior to the development of this vaccine, it occurred to me and a few other doctors in San Antonio that inasmuch as immune globulin contained antibodies for many viruses and had been used to ameliorate hepatitis and severe influenza, perhaps it could be used as a prophylactic measure to help stop the spread of this disease. We gave hundreds of the injections and there seemed to be considerable evidence that it helped. In fact, early in the epidemic I had begun experimenting with weekly self-injections of immune globulin to improve my immunity; perhaps it helped. The supplies of immune globulin were soon exhausted but, fortunately, within several months, the Salk vaccine, and then the Sabin vaccine, became available. Soon nearly every child in and around San Antonio and in most of the Texas areas was inoculated. Today immunization is worldwide, and polio infection rare.

Our experience with poliomyelitis at that time reminds me of what confronts us today in the search for the AIDS vaccine.

We are presently experiencing considerable difficulty in developing an effective vaccine for Acquired Immune DeSciency Syndrome. While the antiviral medication, AZT, is effective against the AIDS virus, it has not cured anyone. It has many deleterious side effects, and has proven to be merely palliative. Researchers have been able to develop both neutralizing antibodies and killer-cell responses for the AIDS virus in the laboratory but, to date, the virus' deadly progress has not been halted in the human.

Vaccines have been developed, consisting of synthetic proteins from the envelopes of the AIDS virus (the surfaces of the viruses) identified as the "GP-160" and the "GP-120" proteins. These were injected after being attached to the vaccinia virus (smallpox) into monkeys and chimpanzees previously infected with the AIDS virus. However, neither of these synthetic proteins were effective in neutralizing the virus. They did not produce neutralizing antibodies. They did not promote cell-mediated immunity. And the killer cells of the body's defensive system did not attack the cells infected with the virus. This phase of the research was disappointing.

Currently, scientists are working with a series of AIDS volunteers who are willing to try every new vaccine — produced in whatever form. Trials have also begun on "CD4," one of the first genetically engineered drugs for Acquired Immune Deficiency Syndrome. Injections of CD4 will be administered to fifty trial patients. The drug is similar to proteins on the white blood cells that the AIDS virus attacks. The theory's rationale is that the virus will be dissipated by the artificial CD4's and not get to the normal white cells. Patients at San Francisco General Hospital, New England Deaconess Hospital in Boston and at the National Cancer Institute are receiving the drug in a trial experiment.

Other investigators are also trying to vaccinate with proteins taken from the core (the body) of the AIDS virus hoping for a protective immune response. The results have been equivocal. Researchers at the University of Chicago and at the Southwest Research Foundation in San Antonio believe that an effective vaccine against AIDS is more likely to be produced from a small, well-defined protein particle (an oligopeptide), rather than the large all-inclusive protein of the envelope or the protein of the core.

As yet, none of the vaccines have been capable of immunization against the deadly AIDS virus or defeating it once it has infected the patient. Dr. Jonas Salk recently suggested at the Montreal meetings the same approach that he did with polio. He speculated that the "killed" AIDS virus would induce cell-mediated immunity and produce an antibody response. But some experts are uncertain that injection of a "killed" AIDS virus would be safe.

Usually, one can inoculate a person with an attenuated or killed virus, or synthetic protein particles and induce the immune system to make neutralizing antibodies to protect against the disease. While this is true for most ordinary viral infections, it has not yet been successful against AIDS.

However, with the massive assault on this distressing problem, a vaccine or drug will be perfected that will accomplish the desired result. Recently, a drug has been developed from the root of the cucumber plant with antiviral effect and now extensive active research is being extended in that area.

*   *   *   *   *

I had attended Mr. Rafel previously. He was a severe diabetic who was difficult to control because he never adhered to his diet, drank heavily, and frequently neglected to take his insulin. He was a very wealthy art connoisseur and lived in a large mansion in the exclusive Chapultapec Heights of Mexico City. The rooms in his home were filled with sophisticated art and sculpture.

Late one evening I received a telephone call from a physician in Mexico City who informed me that Mr. Rafel had been in a deep coma for the past twelve hours and they were unable to control his diabetes. The family had urgently requested that I see him in consultation and arranged to send their jet to pick me up in San Antonio and bring me to Mexico. The patient's family did not permit him to go to the hospital, but had engaged twenty-four-hour nurses and had a small lab set up in the house with twenty-four-hour technicians on hand. The attending physician was trying desperately to cope with the severe diabetic coma.

I arrived in Mexico in the early morning hours and their chauffeured limousine transferred me to their home. I found Mr. Rafel in profound coma with the family members almost in mourning, concerned that his condition was hopeless. His physician was very qualified; he was on the staff of every hospital in Mexico City and Chief of the Department of Medicine at one of the leading institutions. I examined Mr. Rafel very carefully. He was almost areflexic, hypotensive, and had the deep Kussmaul air-hunger breathing of diabetic ketoacidosis. His breath smelled strongly of acetone. The lab work all confirmed the high serum acidity and the very elevated blood sugar. It was difficult for me initially to understand why the patient did not respond to the fluid and insulin therapy which the doctor had administered. Despite the correct therapy, his blood sugar remained between 400 and 600 milligrams, four to six times normal.

In the course of the physical examination of the patient I noticed a very small bruise on the right side of his bald head. I estimated that the bruise was approximately ten days old because of the marked purplish-green discoloration. His pupils were widely dilated. I asked the doctor and the family if he had fallen out of bed, or had otherwise injured his head. They said he had been in the coma for only three days and had not injured himself during that time. I questioned Mrs. Rafel again, "Are you sure he hasn't had a fall and injured his head?" After a few minutes of memory searching she did remember that approximately two weeks ago, returning from a party, Rafel had bumped his head on entering the car and the chauffeur had treated it with mercurochrome and he'd made no further mention of it.

"Did he have an increased frequency of headaches after the bump?" I pursued my questioning.

"Well, he isn't a complainer, but I seem to remember now that he was a bit sluggish after the bump. At night he did complain of slight headaches. He refused to go to several of his club meetings and was very irritable, which was most unlike him."

I called the attending physician into a private room and said, "I believe your patient is truly in diabetic coma, but it is more complicated. The resistance to your treatment points to a complication. I have the impression that Mr. Rafel may also have a subdural hematoma, and this is perpetuating the coma."

"I never gave it a thought," replied the physician. "I figured that inasmuch as he is a severe diabetic and these lab findings indicated diabetic acidosis that this was the primary problem."

Acting on this suspected diagnosis, we admitted him to the American British Cowdray Hospital and the administrator courteously gave me temporary privileges. Therefore, I was free to write orders and call for neurological and radiological consultation. We called upon the finest neurosurgeon in Mexico City and the best team of radiologists. The x-rays confirmed a mass located subdurally, typical of a subdural hematoma. A large clot lay under the lining covering the brain. Typically, a subdural hematoma does not produce brain symptoms or coma immediately after injury, but after the clot breaks down (days later) it absorbs fluid, and as it expands, it acts like a large tumor, pressing on the brain, producing headache, confusion, irritability, and then coma.

The neurosurgeon confirmed my diagnosis, and drilled two holes through the cranium and a large blood clot was evacuated. The patient returned from the operating room at 6:00 A.M. and within six hours we were able to control his acidosis and the elevated blood sugars. Three days later, the patient was well enough to go home. He was alert and lucid. When the family told him what had happened, he was extremely appreciative. I remained in their home to follow this fascinating case for the next four days until he was totally out of danger.

The morning before my Braniff flight back to San Antonio, I had breakfast with Mr. Rafel on his poolside terrace overlooking the city from the heights of Chapultapec. There Mr. Rafel gave me a "tip."

"Dr. Cooper, since you saved my life, I want to do you a favor. In this area there is a new plant that is going to open, a branch of Syntex. They have a secret formula for making cortisone much cheaper than the usual method. They are extracting cortisone steroids starting out with yams. Syntex stock is going on the New York Exchange at a very low rate per share. Since I'm a director of the company, I'm advising you to buy as many shares as you can because their future is going to be great in the pharmaceutical industry."

A couple of days after my return to San Antonio, I had lunch downtown in the St. Anthony Hotel with another physician with whom I discussed the case. Adjacent to our table were seated some of my friends, including one Stanley Jones, whose mother was one of my first patients with intractable sciatica. I related the whole episode to my colleague — both the medical aspect and Rafel's tip about buying into Syntex. Then I returned to my practice and became immersed in catching up with the days I'd missed while in Mexico, and soon forgot about the Syntex stock.

About two weeks later, at lunch at the St. Anthony Hotel, Stanley Jones approached my table and announced, "You know, I owe you a vote of thanks. You did me a real favor."

Puzzled, I replied, "I don't know what you mean."

"Well," he explained, "some time back I overheard you tell somebody about your case in Chapultapec Heights, Mexico. It was fascinating, but more interesting to me was the part about the Syntex stock. Well, I bought it, and I thought you should know that I made a bundle on it. It has jumped up to six-fold per share. I bought several thousands of dollars worth. By the way, how many shares did you buy?"

"None," I answered, embarrassed. "I forgot all about it. But, I'll always remember the intricacies of that complicated diabetic coma!"

DOCTOR, CARRY A GUN

My secretary handed me a letter, sealed and postmarked Seguin, Texas. On the back there was a drawing of a knife with skull and crossbones, no return address or signature. I read the following: "Dr. Cooper, you and Dr. Miller didn't do me no good. In fact, you doctors have made me worse. You don't like me and you have told the spirits to make me feel sick. And after I kill Dr. Miller and his family, I am going to get you and your family next because you deserve it. I know what I must do because my spirit has told me to do this." Signed, Don.

One week earlier Dr. Miller in Seguin had called me in consultation about a nineteen-year-old patient with a most bizarre history, I was intrigued and excited by the diagnostic possibilities. He had attended Don Carley for two years and was confused by the variegated symptoms presented by this young man, who complained about multiple episodes of cardiac irregularity, associated with extreme weakness, lasting thirty minutes at a time, and recurring several times weekly. He also claimed to have frequent attacks of pain in the chest

with associated cough and inability to *take a deep breath* during the episodes. He said he could recognize when an attack was coming, as it
was preceded by episodes of dizziness, light-headedness and nausea.

I scheduled an appointment for the patient for the following
week. During the history inquiry, prior to exam, I noticed that Don
seemed unusually fidgety and nervous. He sweated profusely, looked
about the room aimlessly, never looked directly at me when I asked
him a question, or when he answered, but instead directed his gaze at
the ceiling or floor. He made peculiar grimaces and had an episodic
tic, during which he would squeeze his right eye and retract his right
lower lip. On several occasions during the interview he would jump up
from his seat, pace the room abruptly and hurriedly, and then sit down
again. He was carelessly dressed, having missed fastening two shirt
buttons. He was disheveled, with tie askew, trousers looking slept in,
shoes not shined, and right shoelace untied. On inquiry of his bodily
systems, his answers were fragmentary, inconsistent, and always the
same "Yeah!" For example, "Are you short of breath?" Answer,
"Yeah," "At rest or only exertion?" "Yeah." "Do you cough any?"
"Yeah, when I get upset." "Do you hurt in the chest?" "No, oh yeah."
"When do you hurt in the chest?" "I don't know." "Does your heart
beat fast or slow?" "Yeah, both." "Tell me how you know when you're
going to get an attack?" "What attack, Doctor?" "The ones you described to Dr. Miller." "I never described any attacks to him." "Do
you have any trouble with your stomach or bowels?" "Yeah, both."
"What kind?" "All kinds." "Do you have nausea or vomiting?"
"Yeah." "When?" "Sometimes." It was immediately apparent that his
history was to be of no value. I proceeded with a complete thorough
physical exam, and the findings were all well within normal.

"Do you go to school?" "No, I quit school." "When?" "Three
years ago." "Why" " 'Cause the principal didn't like me, and he made
it tough on me. He had it in for me." "How do you know?" "Well, he
always saw to it that I made bad grades." "How do you get along with
your mother and father?" "My father left home. Mother is mean to me
all the time. She doesn't like me. She is mad that she has to support
me." "Do you ever see your father?" "No, he left home right after I
was born because he didn't want to have a kid." "Do you work?"
"No." "Why not?" "I always get fired." "Why?" "People don't like
me. They don't understand me." "Tell me about your friends." "You
can't trust them," he said. "They pretend to like you and then they rat
on you."

I concluded the exam and held my hand out to shake his hand, but he did not accept it. I told him I would send a complete report to Dr. Miller in Seguin, and that we would work together to try and help him with his problems. He left the office, saying to the receptionist, "Send the bill to my mom, but I don't think she is going to pay it. She never pays for anything I buy." I sent my report to Dr. Miller the following morning, with the negative physical findings, with the conclusion that this young boy was seriously ill psychologically and seemed to border on paranoid schizophrenia.

After reading Don's letter, I called Dr. Miller in Seguin. He told me he had also received the same threat two days previously. I suggested that he have Don picked up at once and placed under immediate psychiatric supervision in an institution to prevent him from carrying out his hideous threats. "I have tried in vain, but we can't find him," answered Dr. Miller. "He is not at any of the haunts he normally frequents. He has been missing for two days."

This was alarming. I immediately called home and cautioned Sally to keep the doors and windows locked, not to let the children out of her sight, and not to leave the house until I returned. Two hours later when I finished at the office, I decided I would skip night hospital rounds. I called my lawyer and asked for suggestions. He replied that it was out of his jurisdiction, and suggested I get a gun and keep it on my person at all time. I told him I had never fired a gun and knew nothing about them. "You'd better get one and learn all about it at once," he said. I then recalled that the District Attorney of the Seguin area, Mr. Baylor, was a patient of mine. I put in a call and explained the situation to him, and he reassured me that he would send a sheriff and deputies to scour the area, and apprehend the dangerously sick boy.

I purchased a Smith and Wesson .22 and some bullets, and joined a rifle range. Before entering my car, I learned to look in the back and under the chassis, and both ways before I made any move. The girls in the office were instructed to buzz me immediately should Don enter the office, and to humor him and keep him in the reception room, until they had alerted me, and to quietly call the police. The next week was filled with constant alarm. Sally kept the children home from school, and had groceries sent in. All doors and windows were kept locked. I went to the rifle range early each morning and practiced for one hour. I soon began to feel quite confident in handling my gun, now a constant companion. I was continuously on guard when parking my car at the hospitals or at my office, and surveyed my own home carefully before entering the garage. My office staff was very apprehensive but alert.

At the end of the week, I received a phone call from the District Attorney telling me that they had apprehended Don, who was safely put away in the state institution. I spoke to the superintendent of the hospital and was told they had studied him intensely, confirming that he was undoubtedly a severe paranoid schizophrenic and he was started on psychopharmological drugs. If his response was poor, they would then subject him to a course of shock therapy. They promised to alert me should he leave the hospital or escape.

I never heard from Don Carley again. I learned from Dr. Miller that Don had been in and out of the institution several times in the next two years, following which his mother and he moved to New Mexico and that, happily, was the last we heard of him.

Since my medical school days I have always felt that psychiatric problems are due to biochemical disorders affecting the brain. I always believed there was more to these problems than reaction to past or present events in one's life, background, sex life or family relationships. I never was convinced that the Freudian analysts, after the many years of therapy, achieved results warranting their approach. I saw patients who came from different social environments with the same psychological problems. It appeared to me that the pathology was a disorder within the person, not the result of environment. The problems seem to be in their genes, effecting chemical-neurogenic-amine-biological disorders. I tried fruitlessly, through the years, to rationalize the psychoanalyst's psychotherapeutic approach. Today they admit that appropriate medication in correct dosages (psychopharmacological drugs) have been quite successful. I anticipate tremendous advances in the next decade with the appropriate use of drugs, and the new diagnostic information gleaned from magnetic imaging scanners.

Schizophrenics are being treated today by major tranquilizers like Thorazine, Stelazine, Haldol, imipramine, and Zanex. These drugs seem to perform their pharmacological help by blocking neurotransmitters, essentially the neurotransmitter dopamine, which seems somehow to be related to brain metabolism. Lithium seems to be of considerable help today for manias, and mood disorders. But it is terribly important to have the optimal dosage levels in the bloodstream. Less is ineffective, and too much would be dangerous. And one must constantly be alert to the side effects, and to the possibility of sensitivity to these drugs. It requires extreme fine-tuning, like for a violin, for best results.

I recall vividly, as a student, my first exposure to a patient receiving shock treatment (electro-convulsive therapy). He had been sedated but I wasn't, and I felt more shocked than the recipient at this brutal, barbaric "therapy." Today electro-convulsive treatment is more humane. It is employed with muscle relaxant (suxamethonium) and an anesthetic administered by a trained anesthetist. The indications for present day use have narrowed considerably to deep depression and schizophrenia not responding to any other form of treatment. It is occasionally used for post partum depression, severe obsessive compulsive illnesses and catatonias. But trials of the psychopharmacological drugs should be administered first.

Psychoanalysis has become a cult in Hollywood — among many pseudo-sophisticates. Under the slightest tension, these people run to their analysts and before they make a decision, they discuss it fully with their "shrink." It seems to be as popular to ask: "Who's your shrink?" as to ask, "Who is your hairdresser?"

Therapeutic results may be manifested in various ways. I'm reminded of the tale of the very depressed man who met his friend on the street. "Bob, you look terrible," he said. "What's bothering you?" "I'm embarrassed to tell you that at my age of fifty-two, I started to wet the bed! I have consulted my family practitioner, and internist, and a urologist all to no avail." His friend suggested that he discuss this problem with a psychiatrist and he did.

They met again by chance two months later and Bob seemed elated. "You look great," his friend told him, "The psychiatrist must have helped and you no longer wet the bed." "No," Bob replied, "I still wet the bed. But now I'm proud of it."

A Star Is Born

Marjorie and Sam Easton consulted me about their problem of sterility. As these were some of my first patients, I was determined to make a good impression. Complimentary word of mouth has always been one of the best ways of starting a new practice. Sam was forty-two years of age, short, sandy-haired, brown eyed, and had a fixed wide silly grimace. He walked with his feet spread out like a waddling duck. His wife, Marjorie, was ten years his junior and was a rather attractive, short, brunette, with deep brown eyes, dark complexion and a furrowed brow which gave her a quizzical, whimsical look. However, she was pleasant and more intelligent than Sam. They had been married for ten years and were unable to have a child. Because of their ages, they were beginning to get panicky and approached me with their problem, stating that they would do anything to have a baby. She had had several early miscarriages. I quickly ascertained that Sam had had a severe urethral infection during his early youth and had been treated then by painful urethral injections of argyrol, with subsidence of the acute infection. However, it was apparent that he had a residual, low-grade prostatitis. Studies showed that he had a very low sperm count. The normal sperm count for fertility requires at least 400,000 to 600,000 sperm per cubic centimeter. His 80,000 was about one-fifth of normal. Complicated by his low-grade prostate infection, this presented a true problem for fertility.

Marjorie appeared to be a normal fertile female. She did not have diabetes, her thyroid was normal, and her menstrual cycles had normal onset and were not abnormal. Physical exam revealed her to be a normal healthy female. On pelvic exam, her cervix was normal and there was a normal sized uterus, in good position. Air insufflation of the fallopian tubes revealed them to be patent, and dye injection showed no abnormality. My initial problem was to attempt to improve Sam's low sperm count. He was relatively normal in all other areas, no diabetes, normal thyroid and steroid hormone levels within the accepted lower limits of normal. I cultured a secretion from his prostate gland and determined the particular bacteria that produced his continued low-grade prostatitis, and he was treated with the correct antibiotic. There had been a recent article in the *New England Medical Journal* describing how one endocrinologist had tried using weekly injections of androgenic hormones for a period of three months. Initially, this severely depressed sperm count, but was always followed by a marked rebound phenomenon. Those who responded favorably had a marked improvement of total sperm count, as much as three to four fold over the numbers prior to treatment.

I suggested this program to Sam. He agreed to comply and faithfully came in for his injections of androgenic hormones which we continued for three months. At the end of that time, his sperm count had dropped as anticipated to 50,000, and we observed him carefully over the next three to four weeks. The only rebound was back to his previous status of 80,000 to 85,000 per cubic centimeter. Discouraging! I suggested that we try another approach, anterior pituitary-like hormone injections with remote possibility that it might increase his spermatogenesis. He faithfully came to my office three times weekly for large injections of the anterior pituitary hormones. At the end of three months, this program was discontinued as there was no improvement.

I suggested to Marjorie that they might consider experimental insemination of Sam's low-count sperm by direct injection into the uterine canal. This was prior to current routine artificial insemination programs or donor invivo inseminations from sperm banks, or invitro techniques which are presently prevalent. First, however, I taught Marjorie to learn her time of ovulation by taking daily basal temperatures, and proposed that once she learned that date by the rise in basal temperature, they established a program of relations for the day prior to the time of anticipated rise in temperature, definitely the day of the rise, and for two days thereafter. Then, there was to be no contact thereafter for one week on the possibility that inception had taken place. She tried this for three months but to no avail. Having failed in all of these measures, we decided to proceed with the attempt at artificial insemination.

I procured from the pediatric department a fine rubber catheter, had it sterilized and placed it, under sterile technique, into her uterine canal. I then gave Sam a sterilized syringe into which he was to accumulate his ejaculate material. Although Marjorie was apprehensive, she assumed the pelvic lithotomy position on the examining table and I proceeded to inject his collected seminal fluid through the catheter, hoping that some of the sperm would travel through the uterine canal into the fallopian tubes and fertilize an ovum. Also, since this was in the days before the use of Clomid, we were depending upon the passage of one egg monthly. This attempt at insemination was repeated five times without success.

I had a conference with a tearful Marjorie and depressed Sam, and told them it looked hopeless and suggested that they attempt adoption. Because of their age and the few babies available for adoption, they were unsuccessful in trying to recruit from the various agencies then in existence. One agency put them on the waiting list and told them it might be two to three years before they would be called. As a desperate chance, I called the Chief Resident in Obstetrics and Gynecology at the Robert B. Green Hospital, one of my former students, explained the situation and asked if perchance a newborn was available for adoption. I told him I had a lovely family waiting urgently and expectantly who would make great parents.

Several months passed without any word from Dr. Jacob at the Green. Late one afternoon he called me excitedly and reported, "We have just received a baby that was abandoned in a dumpster behind an apartment complex. It is a little boy approximately one week old, in horrible condition! He has a badly infected umbilicus, probably a severe yeast infection. He has bacterial conjunctivitis of both eyes, his skin is excoriated with infected scabs and he is extremely dehydrated and starved." I rushed to the hospital to see the bit of surviving protoplasm. I called the Chief of Pediatrics to help in an attempt to save this frail, premature newborn.

After two weeks of intensive care, medication, fluids, electrolytes, antibiotics, and forced feeding, the baby was restored to some semblance of normalcy. I reported my findings to Sam and Marjorie, who were overjoyed at the potential prospect of adopting him. I referred them to their lawyer for legal advice for adoption of this deserted infant. All the proper legal forms were completed, and this little discarded bundle of humanity now became a welcome, well loved asset to the Easton family.

I lost contact with the family through the years, but learned from their friends that they had hesitated to tell the boy, while he was growing up, that he was adopted. But I am sure that he would have learned the story somewhere. His mother, originally from Boston, was very much interested in theater and the arts, and saw to it that her son had an intensive exposure to drama. He was involved in plays in junior high, and had the lead in many plays in high school, and majored in drama at University of California in Los Angeles (UCLA), from which he graduated with honors.

We learned later that he became quite widely known and eminent in the Hollywood scene. He earned an Emmy for a successful popular television series and one year he won an Oscar for best director.

To experience the famous California lifestyle, one need not go any further than LaCosta, a resort-spa situated in the tiny community of Carlsbad, some twenty miles north of Lajolla. With its ideal climate and proximity to San Diego, the ocean and the mountains, it is an ideal getaway spot for serious spa-goers, golfers, and tennis enthusiasts. Hollywood celebrities, the particularly rich, and partially famous sojourn in LaCosta. In October of 1983, Sally and I were invited to spend a week with friends who own a large condominium in the LaCosta complex. We accepted this invitation readily. I had been working exceptionally hard and I needed some "time out," I thought I would like to experience the lifestyle of the jet setters. Also, I was most anxious to take a series of tennis lessons from the famous professional, Pancho Seguiro. Fortunately, I was able to rearrange my office and hospital schedule and my associate would be available to handle my practice during my absence.

After my sixth lesson of tennis trial and error (mostly error), Mr. Seguiro finally complimented me on my progress, saying, "Doctor, if you keep improving like this, and continue to practice, and forget your office when you are on the court, you will finally be a relatively decent player." I noted the word "relatively." However, I was feeling quite good with the comment from the famous professional. Fatigued, wet with perspiration, but happy, I met Sally in the Tennis Pro Shop and we browsed and chatted as we looked at the displays of tennis gear. A handsome young man came near. He was about thirty-years of age, tall, muscular, blond, blue-eyed, with an enviable California suntan. Accompanying him was a good looking brunette woman about the same age, both in very attractive tennis clothes. They apparently had just finished playing a match. "Here are some people I know from San Antonio," we heard him say to his companion, "and I want you to meet them."

We turned expectantly as this tall young Viking approached. With arm outstretched, he shook my hand, and said, "Dr. Cooper, I recognized you immediately even though I've been gone from San Antonio for twelve years. My name is David Easton. You may remember me. I am Sam and Marjorie's son. And may I present my wife Carol." Of course, when he identified himself, I recalled immediately the Easton infertility problem and the adoption of the sickly waif. But not knowing how much of his history he actually knew, I merely replied that, while not immediately recognizing him, I certainly did remember him. I told him I had followed his career as a television and movie producer, Emmy and Oscar winner, with great interest and complimented him. "Doctor," he said, "It's okay. You don't have to be careful what you say. My parents told me the whole fascinating story. I just want to take this opportunity to say, thank you, doctor, thank you."

AN ITALIAN OPERA

I was consulted by a prominent ear, nose and throat specialist regarding a patient suffering from intractable, unbearable headaches for the past three weeks. This patient had had a history of sinus trouble for two years. The usual treatment for sinusitis at this time did not seem to alleviate any of his pain. The doctor was told to send the patient to my office the following morning.

When I entered the examining room, I found a small elderly, obese gentleman sitting in the corner of the room, holding his head and grimacing with pain. He identified the pain as being predominantly at the back of the neck, spreading forward over the head and also down over the shoulders. After a lengthy, poorly-given history, heavily accented in Italian, all I learned was that the pain was different from his usual sinus headache; that there had been no head trauma and that he was afebrile throughout this recent episode. I had no additional clues. I asked the patient to start undressing and said I would return to examine him when he was unclothed. However, just before I left the room, I noticed that as he crossed his legs and bent forward to remove his shoes, there was a marked stiffness and rigidity of his neck. He was unable to bend his head forward more than a half-inch without painful contortions. This presented an interesting clue, and prompted me to consider the possibility of meningeal irritation. I sent in one of the nurses to help him undress, and to place him flat on the examining table.

His wife was in constant attendance, patting his hand, soothing his brow, and caressing his cheeks. He, however, was quite irritable and told her to leave him alone, cursing her in Italian! Embarrassed, she withdrew and cowered in a corner of the room.

I approached the patient and initially tried to elicit signs of meningeal irritation by the Kernig's and Brudzinski's reflex reactions. When the hip and knee are flexed to 90 degree angles, any attempt to extend the knee is resisted and causes pain in the hamstrings. Any attempt to flex the neck causes involuntary flexion of the hips. Both tests were highly positive, establishing my suspicion. The rest of the neurological exam was confirmatory. All the other systems were completely negative with the exception of an elevated blood pressure and slightly enlarged heart. He was seventy-three-years of age and had had hypertension for a long time. His pupils and cranial nerves and sinuses were unremarkable, and the rest of the neurological exam was essentially uninformative.

My diagnostic impression was that this man was not suffering from severe intractable sinusitis, but instead had irritation of the meninges of his brain and spinal cord. Since his blood count was normal, and the sedimentation rate was negative, and since he was afebrile and had not been exposed to any viruses, and his eyegrounds were not affected as by tumor pressure, I felt it was imperative to do a spinal tap to determine the origin of the irritant to his meninges.

Mr. Lassio was hospitalized immediately, and the spinal tap revealed the presence of a considerable amount of old blood in the spinal fluid. I removed about 20 cc of spinal fluid until it began to clear. The first part of the tap revealed old, gritty brown material indicative of past bleeding. I knew, therefore, that the blood was not coming from my tap, as that would have shown fresh blood. Almost within minutes after the removal of the old bloody material, the patient reported that his headache was beginning to subside. I also noticed about a fifty percent decrease in the rigidity of the neck. Twenty-four hours later I tapped him again and there was still some residual old coffee-ground bloody fluid, but considerably less than we found the day before. Forty-eight hours after the second tap, the spinal fluid was completely normal and the patient was completely symptom-free, with no residuals.

This Italian couple was very popular, and I continued to get phone calls from their neighbors and friends and many of the Italian families in San Antonio who wanted to know his progress and prognosis. After a week's hospitalization, with no more evidence of bleeding, the patient was totally symptom-free and he was discharged. I was never totally sure of the original cause of the bleeding, but assumed that he apparently had ruptured a small varix, a dilated vein. For the following eight years that I continued with his care, there was never a recurrence. His problems, thereafter, concerned gradual enlargement of the hypertensive heart, and in later years, occasional small strokes, and finally a large massive stroke to which he ultimately succumbed.

After his recovery from the irritant to the meninges, I had a talk with his wife, who seemed to be genuinely pleased that he had recovered and was back to his normal self. What I did not know then was that in his normal state he was actually a dictatorial, selfish, inconsiderate man. Their friends told me that he was a despot, hostile to friends and relatives, and especially abusive to his self-effacing wife. He was thirteen years older than she, and through their lifetime he dominated her constantly and completely. He was a typical chauvinistic male, demanding that she wait on him hand and foot. He never showed any appreciation for the attention she offered him, in overabundance. In retrospect, I realized that she had been fearful of him throughout their marriage. When her friends congratulated me on the great job I did in helping Mr. Lassio recover, they would shake their heads sadly and say: "I'm not sure you did Mrs. Lassio, the martyr, a mitzvah, a good deed in bringing him back to normal, because in actuality he is a tyrant."

IT'S A ZOO

I once heard a comedian remark: "Don't bother to watch animals in the zoo to see funny behavior. Observe people: they are by far the funnier." After years in medical practice, observing people and their reactions to medical problems and treatments, I realized that the comedian was absolutely right. Some of the peculiar behaviors I saw were far more bizarre than those of any animals in a zoo.

The Ox (A cud-chewing mammal)

The president of a large bottle company started his career many years before as a bottle washer in a factory. Industrious, energetic, and very likable, he eventually rose through the ranks to become the owner of one of the largest bottle manufacturing plants in Texas. He would come to my office at six-month intervals for "executive" examinations. He wanted thorough complete physicals with stress tests, echocardiograms, ultrasonic studies, colonoscopic evaluations, as well as all lab urinalysis and x-ray studies. He also had all of the executives of his company come in for periodic evaluations, as the company insurance plan covered it. The only diagnosis I made on Charles Anson was that of external hemorrhoids, and since they were not too troublesome, he refused to have any surgical procedure for relief. One day he called the office to report to the nurse he was experiencing severe pain from his hemorrhoids. They were not bleeding, but he had excruciating discomfort prior, during, and after evacuations. I suspected from his history that he probably had developed a painful rectal fissure. Charles was quite stoic and would only complain if it hurt severely, and rectal fissures do hurt badly. I prescribed Lidocaine Jelly for local relief and twelve hemorrhoidal rectal insert suppositories. My nurse called the prescriptions to his pharmacist. He called back two days later and requested to talk to me directly, reporting, "I am not a bit better. Actually, I think my rectum is worse." "Have you applied the ointment two or three times daily as suggested?" "Yes, but those 'enormous' pills you sent me, I had a devil of a time chewing and swallowing them. Also, I think they were coated with some sort of aluminum, and they scratched the hell out of my throat." This was unbelievable! The president of a large plant, an intelligent, successful business man — was swallowing his rectal insert suppositories — and without even removing the aluminum wrappings! I had heard of the longstanding joke about the man who reported that, for all the good hemorrhoidal suppositories do, he might just as well have inserted them into the rectum for relief. But this was no joke. My nurse did not explain the directions clearly to him. The box said: "Use one three times daily." And Charles was indeed trying to swallow them three times daily with a glass of water. This posed a dilemma. How was I going to handle this without humiliating this executive? "Charles," I said, "sometimes, those large capsules don't dissolve quickly enough, nor do they remain intact by the time they reach the rectum. Don't try chewing them before swallowing. You'll have better results if you remove the aluminum, and insert them directly into the rectum for relief." I believe he caught on. He called back two days later to say his symptoms had abated completely, but he still refused to have a hemorrhoidectomy. Recalling my own discomfort with hemorrhoid surgery, I thought he made a wise decision.

The Skunk Did Smell

In the '40s, hypertension therapy was a frustrating and vexing problem. It was associated with a high mortality and morbidity. Patients would develop marked enlargement of the heart, since this pumping organ was forcing blood through narrow spastic vessels and had to work hard. The enlarged heart would begin to fail, and the patient would succumb to severe cardiac congestive failure. The elevated blood pressure would wreak havoc on fragile atherosclerotic blood vessels, and many had catastrophic strokes. Headaches and visual disturbance also accompanied hypertension. Patients would develop hypertensive retinopathy (damage to the retina), with narrowing of the vessels which would rupture and cause small hemorrhages to leak into the back of the eyeball. Also, the small vessels of the kidney filtering system would be damaged and renal failure ensued.

Before the days of low sodium diets, diuretics, beta blockers, calcium channel blockers, and A.C.E. (angiotensin converting enzyme inhibitors), control of hypertension was very difficult. Patients were given sedatives, and various preparations of nitrates, theobromine and other xanthine derivatives. Later, the Indian root drug, Rauwolfia serpentina, named after L. Rauwolf, a 16th century German botanist, was developed and gave moderate relief. When Kempner promoted his rice diet at Duke University, people thronged to the university to eat rice in all its forms three times daily. It definitely had merits, but in the end proved to be merely a form of ingesting a low-sodium diet.

Soon all common therapy required patients to restrict their sodium intake.

Bill Martin suffered severe hypertension. He was short, squat, muscular, a classical male mesomorph. He had the barrel chest, the bulging muscles, wide diaphragm which was elevated, impeding him from *taking a deep breath*. He was quite strong, having been a carpenter before he became a successful contractor. But the control of his blood pressure was indeed difficult in the early days, with the limited drug therapy available. The sedatives, the nitrates, the xanthines and the low-sodium diet were all tried on Bill, but with only moderate success. It was finally decided that Bill was a candidate for a sympathectomy, an operation which was in vogue for several years at that time. By surgically cutting the sympathetic nerves that went to the various blood vessels, a moderate reduction in hypertension ensued. The reduced pressure would continue for several years remission, but then the hypertension would recur. Fortunately, high blood pressure is no longer the ominous threat that it was in the '50s and '60s. It is still as widespread today, but more easily controlled with the various successful present day medications.

Bill, however, presented one serious additional problem — perhaps not so much to himself but to those around him. Bill had the most revolting, strong body odor that I encountered in my many years of practice. It was a combination of ammonia, locker room perspiration, and decay. When he sat in my reception room waiting his turn, other patients sitting near him would quietly get up and move to the furthest corner to avoid the overwhelming smell. On one occasion when I was running late, two patients, according to my receptionist, walked out of the waiting room and told her quietly that they would wait in the hall. The nurse would place him in an examining room, order him to undress and put on a gown, and then beat a hasty retreat. I always knew when Bill was in the office, even before I saw him. And for some time afterwards, his memory would linger on even with the liberal use of deodorant spray.

At one of his visits, I could no longer contain myself. I suggested to Bill that there was a new approach in addition to what he was already using for his hypertension. Namely, hot baths. I told him that one must use Lifebuoy soap liberally all over the body before entering the bathtub, then soak in the hot tub for 20 minutes, then shower, and then once again repeat the liberal use of Lifebuoy soap, and soak again in the hot tub for twenty minutes. I said, "It will do wonders for your hypertension." "How often do I have to use that treatment," asked Bill, who previously, it seems, would even skip his weekly Saturday night baths. "You must do this every day after work, to produce a good effect on your blood pressure, and always just before you come to the office." I said. He was to cooperate with his medicines and with his new Lifebuoy hot tub regime for the control of his hypertension. In a short time, we were able to tolerate his presence as he now had replaced his body odor with the odor of carbolic acid in the Lifebuoy soap. In later years, Bill was placed on beta blockers, and between those and his frequent hot baths with Lifebuoy, both he and the blood pressure were tolerable.

The Squeaky Cardinal

Several weeks after I presented a lecture on cardiac pacemakers at the medical school, Dr. Paul Gomez, an internist in Monterrey, Mexico, called me in consultation to attend one of his longstanding patients with advanced rheumatic heart disease and chronic failure. I was highly complimented. He explained that she was the wife of one of the leading industrialists in Monterrey.

Arrangements were made at the Santa Rosa Medical Center to reserve the large corner suite for her and for two adjacent rooms for members of the family. Two hours prior to her arrival from Monterrey, I received a phone call from her son. "Dr. Cooper, I want you to know," he began in an elegant Mexican accent, "Mama is a bit eccentric. She is very superstitious, and is addicted to the color red, any and all shades of red. She believes it brings her good luck!" He laughed when I told him I wasn't a redhead, nor did I have a ruddy complexion, nor was I a communist. But I promised I would wear a red shirt and tie, and red socks, to help start her off psychologically "on the right foot."

Mrs. Adolpho arrived at the Santa Rosa Medical Center, speaking very little English in a squeaky, high pitched, irritating voice. She was accompanied by an interpreter, two daughters, her son, two maids, and a security man. They each and every one wore an article of clothing in red, a tie, or a skirt, or a blouse, stocking, or shoes. It was comical but festive. She was ensconced in the corner suite, and the rest of the entourage settled into the adjoining rooms, using the hospital as their hotel. When I entered her room for the initial examination, this thin nervous woman in her early sixties was coughing slightly and breathing with difficulty. Each *deep breath* was punctuated with a grunting cough. Looking worried and apprehensive, dressed in a red nightgown, red bathrobe and slippers, her cheeks painted with circles of bright red rouge, she cut the figure of a small, sad, ridiculous looking clown. I understood enough Spanish to recognize that she was telling her family that she thought I looked very nice in my red shirt and tie, and she knew we were going to get along very well. I had already obtained a long, detailed history from Dr. Gomez and studied the accompanied chest x-rays, EKGs, and lab findings from studies made in Monterrey.

Mrs. Adolpho had a markedly enlarged heart, particularly on the right side. She had both advanced mitral and aortic valvular involvement, chronically stenosed (narrowed), as a result of longstanding old chronic rheumatic heart disease. She had a tachycardic pulse (the rate was elevated to 110 beats) but regular. Her neck veins were markedly distended, indicating cardiac failure. Her venous circulation was not returning rapidly enough into the heart and was backing up into the systemic neck veins. There was fluid in both lung fields, making a dry-leaf crackling sound heard in the presence of fluid known as "rales." The liver was markedly enlarged and was extremely tender and congested due to right-sided heart failure. There was considerable swelling of the lower extremities. She was unable to lie down because of the fluid in the chest, and found it necessary to sit upright to breathe more easily. She squeaked her complaints while breathing with considerable effort and constantly coughing.

Her rapid heart beat added insult to injury of the already badly functioning, crippled heart. Her blood pressure was interesting diagnostically. She had a high systolic of 180 and the lower diastolic reading was down to 60. This left her with a large pulse pressure (the differential between the high and the low pressures). It was 120 millimeters versus the normal of 40. She was extremely nervous, sweating freely, and exhibited fine tremors of the hands. She stared wide eyed and revealed a definite exophthalmus (protrusion of the eyes). She had all the physical signs and symptoms of over activity of the sympathetic nervous system, which led me to decide to evaluate her thyroid gland. Standing behind her, I placed both hands around her neck gently and asked her to swallow. As I suspected, the thyroid gland was enlarged, irregular and spongy. I ordered blood tests for thyroid activity and as anticipated, the results came back strongly positive for a markedly overactive thyroid gland. We now had the answer for her intractable "heart failure." She had been correctly treated for heart disease in Monterrey with diuretics, digitalis, antiarrhythmics, low salt diet, and antibacterials for the pulmonary infection. However, the "unrecognized" hyperthyroidism (the overactive thyroid gland) was the culprit whipping this already damaged heart.

Mrs. Adolpho was immediately given radioiodine to depress the thyroid activity. While waiting for its slower effect, large doses of the antithyroid drug, propylthiouracil, were administered for immediate reduction of thyroid hormone production. Due to her cardiac failure, she also received oxygen. By the seventh day her pulse was down to a normal 68. The extraneous fluid in her lungs had receded, the nervousness had abated considerably, and the hand tremors were beginning to decrease and Mrs. Adolpho was much more comfortable and her voice had improved. She certainly wasn't out of the woods yet, but the prognosis was more optimistic. On the eighth morning, on my early rounds, I asked if there was anything we could do for her. She smiled and said: "I would like very much to have a red canary in a red cage." A red cage was no problem, but a red canary presented a real challenge. But her private duty nurse went down to the Mexican market, bought a canary and had one of the local artists paint the feathers red!

Three weeks later, she put on her red dress, her red shoes and stockings and her red hat with its red feather. Clutching the red bird cage containing the red canary, with many of the yellow feathers already showing through the red paint, Mrs. Adolpho left the Santa Rosa Hospital for continued treatment in Monterrey. My finding of her undiagnosed overactive thyroid was indeed a boost to my reputation and soon many doctors in Monterrey began referring their difficult diagnostic problems. The arrival of "The Lady in Red" from Monterrey proved to be, thankfully, a Red-Letter Day early in my career. That case reminded me of Dr. Louis Leiter's admonition in my third year of medical school, "If there are symptoms that don't fit the primary diagnosis, look for an additional medical problem that may be concurrent."

The White Rabbit

Ted White was the owner of a large retail store in San Antonio. He suffered from hypertension and minimal cardiovascular disease. He was seventy-four, thin and angular, had lost most of his hair and wore thick spectacles. As a deacon in his church, he and his wife attended services every Sunday morning and bragged of a thirty-year attendance. They also attended evening bible studies on Wednesdays.

Priscilla White, his wife, had a name that befit her appearance.

She was a thin, seventy-two-year-old, straight-backed, grim looking woman with gray hair piled high upon her head in a knot, not unlike the style of the 1920s. When she came to the office she wore no make-up, a dull gray cotton dress, a bit too long, white shoes, white gloves, and she carried a child-size small white purse and looked down when she talked.

It seems that Mrs. White's complaints were not those of an internal medical diagnostic problem. She asked me to dismiss the nurse, which I did, and then she quietly referred to complaints in her urinary and vaginal tract. For the past week she had had severe urinary frequency and burning and thin tenacious vaginal discharge which embarrassed and disturbed her. After completing my studies, including urinalysis and microscopic bacteriological exam of the vaginal secretions, I was amazed to find the report indicating that she was infected by Chlamydia trachomatis. This is a bacteria which is spread only through sexual intercourse, a type of venereal disease. I dismissed the nurse at the time of consultation and reported my confidential findings to this shy, elderly, quiet bible student. She was terribly self-conscious when she learned that this disease was spread only through intercourse. I told her that treatment was simply the use of a broad spectrum antibiotic, and suggested that her husband should also be given the medication. Smiling broadly, she confided to me in a whisper like a titillated conspiratorial school girl, that the sexual partner was not her husband. With a sparkle in her eye she explained, "You see, every Tuesday I meet with Mr. Samuels, the head salesman of our store, who is fifty-two, quite robust and virile. We meet in a hotel room at the St. Anthony Hotel downtown. We have been meeting like this for two years." It was then she asked how long the incubation period was for this infection. "Seven to ten days," was my answer. Now looking me straight in the eye she said: "I guess we have a problem, Doctor. You see, I also meet with our accountant, Harry Stone, on Thursdays. I also engage a room at the St. Anthony Hotel and we have been meeting there for about one and one-half years. And maybe he is the infectious one." I was prepared to disbelieve her, but then she told me on Saturdays, she reserved a room at the hotel to meet with one of the truck drivers from the company, and she identified him as a forty-four-year-old bachelor. It was than I remembered the time-honored axiom: "You can't tell a book by its cover."

I told her that I would guarantee her confidence and that she was to have each of these men call me and I would prescribe accordingly. I then suggested that she approach her pastor for counseling, not that I was surprised at her sexual prowess, but that her promiscuity was of concern. She laughed broadly, "Doctor, I know you're not going to believe this, but I believe the Reverend has shown an interest in me too!" It was then that I decided that the only proximity this Sunday bible school student had to sainthood was in the name of the hotel that she frequented three times weekly.

I treated her and each of her hotel roommates separately, independently and confidentially, and suggested to each that they contact their partners to be sure to take proper medication. If Ted White died and did not leave her any income, there was no need to worry as Priscilla could easily have become the "oldest woman in the oldest profession." But Priscilla would be comfortable, as all hotel rooms have bibles in the desk drawer.

The Dumb Bunny

When Rose Mansky presented herself for an evaluation, I listened carefully to her history, which concerned itself with frequent episodes of migraine headaches, transient pains in the chest under the breast bone with minimal radiation, but often associated with tension and exertion. She also experienced shortness of breath and frequent attacks of palpitation. Rose was only twenty-two-years of age and the remote possibility of coronary heart disease was quickly dismissed. When I listened to her chest, she could *take a deep breath* without effort and there were no abnormal sounds during the respiration. But when I listened to her heart, there was a rough click associated with a midsystolic timing of a murmur, which radiated around the left fifth rib space. This cardiac valve murmur in a young woman was classical for a common disorder, "mitral valve prolapse." An x-ray of the chest was negative, and the EKG was well within the normal with the exception of an occasional premature systole, an innocent ventricular beat that comes ahead of time. But her echocardiogram was classical for mitral valve prolapse. At the final consultation, I spent considerable time explaining mitral valve prolapse, and how she was to live with it. I told her immediately that it was a frequently seen disorder, was not fatal, and that anywhere from ten to fifteen percent of all people have a variant of mitral valve prolapse. Very few people are aware that they have this disorder, and those patients who have occasional chest discomfort or palpitation or intermittent slight arrhythmias (irregular rhythms) should not be alarmed as the symptoms do not indicate a poor prognosis. I explained further that as she had a prolapsing mitral valve, between the left atrium and left ventricle, the best way to protect that valve was to prevent secondary infection. She was to alert all surgeons prior to any surgical procedure that she had this condition and they would protect her with antibiotics. I suggested that she was to take antibiotics twenty-four hours before any dental work, and for two or three days afterwards. If she had any severe respiratory infection or if she was to have any pelvic surgical procedure, even minor cautery, she was to be covered with prophylactic antibiotics.

Finally, I cautioned her that if she had any unexplained fever, to report to my office promptly. Two weeks later she came to my office, claiming that she had for the past three days an unexplained temperature of 100 degrees. Her white blood cell count was slightly elevated. My technician reported finding pus in her urine. A catheterization urinalysis was done in order to decide whether the pus was coming from the bladder or from the vaginal tract. The catheterized urine direct from the bladder was completely normal. I questioned her about vaginal irritation, discharge or infection. She said, "You told me that I must be extremely careful to control all infection. I've had a low-grade vaginal discharge for many months, and decided to use a daily douche. I heard all the wonderful attributes of the cleanser '*Mr. Clean,*' and started to douche with Mr. Clean." Upon checking her pelvis, I discovered a severe, raw vaginitis. "How often do you use the preparation, Mr. Clean?" "Twice daily," came the prompt answer. "The chemical," I said, "produced your infection," and I sent her to a gynecologist for relief. I knew Mr. Clean was an effective liquid cleanser for toilet bowls, bathroom walls and kitchen floors, but the vagina? I presume that if she hadn't improved, this innocent might have started using cleanser or brillo.

The Lemming Commits Suicide

In the early days of my practice, I decided to spend a month at the famous Massachusetts General and Beth Israel Hospitals in Boston. Some of the finest internists and cardiologists were associated with these hospitals. Two of the world's most eminent cardiologists, Dr. Paul Dudley White and Dr. Samuel A. Levine practiced in Boston at that time. It was very rewarding to make hospital rounds with these medical titans.

One morning Dr. Harry Stone, a younger colleague of the chief of the departments, discussed hypertension at grand rounds. He stopped abruptly in mid-sentence and said to the gathered audience of doctors in the amphitheater, "Gentlemen, I think I am having a rupture of an aneurysm at the base of my brain at the Circle of Willis. I have suddenly developed an excruciating headache and my neck is becoming increasingly stiff as I talk to you. I am seeing double, my right arm and right leg feel weak, and I am gradually losing consciousness." We all thought that was a dramatic discussion but with sudden horror realized the actuality of Stone's terse statements. He crashed to the floor and lapsed into a deep coma without any additional audible outcry.

He was rushed to the Intensive Care Unit and attended by the heads of the departments, who confirmed his dramatic, spectacular, descriptive diagnosis, and the following morning he was dead. This vascular accident being so vividly described as it occurred, by a precise internist, would remain forever in the minds of those who attended that meeting. I certainly never forgot the description of this tragic occurrence, and have ever been alert to this as a diagnostic possibility.

My dentist, Sandy Kahn was a patient complaining of severe backaches. I was able to relieve him of his muscle spasms quite promptly after noting how he constantly leaned to the right as he approached his patients. I merely suggested he change the position of the stool and start leaning to the left. It was apparent that he was developing an intercostal nerve neuralgia secondary to the positional rubbing of the lower thoracic vertebrae. Over a period of time, a low grade arthritis ensued from the developing calcium spurs. The dentist was a workaholic. He performed exceedingly fine, detailed dental repair work, very slowly and very meticulously. He was hesitant to accept new dental procedures, but he had refined his usual regular approach to problems to a degree of perfection. He would constantly comment, "Why do I have to change, when my results are so good?" Sandy was small in stature, approximately fifty-five-years-old, had very gifted hands, moved slowly, but purposefully. A classical obsessive creature of habit.

One afternoon he calmly called me from his office to tell me that his daughter brought his wife, Evelyn, to his office because she was feeling badly. Early that morning she had suddenly developed severe generalized headaches, was seeing double, and developed some weakness of the left arm and left leg. Soon, she said, the diplopia (double vision) had disappeared, but the headache continued. He seemed somewhat concerned, but not alarmed. I asked him to have his daughter bring his wife to me immediately. Our offices were on separate floors of the same building.

As she came into the examining room I noticed that she was holding her head with both hands, apparently suffering agonizing head pains. She also held her head stiffly and was tearing, and complained of experiencing double vision early that morning. The reason for the visual defect was a partial paralysis of the sixth cranial nerve, which allowed the eye on the right side to turn in. She said the weakness of the left arm and left leg had disappeared. The pupil was slightly dilated on the same side, and she obviously seemed to be suffering some confusion. Her blood pressure was slightly elevated. The rest of the physical examination was negative. She was only forty-years-old and had no evidence of atherosclerosis. She was not a diabetic, and I did not suspect a vascular stroke. I was concerned with the possibility that she was leaking from an aneurysm of the Circle of Willis at the base of the brain, and reported my findings to her husband, suggesting that she be hospitalized promptly for further studies. He retorted sluggishly, "Perhaps it's just a severe migraine. Let's wait until tomorrow before we take any action." Dr. Kahn, as we all knew, was slow to make decisions and did not like changes. I argued him out of his indecision and ordered immediate hospitalization!

Their fifteen-year-old daughter, sitting in the reception room and overhearing my phone call to her father asked me to explain what an aneurysm was and exactly where it was. I told her an aneurysm is often a congenital dilatation, a weakness, in a vessel wall of one of the arteries, sort of a blister. As time passes, the blister gets thinner and thinner and then, as a result of its developmental weakness, may start to leak. Once it leaks, there is always the frightening aspect of a severe hemorrhage into the brain from a complete rupture of the aneurysm. Should this occur, the symptoms that she suffered initially would be repeated, but with the continued bleeding into the brain she would lose consciousness. If the hemorrhage were severe enough, and they often are, it could be fatal within minutes, hours, or days. "The Circle of Willis," I explained, "is the confluence of blood vessels at the base of the brain and actually produces a circle around the pituitary gland. This is an area where most commonly weaknesses of blood vessels occur, producing the so called aneurysm or berry aneurysm."

The next morning, after carotid artery and vertebral artery angiography was completed we could easily visualize the Circle of Willis at the base of Evelyn's brain and there was a small saccular aneurysm leading off one of the vessels by a tiny stalk. The CAT scan showed evidence of a tiny leak into the brain, but as yet no massive hemorrhage. On tapping the cerebral spinal fluid, there was fresh blood; and on physical examination, the weakness of the sixth cranial nerve producing the double vision and the crossed eye effect was again evident. I met with Dr. Kahn and explained the seriousness of the situation. It was necessary to keep her arterial blood pressure under control with medication; that she was to be at complete bedrest; and to avoid coughing, sneezing, and exertion of any kind. She would be placed under sedation and given the drug Dilantin to prevent the possibility of convulsions. Furthermore, I was going to consult with a neurosurgeon to clip the stalk of the aneurysm at the base of the brain. I felt that surgery should be done within the next three or four days, as soon as her condition stabilized.

Dr. Kahn was hesitant, as usual, stroked his chin several times and said, "Dr. Cooper, is all of this really necessary?" "Don't you think that if she just stays in bed a few days the artery will seal itself and we will be over the problem?" "That is not the usual course of this condition," I explained in frustration. "The usual course is that within days or weeks or months the thinning wall, which has already indicated leakage, will rupture completely, produce a massive hemorrhage, and you will lose your wife." It disturbed me to be so brutally frank with Dr. Kahn, but he reminded me of the mule who has to be struck violently with a board between the eyes to get his attention. And only then could suggestions be made for him to move.

Forty-eight hours later, as the patient's condition stabilized, I called the dentist and said, "We should schedule surgery in the morning." His answer was, "Please don't do a thing until I come to talk to you," which he did later that day, and once again procrastinated. "She is doing fine, she looks good, I hate to subject her to such dramatic surgery, my wife is willing to take chances, as she is also convinced she is going to be all right without the surgery." Once again I pleaded with the doctor, "This is not the usual history of aneurysms. We are lucky that she did not rupture initially, but she will sooner or later. I am strongly urging and advising you to have the ligation done, and have that stalk clipped now." I explained that this is all done under microscopic operating technique and in the hands of the selected neurosurgeon, she would do very well.

The following morning, on rounds, I found his wife, Evelyn, completely dressed walking around the room with all of her hospital clothing carefully packed in a small suitcase. She told me she wanted to be discharged and thought that perhaps she needed a trip. She was going to go to Canada in the morning to visit her sister and relax and overcome all the frightening exigencies. Once again, I repeated my warnings of the urgency and the fear of letting the aneurysm rupture.

But the following morning, all the Kahns went to Canada. Two days later, a distraught, subdued Dr. Kahn called me from Canada to tell me that Evelyn had died. Unthinkingly, she lifted a suitcase onto the bed in preparation for unpacking, had a recurrence of sudden headache, lost vision and consciousness, and lapsed into a deep coma. She lost all reflexes, and within thirty minutes died!

What an unnecessary fatality! Evelyn lost her chance for survival by not undergoing the surgical procedure. And Dr. Kahn must live the rest of his life with a guilty conscience knowing that his obstinacy contributed to her death. Evelyn showed no will of her own, deferring to her husband unquestioningly. Like the lemming, she seemed to be pushed, by events she was helpless to control, to her own destruction.

GRATITUDE

Throughout the course of the practice of medicine, one is not only learning and re-learning and un-learning different phases of medicine as it is developed, but one is also constantly learning the various relationships between doctors and patients. It is often unpredictable and frequently full of surprises. Mrs. Gold taught me never to assume or anticipate a patient's gratitude for a job well done. If gratitude is extended, accept it graciously. But one should not practice medicine in anticipation of it.

Mrs. Gold accompanied her son Charles, age nineteen, to the office during my early years of practice. This sound-looking youth had suffered from high fever, chills, generalized malaise, cough, and pain in the chest of four day's duration. He looked quite pale and was obviously very sick. His white blood count and sedimentation rate were elevated. A chest x-ray revealed haziness in the central hilar regions. The EKG showed diffuse slight elevation of the ST segment in all of the leads except AVR (suspicious of inflammation of the lining of the heart). I learned from his history that he had had what he assumed was an upper respiratory infection one week prior to the onset of the present symptoms. When he *took a deep breath* there was sharp pleuritic type of pain in the anterior chest. This pain was superimposed on the constant pain that he felt sitting up, and the same chest pain was markedly aggravated when he was lying down. For relief he would sit up and hunch forward. The rest of the physical was negative.

There was no evidence of lobar pneumonia on x-ray, and he was a bit young for coronary heart disease. Charles' description of the aggravation of the pain upon lying down, associated with the pleuritic pain on *takng a deep breath* seemed to indicate that we were dealing with pericarditis, an acute inflammation of the lining around the heart.

The differential diagnosis was the next problem. What indeed did cause this acute pericarditis in a previously normal, healthy male? He had no evidence of tuberculous infection of the lung which conceivably could produce a tuberculous pericarditis. He had no lung involvement other than the evidence indicating slight inflammation of the lining (pleurae) of the lungs. There was no evidence supporting a diagnosis of uremic pericarditis because the urinalysis was normal and the blood chemistry showed no disturbance of kidney function. There was no evidence of rheumatic fever, as he had no involvement of the joints, no cardiac murmurs, and no arrhythmia. His respiration was quite labored and he was chilling. I told Mrs. Gold that he was seriously sick and needed immediate hospitalization. He was admitted to the Santa Rosa Hospital with a diagnosis of acute pericarditis, possibly viral in origin. He was placed in an oxygen tent to support his decreased oxygenation. He was given medication for the pain, advised not to lie flat as this exaggerated his discomfort. His chemistry and electrolytes were carefully controlled to remain normal. I ordered antipyretics, such as aspirin, Bufferin, and acetaminophen, to reduce his temperature.

The following day his condition became more acute. He was unable to take full deep breaths because of the severe pain. The number of cycles of shallow breathing per minute increased from the normal sixteen to thirty. There was now evidence of fluid accumulating in the lung bases, known as effusion. And on percussion, the borders of his heart seemed to have increased considerably. X-rays were positive for pericardial effusion, as the cardiac silhouette now had the water bottle configuration, indicating increasing amounts of fluid in the sac surrounding the heart. At that time neither echocardiography nor angiocardiography were available. There seemed to be no point in using any specific antibiotic inasmuch as we had no definite evidence of bacterial or fungal infection. His blood cultures were all negative. His heart valves were not involved with bacterial elements as in endocarditis.

He had characteristic physical findings of pericarditis with fluid. When he *took a deep breath,* his systolic blood pressure dropped more than 20 millimeters of mercury because when his lungs were markedly inflated with the deep breath they would press upon the fluid sac around the heart. This in turn would press upon the heart itself, decreasing the blood pressure. Upon expiration, the blood pressure would increase. His neck jugular veins were engorged, indicating disturbance in the return of the blood flow to the heart.

The patient was getting sicker by the hour due to his cardiac failure. EKG showed continued extension of his pericarditis, and he was having increased difficulty in getting sufficient oxygen to his red blood cells. By the fourth day of his hospitalization, his condition was indeed critical and I was afraid that I was going to lose this young man. For confirmation of my diagnosis and approach to his problem I felt it would be helpful to consult with another cardiologist and a pulmonary specialist. Each spent considerable time studying the chart and the patient, and all agreed that there was nothing that could be added at this point and that the prognosis was very poor.

On the fifth morning, Charles continued to deteriorate, he was now quite cyanotic (bluish hue) in spite of being in an oxygen tent. He was intermittently semiconscious, had forsaken all food. His blood pressure changes were classical for pericarditis, and he had the so called paradoxical pulse (waxing and waning in pulse volume associated with the breathing cycle). I had requested one of the thoracic surgeons to tap his pericardium and draw some fluid for relief. This brought temporary relief, but within six hours he was as sick as before, with re-accumulation of the fluid.

The following morning, in spite of all the help that was mustered, he was slipping out of control. I called Charles' mother to the patients' waiting room and confided to her what she already suspected: that in spite of all the approaches we used, and with three doctors actively on the case, he was going to succumb to this disease. She cried and clutched me tearfully begging, "Doctor, do anything, do anything you can to save my son. He is my only child." Of course this was extremely hard to take and I sat trying to comfort her for most of the day!

Finally, exhausted, I went to bed and awakened at 2:00 in the morning, remembering that during a recent medical meeting at Brooke General Hospital I learned that the endocrinologists were using a hormone experimentally known as adrenocorticotrophic hormone, or ACTH. Its primary use was to stimulate the adrenal gland. This was a

preparation taken from the pituitary gland of cows. It was used paren-
terally, that is, injected intramuscularly, suspended in a thick tenacious material of beeswax. On reviewing all of the known physiological
functions of ACTH at that time, I remembered that in addition to
stimulating the adrenal gland with the resultant effects of adrenal hormone production, it also acted in a capacity of being anti-inflammatory. "This may be the answer," I thought to myself, and hastily
dressed in the early morning hours and rushed to the Brooke General
Hospital. Fortunately, the nurse on duty in the early morning hours
had been one of my students. She was in charge of the medication,
knew where the ACTH was, and when I explained my predicament
and told her what I was thinking of trying, she surreptitiously gave me
six ampules of the hormone. We both promised to be discreet about
this.

Tucking this "treasure" under my arm, I rushed back to the Santa
Rosa Hospital, arriving there at 3:00 A.M. Mrs. Gold was sitting in her
son's room, head bent and weeping. Charles' condition was even more
precarious. I motioned for her to come out of the room. When she saw
me, she became even more frightened. She was absolutely sure that his
life was terminating and that was why I was there at that early morning hour. I sat her down, put my arm around her, and said, "Mrs.
Gold, with your permission, I would like to try a new medication. It
might help, and we have nothing to lose by this trial. This drug has
been used only experimentally to stimulate production of adrenal hormones, but one of its beneficial side effects is that it acts as an anti-inflammatory." I explained that Charles' condition was the result of massive inflammation that was uncontrollable. It was a shot in the dark,
so to speak, or in this case, a shot in the buttocks. It couldn't compli-
cate his desperate condition, as we were carefully controlling his fluid
balances and his cardiac output. I reminded her: "You asked me to do
anything, and I am willing to try it. Are you willing to allow me to try
it?" Once again: "Doctor, please do anything. Save my son. Please.
Try anything, of course you have my permission."

I called for the nurse on the floor and gingerly we turned semiconscious Charles on his right side, exposing his left buttock. I prepared the medication for injection. It was thick and tenacious and it
was necessary to run it under very hot water to make it less viscous in
order to enter the large 20 gauge needle. I injected 80 units of the
ACTH, turned him back on his side, and said a silent prayer. It was
now 4:00 in the morning. I watched him for one hour and there were

no immediate adverse reactions. I told the nurse to call me if she had any additional problems other than those which she was already facing. I told Mrs. Gold that I had to go home to get some sleep and that I would see her at 8:00 A.M., hoping, but doubtful, that he would survive the rest of the night.

I rushed to the hospital at 7:00 A.M., unable to sleep any later, rushed into Charles' room, and couldn't believe what confronted me. Charles was smiling and sitting up, out of his oxygen tent, having his breakfast, his bedside radio blaring the "oldie" popular song, "Am I Blue." Looking at his improved color I mused to myself with elation, "You certainly were before the ACTH." His temperature had dropped by two degrees; his respiratory cycle was down to twenty. He said that the pain in the chest had practically left him. His blood pressure did not show any changes on respiration. His pulse rate was an even 86, and he was more alert than he been for the past week. It was difficult to believe! I wasn't ready to accept this at full face value. When eight hours passed from the time of his last injection, I gave him another injection of 80 units of ACTH, and then went to make my rounds. Before I did, I searched for Mrs. Gold, but she apparently had gone home to sleep for a few hours.

At 2:00 that afternoon, after a quick lunch at the hospital, I rushed over to see our critical patient and, once again, found him sitting up comfortably, with no pain. He was fever free, blood pressure normal, pulse rate normal, and the EKG revealed some lowering of the elevated ST segments. Once again, I was not prone to accept this resolution, although I had to admit to myself that I was terribly excited and elated. I checked him again at 8:00 that evening, and there was continued improvement. He received his third injection of the ACTH eight hours after the last one.

The next morning on my seven o'clock rounds, I found Mrs. Gold in the room talking excitedly to Charles. Of course, he was eating again. "Charles always ate when he was feeling good," mother said. He threw back the cover of the oxygen tent saying he didn't need it anymore, and was reluctant to even accept the nasal oxygen cannula which was flowing at only four liters per minute. Upon physical examination the cardiac fullness had decreased considerably, his lung fields seemed to be clear. He could *take a deep breath* without pain! There was no cough. There was no fever. He had flushing of the face, but seemed quite normal. He no longer had the paradoxical pulse of pericarditis.

Now I accepted his improved status and felt that indeed the

ACTH had done its incredible job, and I was willing to continue with it in gradually decreasing doses for the next week. I called Mrs. Gold out into the hall, put my arm around her, and said in an expansive mood, "Well, Mrs. Gold, isn't it wonderful! Doesn't Charles look great! All seems to be going well. The new medicine did the trick!" I was waiting to hear her effusive gratitude. Instead she looked up at my face, quietly frowned, and said: "Dr. Cooper, why did it take you so long to think of that?" I wasn't sure that I'd heard her correctly. "I'm sorry Mrs. Gold. What did you say?" Once again: "Dr. Cooper, why did it take you so long to think of that?"

Actually Mrs. Gold was right. I was in control of the whole case. I knew all the problems and the complications. I had been previously exposed to the pharmacological properties of ACTH. Why hadn't I thought of it earlier? I decided not to agonize any further and I went to see my next patient, thoroughly pleased with myself.

*   *   *   *   *

Robert Leonard was a tall, dark-complexioned, handsome, prematurely gray, very successful oil developer. He had a broad smile and frequently flashed his pearly-white teeth. On each cheek there was a deep dimple that would be the envy of Tom Selleck. He had an excellent reputation among the members of the oil industry. He was a gentleman and one could always rely on his word. At the age of forty-two, Robert Leonard, who never seemed to be a Type A personality, had his first coronary occlusion. Fortunately, it involved the posterior coronary vessel, which is the least serious of the three coronary vessels. He survived his first episode and was not left with any residual handicap.

Mr. Leonard was referred to me by Dr. Norman, a close friend of his, when Robert began to develop angina pectoris with physical effort. The angina was not severe but it was classical: chest compression under the breast bone radiating into the neck and into the inner aspect of both arms. Robert was an avid golfer and he would have anginal episodes when he climbed the hill of the 17th hole at the country club. The chest pain would also occur when he over-ate or whenever he was especially tense during drilling of expensive, deep wells.

His EKG showed residual evidence of the previous posterior coronary occlusion, and his stress test was positive. It also revealed, at this time, major damage in the anterior coronary vessel, the predominant one, and there was suspicion of atherosclerosis of the circumflex (the third coronary vessel). He was not troubled with any arrhythmia and responded very well to vasodilators in the form of nitroglycerin inserted under the tongue, and to nitrates taken orally four times daily. He was placed on a low fat, low cholesterol diet, asked to discontinue smoking, and to reduce his alcohol intake to two ounces daily. He lost weight, and with cooperation on the medical program and diet, did very well and the angina abated. Soon Bob (Robert) and his wife became social friends of ours. However, we were not in the same category as most of his very close friends who were charter members of the very elegant, conservative German Club, and the San Antonio Country Club, which had a tight membership. He and many of his close friends in the oil business had their own jets and flew all over the country for business and pleasure.

Bob and his wife invited Sally and me to join them in a jet flight to Las Vegas as their guests for four days of fun. We met the rest of their group and all checked into the MGM Hotel. After the evening dinner shows the groups would hasten to the dice tables and gamble unbelievable sums until the early morning hours. Bob and his friends used one hundred dollar chips to play the table, and it never troubled them to loose twenty or thirty chips in an evening. Sally and I played the "one-armed bandit" machines and had our fun.

The first night at the MGM, Milton Berle was the comedian on stage. He told joke after joke, half of them in "Yiddish." In the others, he freely used Yiddish expressions. Bob and his friends laughed heartily at all of the jokes. Sometimes their laughter was so uproarious it was all they could do to keep from falling out of their seats as they applauded wildly. This I couldn't understand, because none of these "jet setters" were Jewish. After the show I approached Bob. "I am amazed that you understood Milton Berle's jokes, I thought it would take an Eastern audience to appreciate them." Bob and his Aryan-looking gang laughed and said, "You'd be surprised how much we guys know. Sam Levine, who sells us our equipment, teaches us Yiddish."

I decided to have some fun and test them. I asked, "Do you know what a schlemiel is?" Bob answered, "Sure, it's an oil developer who doesn't pay attention to his geologist." "Then what does it mean to be mazeldik?" "That's easy," Bob said. "That means when you drill twelve holes and ten come in successfully." "Okay. What's a schnorer?" "A schnorer is an oil developer who tries to keep his investors from earning as much as he does." "Very good. But now I think I've got you. What is a shlimazel?" "That's when you're sleeping with your partner's wife and he finds out," Bob replied, laughing. So now I understood why they appreciated Berle's jokes. Sam did a great job educating them.

Thereafter Sally and I were careful not to use any Jewish expressions that were not complimentary. We had a wonderful time. Sally won $8 and Bob Leonard came home with $12,000 in winnings. On the trip home, I couldn't resist telling Bob and his friends comedian Bob Hope's favorite story. An oil millionaire went to Las Vegas and came home with half a million dollars. He went there with a full million! Bob laughed, "I think my twelve grand take home was pretty lucky." "Bob," I said, "I think you are lucky in all your financial undertakings and I hope that your health continues with parallel luck." He turned around, smiled, shook my hand, and said, "That's what you call mazel." Once again he floored me!

About two months after the Las Vegas trip, Bob called me to his office to discuss an interesting proposition. He reported that in collaboration with the Sun Oil Company and another oilman, they were going to drill the deepest well in West Texas, one and a third miles into the bowels of the earth. It would take well over a year. He handed me a document, signed and notarized, that read as follows: "Robert Leonard hereby awards Dr. Elmer Cooper and his family a 1/8th participation in his (Robert Leonard's) 1/8th earnings of the Sunset #1 to be drilled by Sun Oil and others." I was startled and embarrassed. "What's the meaning of this, Bob?" "Dr. Cooper, my wife and I have become very fond of you and your family. If this oil well hits, as I'm hopeful it will, and you get 1/8th of my 1/8th, you will be able to retire and your children will never have to want for the rest of their lives. All I want in return is your friendship and help in keeping me alive as long as possible." This was the most generous gesture I encountered in my entire medical practice. The well took a year and a half to drill. Unfortunately, it was a dry hole! Although we were all disappointed, I rationalized that I wasn't ready to retire yet and loved the practice of medicine. And so, I continued another ten years.

Two years after the dry hole experience, Bob Leonard was playing golf at the Country Club with his buddies, had just completed a beautiful drive 270 yards straight down the fairway, when he turned to his friends and said, "I don't feel well." With that, he turned pale, dropped to the tee and despite heroic cardiopulmonary efforts by his group, it was of no avail. Robert Leonard apparently had a ventricular fibrillation and died. He was not yet fifty. His mazel ran out.

* * * * *

Highway 181 runs south from San Antonio to the Gulf Coast. Sixty miles south of San Antonio on this highway there are two towns, Karnes City and Kenedy. They are very similar in their layout, with similar size and populations. Each town is surrounded by rolling hills and green pastures, and the cattle industry flourishes. Like twins everywhere, the towns were constantly competing with one another for prominence. Both Chambers of Commerce were extremely active. Their high school football teams regularly battled it out on the field. Each developed a small, very well equipped hospital. Each had a small motel, a progressive civic center, and popular cattle auction theaters.

When David Mason developed diabetes and coronary heart disease and arthritis, he was told to leave his home in Chicago and go to the Southwest for his health. Karnes City, anxious to outdo Kenedy, advertised in the *New York Times* for someone to manage a new movie theater that was planned. David Mason, who looked like a younger version of George Burns, including the ever present cigar, happened to read the ad, applied for the position, and was immediately hired after he came to Karnes for a personal interview. Mason was a short, pleasant, affable man, very appealing, and knowledgeable in theater management.

Once he settled in Karnes, he was referred to me for the care of his diabetes, coronary heart disease and low-grade arthritis. I found him friendly, cooperative, and intelligent and I enjoyed our relationship very much, although I couldn't tolerate his cigars. His diabetes was controlled with diet and small doses of insulin. The coronary heart disease responded to nitrates, and his angina was markedly reduced after he lost weight, stopped smoking, and decreased some of the tension that he experienced in Chicago. He gradually converted himself from a Type A personality living in the Midwest to a Type B personality living in the Southwest.

His wife, Sarah, was in menopause, suffering severely from hot flashes, nervousness, and irritability. She found the move quite a shock to her nervous system. She consulted me for help and was placed on endocrine replacement therapy. She was told to take estrogen from the 5th to 25th day of her cycle, and progesterone from the 15th to 25th. This regimen regulated her periods and allowed her considerable comfort as the hot flashes abated and the nervousness and irritability disappeared. She soon became a happy Texan and she and her husband acclimated nicely to Karnes City.

The theater was very popular and drew its audience from a populace in a thirty mile radius. After two years, David Mason's popularity increased greatly and soon the Chicagoan was elected mayor of the city. He was not a Texan, not a cattleman, knew nothing about oil, and had never farmed or ranched, and although a city boy at heart, he became an excellent and popular mayor for the city.

During one of David's routine check-ups he mentioned that Bob Tolson, who had a 208 acre farm on the outskirts of Karnes City, was in dire need of money, having had several crop failures, and needed to sell his acreage at a sacrifice. While most acreage there was selling for about $1,000 to $1,500 per acre, Tolson would let his land go at $700 an acre for a quick cash sale. David suggested that I should take advantage of this. "Doctor, you work very, very hard, and I think it would be wonderful for you to have a little farm close to San Antonio. You could reach it in an hour and a half and spend relaxing weekends there riding your horses. Bob Tolson is a bachelor and would like to continue to live on the farm in his two-room decrepit house. He would take care of the farm and your horses and raise some crops." David continued, "Look how well I am doing since I left the big city of Chicago. I think it would be equally as beneficial for you to get away, ride your horses, walk in the fields, and *take deep breaths* of the fresh country air."

I told him I would give it some thought and get back to him within a week. That evening I called my brother-in-law, Herman, an astute business man whose judgment I respected. I described the 208 acres and its location, and told him about Mason's idea. I proposed that perhaps the two of us should buy the farm for both families to enjoy. Herman was equally enthusiastic, and said that since I was too busy to get there, he would drive down to evaluate the farm. After studying the site and its potential, he would meet with me for a decision.

When Herman returned from his exploration of the Tolson property, he called and said, "That farm is not for us! I saw no active crops growing. There is no good soil there. It is gravelly, rocky, and strewn with black rocks and yellow mud. I thought I smelled sulfur there. I met Mr. Tolson, an elderly gentleman, who had had no successful crop for five or six years. He is in dire need of cash and looks sickly. My impression is that we would be throwing away money to buy this worthless acreage." His reasoning seemed valid and I called David Mason, thanked him profusely for allowing us the opportunity to pick up a bargain, and told him I decided against this opportunity.

When I saw David Mason again approximately six months later, he said, "Doctor, I have a sad tale to tell you. One of the oil developers was flying over our area in his private plane looking for potential sites for drilling. He happened to have a Geiger counter on board his plane, and while criss-crossing an area between Karnes City and Fall City, the Geiger counter went absolutely wild. He checked and re-checked and finally landed the plane in Karnes City, rented a car, and criss-crossed the area again until he pinpointed the source of maximum Geiger counter activity. The area with the most intense radiation was Tolson's 208 acres." "Within a week" he said, "geologists and surveyors were clambering all over the Tolson farm." Tolson's farm turned out to be the site of one of the largest uranium deposits in Texas. The entrepreneur quickly bought Tolson's land and additional land around it, and started one of the larger uranium processing plants in the USA. For the next few years I could not restrain myself from berating my brother-in-law. "Nothing but a bunch of black rocks! Gravel and stony soil! How come you couldn't tell it was uranium?"

Several years later I heard that Mr. Tolson died. Try as I might I was unable to learn the cause of his death. According to his local physician he gradually lost weight, had severe anorexia, and problems with his gastrointestinal tract. The local doctor treated him for ulcers. Unfortunately no complete physical, x-rays, or lab studies were done, and the patient died two months after consulting his physician. It would have been of great interest to learn whether or not Tolson died as a result of radiation exposure. He lived for a lifetime directly over the areas where all the uranium deposits were found. Could he have died of cancer of the thyroid or bone or lung with metastases, or did he have leukemia? Any of these complications and many others could have come about as a result of exposure to radiation over a prolonged period of time.

One Sunday while driving home at my usual illegal speed from a fishing trip on the Texas Gulf Coast, I failed to slow down as we passed through Karnes City. Sally was sitting up front and my three children were in the back seat. Suddenly, we heard the shrill siren of a motorcycle policeman. When I glanced at my speedometer I realized that I had been doing eighty miles per hour. My children were petrified seeing this police officer directing me to the side of the road. I told them, "Kids, don't worry. This is my town. I've got it sewed up. I have patients all over this town. Why, David Mason, the mayor, is one of my patients." I stopped and rolled down the window. The young officer, about twenty-one, leaned into the window and asked for my driver's license. As I handed it to him I said, "I'm Dr. Cooper. I have many patients in this town. It's a great town." The officer said, "Yeah, I know." I continued, "You know David Mason, your mayor, has been my patient for five years and is a close friend. Please give my regards." He said, "I will. I know you're David Mason's doctor." I turned and winked at the children. Then I saw him pull out his book of tickets. Getting a bit apprehensive, I continued, "Now you know Mrs. Garner, the principal of the high school, has been a patient of mine for twelve years. She's a good friend of mine." The tall lanky policeman with his Texas drawl said, "Yeah, I know." "By the way," I asked, "Do you happen to know her son John? He would be about your age. He used to be a patient of mine too." "Yeah, I know. I'm her son John!" With that, he handed me the ticket for speeding. "You did a great job helping me with my growing joint pains, Doc. And I'll always appreciate that." As he started his cycle he said, "See you in court next Wednesday at 2:00 P.M. Goodbye Doc." I rolled up the window, embarrassed and frustrated. Bleakly, Sally and the kids said in unison. "Yeah Doc, you've got this town made." Then they all burst out laughing. Trying to redeem myself with my family, I said, "You heard him mention his problems with growing joint pains? Well, I certainly did help him. Did you notice he was six-feet four-inches tall?" Sally smiled and said, "Not good enough, Doc."

*   *   *   *   *

The juvenile diabetes, often called unstable, brittle diabetes that occurs during childhood, is more serious and more difficult to control than diabetes that occurs during adult years. It is characterized by wide swings in the amount of glucose available to the brain — either more glucose than necessary (hyperglycemia), or less glucose than necessary when responding to overdosage of medication or exercise (hypoglycemia episodes). It is more serious than any of the other types of diabetes inasmuch as the illness continues for a long time, having started in childhood. It is also complicated by the other endocrine problems that are involved during growth, maturation, and sexual development. Control is difficult, and most juvenile diabetics have some degree of emotional reaction to their diabetes. Juvenile diabetic patients are often understandably uncooperative. Being young, they resent having to adhere to their diet and are not good at taking medication, even when under supervision by adult members of the family.

I was first consulted to see Muriel Dawson at age seventeen, a classical case of juvenile diabetes. Her diabetes was first recognized at the age of three. She had been in a diabetic coma at least eleven times prior to my seeing her, and had suffered innumerable episodes of diabetic hypoglycemia shock. Some of these complications were due to her basic physiological responses and some were brought on by her careless approach to her condition. When I first saw her at the hospital, she was in a deep diabetic coma, with blood sugar of 640 (normal is 80 to 120 mg), and she was in diabetic ketoacidosis. She had the classical Kussmaul air hunger, labored respiration, acetone breath odor, and was almost in a state of areflexia (depressed reflexes).

Her mother had died several years earlier and she lived with her father. He was a short, thick-necked, wide nosed, florid faced, fast-talking, cigar smoking individual. He was gaudily dressed, sported a large gold chain about his neck, and an ostentatious gold and diamond studded Rolex on his wrist. He was abrasively obnoxious, dictatorial to the nurses, demanded immediate attention, and seemed more concerned with his own comfort than with his daughter's precarious condition. He demanded, and I helped him receive, permission to spend the nights in his daughter's hospital room. Immediately he criticized the rollaway bed that was brought in and ordered an additional complete hospital bed for his comfort. This made the patient's single room quite crowded. The special duty nurses that he had requested were handicapped by his irritating presence and the room continuously reeked from his cigars.

For forty-eight hours it was necessary to maintain close supervision of Muriel's severe diabetic condition. In addition to her uncontrolled diabetic acidosis, there were considerable signs of kidney involvement and I was fearful that she had already developed diabetic nephrosis (Wilson Kummelstiehl's disease), which portends early fatality. While Mr. Dawson slumbered and snored and, when awake, puffed on his cigars, I was busily studying her blood sugars, blood gases, and electrolytes, trying to get control of this difficult condition. Finally, on the third day, she came out of the coma, quite alert and cantankerous, but saved. That afternoon, Mr. Dawson asked me to meet him in the hospital hall. I was sure he was going to discuss her future care, or at least to indicate his reaction to all of my efforts. He did, indeed, thank me and vociferously and foolishly offered me a cigar which I declined. He shook my hand, told me what a great job I did and what wonderful care I gave his daughter, and declared he wanted to show his appreciation.

As he was in the oil business and very successful, he said that out of gratitude he would like me to become a part investor in some extremely rich oil royalties. He claimed that he had ten wells in a certain area in West Texas and was going to drill an additional eight more. He maintained that he didn't expect me to participate in the cost of the wells, but was willing to sell me a relatively inexpensive participation for $10,000. I would soon, he said, be the recipient of at least $50,000 a year of oil income for years. He kept saying, "I'm most anxious to do something for you and I know you don't want a charitable contribution. Therefore, with this limited small investment, I am guaranteeing you several hundred fold return on your money."

I replied that I would think it over carefully and was appreciative of his wonderful offer. At dinner that night, Sally told me, "You see, it does pay to be a conscientious doctor."

The following morning, before the patient was discharged to continue treatment at home, Mr. Dawson brought me charts and plats of the area of this oil production. It seems that it was adjacent to land that had wells developed by the Humble Oil Company. There were, according to his charts, flowing wells all over, and, as indicated on these plats, he had ten wells in production, and he indicated where eight more would be drilled. He had me sign papers and I proceeded to the bank and submitted a cashier's check made out for $10,000. He receipted this, left me all the charts and promised to keep me informed on the progress of the drilling. He appeared to be promising me 1/8th of all the income from eighteen wells hereafter, with only one initial outlay of money. There was to be no participation in any of the future drilling expenses or in the cost of maintaining the wells. This seemed a real bonanza! I carefully folded all the charts and took them home with me.

The next morning, Sunday, I slept a bit later, and phoned my friend and patient, Arnold Hunter, who had been in the oil business for twenty-four years and explained the details of Dawson's offer. "Your friend is certainly trying to show gratitude for what you've done for his daughter," Hunter said, "and he wants you to take care of his daughter hereafter and be somewhat indebted to him." He asked me to bring all of Dawson's charts, drawings, plats, and descriptions to his office. On Monday morning, on my way to the hospital, I dropped all the information with his secretary since he had not yet arrived, and went to the hospital.

That evening, Sally told me that Mr. Hunter had asked that I please call him at his home, immediately! "Dr. Cooper, I have some disturbing news for you. Those maps, those charts, those plats, that information, none of it is authentic. There are no wells in that area. There are none being contemplated. There have been seismographic studies done previously, and all indicated that there is no oil in the area Dawson designated. The information is fraudulent!"

Furthermore, he said he learned that Mr. Dawson had a reputation for being an oil swindler. It was hard for me to reconcile this. I knew that I was vulnerable and could possibly be subjected to fraud by an oil man. But to think that this man, whose daughter's life I'd saved, used that premise as a basis for manipulating me was more than I could gently tolerate. Muriel had a charming personality but was a dependent apathetic young lady, so I was reluctant to upset or alarm her. I told her, "I would like to talk to your father." She told me that he was in West Texas but she knew how to get hold of him. I asked her to please give him a message tonight. I did not want to alert her as to what had transpired, nor allow her to be disturbed by what her father was up to. "Tell your father to send me a check for $10,000 by tomorrow noon and we will conclude our business. If the check does not arrive in my office by tomorrow noon, he will need the help of the district attorney to complete our transactions." She was totally naive about the content of the conversation, but cheerfully told me that she would deliver the message, and reported that she felt well, thanked me again, and said she would see me in my office the following Monday.

At 11:15 the following morning, after I returned from hospital rounds, there was a Western Union telegram awaiting me with a withdrawal slip for $10,000 to be presented at the downtown office. Nothing was further said by either of us, and I debated whether I wanted to continue with Dawson's daughter's care. Although I enjoyed the challenge of treating the young lady, I realized that the relationship between her father and me was such that I could no longer feel comfortable being responsible for her health. I was sad to interrupt our relationship because we had established an excellent rapport. I referred her to a diabetic specialist, and learned unhappily two years later that she had died from diabetic kidney failure due to diabetic glomerulosclerosis. I read with no surprise, several years thereafter, that her father was charged in West Texas with fraud, found guilty, and sentenced to four years in jail.

*   *   *   *   *

Several years ago, Sally and I were returning from Paris on Air France, sitting in row thirty-six, in the very crowded coach section. I was busy reading the *Eye of the Needle*. We were halfway home, mid-ocean, when over the intercom came the urgent call from the stewardess, "Is there a doctor on the plane?" "We need a doctor immediately." "Please, is there a doctor on the plane?" Sitting way back in the coach section, I fervently hoped that there was a doctor in first class who would be available, or perhaps one in the first thirty-five rows. No one arose to attend the patient. Once again, over the loud speaker, "Please, we need a doctor immediately in first class." "Is there a doctor on board the plane?" Since no one answered this last plea, I reluctantly left my crowded section and wound my way through the narrow aisle to the first class section. Of course, I had no medical instruments with me, but I would see if I could be of any help.

Lying on the floor between the seats in the middle of the aisle next to seat number two was a tall, very dark, relatively good looking mid-Eastern appearing young man. He was hyperventilating in a remarkably rapid fashion. His head was rolled back and slightly stiff, and his eyes rolled back up. His hands were clenched in a typical carpopedal position (the thumb was compressed into the other four fingers in a spastic condition). There was marked pallor around his lips. The history the stewardess gave me was that this man was very nervous, had been pacing back and forth down the aisle, looking at his watch, sighing, and constantly asking, "How many hours to go before we reach New York?" He had been sweating profusely and drinking heavily. He was well-dressed and constantly offered to pay $10 for each of the drinks even after it was carefully explained to him that in first class drinks were free. She noted that after perspiring freely and becoming increasingly tremulous, his sighing increased, as did his rate of breathing. When he stood up, he apparently felt dizzy, as he held on to his arm rest, and then collapsed.

This was a classic case of "hyperventilation syndrome." Under extreme tension, many people begin to breathe deeply automatically and then voluntarily try to regulate the respirations. The hyperventilation is a characteristic syndrome. Normally, breathing is regulated by the concentration of the carbon dioxide in the bloodstream, which affects the respiratory center in the base of the brain. This is all done automatically and one does not have to concentrate on breathing. Under states of tension, many people start out by deep sighing. They take in a deep breath and sigh through the expiratory phase, which becomes longer than the inspiratory phase. In this way, they begin to wash out necessary carbon dioxide, which is the stimulant for respiration. As they continue to do this, more and more carbon dioxide is washed out and soon the normal stimulus for respiration becomes impaired. One does not die of this condition because it is impossible to block the respiratory system completely in this manner, but the concentration of CO_2 being gradually washed out causes the breathing cycle to become slower. As the breathing becomes slower under this state of tension, the patient begins to suspect that he is losing control of his breathing and starts to voluntarily take deep breaths and effect deep expiration. As a result, he washes out more CO_2. When this becomes progressive and he develops respiratory acidosis, the patient displays the typical lightheaded fainting and carpopedal spasm of the hands. This is what happened to the young man on Air France.

Recognizing what was confronting us, I asked the stewardess for one of the usual paper bags used for air-sickness and placed it over his nose and mouth, allowing him to proceed rebreathing his expired air and thus reaccumulate the proper amounts of CO_2. Within five minutes his breathing cycle returned to normal. The faint over and revived, he looked around, stood up, and appeared to be in complete control. He was about six feet tall, outfitted from head to toe by Gucci, apparently from oil money. He promptly sat down in his seat, never looked at me, never offered to shake my hand, and never bothered to thank me. I returned to my seat, thinking, "What an ungrateful bastard."

Shortly after I returned to my seat, the stewardess came and thanked me profusely, saying the Captain wanted me to have a large bottle of champagne as a token of their appreciation. I thanked her, popped open the corked bottle, and Sally and I began to enjoy the bubbly champagne. As I was sipping, I noticed the young man coming down the aisle toward me. I thought, "Finally, he is feeling well enough to come and show some recognition and some appreciation." He came closer and closer without smiling, and then before I realized it, he was passing my seat.

As I turned around to approach him and ask him how he felt, he bumped my elbow and the champagne poured all over my suit. Without any apology, let alone thanks, he continued to walk up and down the aisle, apparently to increase his circulation.

We arrived in New York that evening and since we had tickets to the production of "Cats," we rushed by cab to the theater. During intermission, someone tapped me on the shoulder and I turned around to see a well-dressed middle aged man. "My name is Norman. I'm CEO of Alexander's store." I was on Air France sitting in first class when you saved the life of that fellow. You did a beautiful job."

I explained that actually the treatment was very simple, once the diagnosis was recognized, and told him the rest of the story including the part about the champagne. Incredulous, he shook my hand and walked off sadly, shaking his head, muttering, "That's gratitude."

Everyone Wears a Different Hat — The Unforgettables

Health, equanimity and memory are assets necessary for successful living. The loss of any of these is a disaster. Although somewhat narcissistic, nostalgia is comforting and adds continuity to one's life. Certain past relationships remain vividly unforgettable.

Dr. Shotts

Colorful, glamorous, and charismatic would describe Dr. Larry Shotts, a highly skilled chest surgeon who had lurid fantasies of his worth to the world. Tall and robust, he had brown curly hair, deep-set brown cunning eyes, and a wide smile revealing pearly, orthodontic corrected white teeth. He sported an eighteen-carat gold chain around his right wrist and wore a large gold watch studded with diamonds on the left. The neck was encompassed by a heavy chain of gold, and he wore a large diamond ring on his right hand. Dr. Shotts wore custom made French cuff shirts with gold and diamond links, his nails were always neatly manicured, his Italian shoes highly polished. He was ruggedly handsome, extremely articulate, and suffered from a case of egomania. He would stride down the hospital corridors, brisk and erect, looking very glamorous, and nurses would sigh as he passed their desks.

During World War II, he was chief of thoracic surgery for the 4th Army and performed spectacular chest surgery under the most trying conditions in European areas. After the war, he was one of the consultants in thoracic surgery for the Army and quickly gained a professorship in surgery at the new medical school of the University of Texas in San Antonio. He was the leading thoracic surgical consultant for the hospitals in San Antonio. Every Wednesday evening he would present a symposium on diagnostic chest problems at the Brooke General

Army Hospital, and physicians would come from far and wide to hear his interesting, thunderous, well-demonstrated theatrical medical presentations. Each time, it was "I did this, and I suggested that, and then I operated and I had spectacular results."

Not surprisingly, he married a New York cabaret torch singer of considerable renown, and she was as beautiful and feminine as he was virile. They were an exciting couple and very impressive socially. They were each prima donnas and they fought constantly. He would pound his fist, and she would throw things — hair brushes, mirrors, and plates were her specialty!

It was always exciting to be called in consultation to see one of Shotts' cases before or after surgery, for to work with him was an unforgettable experience. When he entered a patient's room, he always demanded an entourage to accompany him; the head nurse of the floor, at least one other nurse, the intern, the resident, and the orderly. If there was an extern close by or another consulting physician on the case he would make sure that they came along also. He thrived on audiences, and seemed to anticipate applause and requests for encores whenever he presented a case.

Manuel Gonzales, of Mexico City, came to see me because of a persistent cough with pain in the chest and bloody sputum. He had lost weight and was a two pack a day cigarette smoker. My suspicions were confirmed after listening to his story, and his x-rays revealed a large tumor mass in the left upper chest. Dr. Shotts and I consulted on the case and we decided that the tumor was operable. The patient was very wealthy and was a member of a very prominent family in Mexico. Dr. Shotts charmed all the members of the family and in his first meeting with them boasted of his surgical merits, his successes and his various academic appointments. The surgery was long and difficult but the outcome successful. Dr. Shotts dramatically described his procedure in great detail to the assembled family and awed them with his skill.

On the patient's third postoperative day, Mr. Gonzales was doing very nicely and by chance both Dr. Shotts and I entered the room simultaneously. Of course, his usual entourage was present — the head nurse, another nurse, the intern, an orderly and an extern, as well as the private duty nurse — standing attentively at the bedside as he pontificated. Waiting until all eyes were upon him he cleared his throat and said to the private duty nurse, "If Mr. Gonzales continues to have this hacking cough, I want you to call the pharmacy and ask them to

send you 'Shotts' special cough mixture'." I knew very well that the
"Shotts," special cough mixture was just a routine pharmaceutical over
the counter drug known as Brown's Cough Mixture. He then turned to
the nurse again and said, "If this patient has difficulty in bringing up
sputum, I want you to hold a pillow on his chest firmly while the patient coughs so there will be no pain." He demonstrated this procedure, "This," he said to the concerned family gathered around the bedside, "is called Shotts' cough maneuver." Of course, this was a
maneuver that all of us had learned in third year medical school.
"Next," he said, turning again to the head nurse, "I want you to bring
me the Cat-of-nine-tails to wrap his chest so he will not experience
pain as he moves about. Bring me the Shotts' Cat-of-nine-tails." The
so-called "Shotts' Cat-of-nine-tails" was a binder for the chest which
had been in common use in all hospitals for about ten years and was developed in Australia. At about this time I felt he had captured the audience as they stood around and watched him with total admiration,
ordering, gesticulating, and "Shotts-izing." I could not help myself. I
turned to the nurse, saying, "and if Mr. Gonzales does not have a
bowel movement by tomorrow morning, be sure and give him a
"Shotts' enema." and I walked out! Larry Shotts became red in the
face, and I am certain his blood pressure rose 20 to 30 points. For two
weeks afterwards he would pass me in the hall and merely nod; he
would not recognize me. This was his form of punishment.

*   *   *   *   *

Several weeks later, he did consult me on a case of a bizarre type
of lung pathology. The patient was a man in his early forties who was
referred to him by one of the local family practitioners for a possible
cancer in the *right* middle lobe of his lung. I was asked to see the patient as Shotts was not quite convinced that this was a typical carcinoma of the lung. On x-ray, the infiltrate was a bit hazy and glassy and
showed no calcification or other specific definable characteristics of
lung cancer. The patient had lost some weight, had a hacking cough,
and was slightly febrile. When I entered his hospital room he introduced himself to me as Lou Taylor. During the history-taking, he told
me that he worked at the local department store across the street from
my building. He said he had been coughing for several weeks, had malaise, headaches, anorexia, sweated and had a low-grade fever.

Routine lab studies were negative. Physical examination revealed
a well-developed male, moderately ill, perspiring freely, with a con-

stant hacking cough. This was aggravated whenever he *took a deep breath*. His throat was red, his temperature was 102 degrees and he had normal blood pressure. On auscultation of the chest, I heard rales and bubbling noises on the right side with lesser amounts in the lower lobe of the left lung. (In the history-taking he replied with negatives to questions regarding recent contact with rabbits, cattle, birds, polluted water, and insect bites.) The x-ray, taken two days previously, revealed a normal heart and *left* lung, but there was now a definite widespread hazy involvement of the *lower* lobe of the right lung suggesting pneumonitis (a type of pneumonia). The x-ray surprisingly showed more involvement than was anticipated from physical findings, which is a reverse of the usual chest pathologies. My initial impression was primary atypical pneumonia. Agglutination tests for typhoid and paratyphoid, tularemia (rabbit fever), and brucellosis were negative. Sputum smears for acid-fast bacteria, that is, for TB, and smears for fungi were also noncontributory. Skin tests for fungus, namely histoplasmosis and coccidiomycosis were also negative. The patient's condition was steadily deteriorating. Two days later at re-examination, his temperature was 104 degrees and his spleen had enlarged. It is rare to have an enlarged spleen with the usual bacterial or viral pneumonias. The influenza pneumonia viruses were ruled out by negative throat washing.

The history and progress of this case, the physical findings combined to lung and spleen, and x-ray changes of a suspicious hazy pneumonitis with the pathology predominantly close to the hilar (central) region of the lung brought to mind a rare condition know as psittacosis or Parrot fever. On a hunch I sent his serum for complement fication tests to the Austin Contagious Disease lab. The missing link in this diagnostic puzzle was the absence of bird or animal history of exposure by this luggage store salesman.

Once again I questioned this very sick apprehensive man, "Do you have parrots, or parakeets, or canaries at home?" The answer was again, "Absolutely not."

The serum that was sent to Austin for complement fixation test studies for psittacosis came back strongly positive. A repeat study within several days showed an even increased titer. This disease, very rare in the United States and Canada, is caused by the psittacine virus which is intermediate in size between the rickettsia bacteria and true viruses. The disease is rare and only occurs in people who are exposed to groups of birds such as parrots, parakeets, cockatoos, and budgerigars. Occasionally canaries, finches, pigeons, turkeys, pheasants and chickens have been recognized as potential sources of exposure. The virus is usually present in the droppings and nasal discharge and saliva of birds. Once a person is infected or becomes a carrier, human to human spread is possible. There had been a paper, I recalled, reported two years previously, wherein human to human spread in a hospital produced thirty active cases of psittacosis in nurses. Four died of overwhelming infection.

I questioned the patient once again, in the presence of his wife, regarding exposure to birds. His wife's eyes shone with sudden recall, "I remember," she said, and then told us of an incident that occurred two weeks prior to the onset of Lou's illness, which he apparently had completely forgotten. A parakeet had escaped from a cage in the bird department, three floors below the luggage department on the main floor of the department store and momentarily alighted upon his new luggage display, soiling it extensively with its droppings. The bird was recaptured by the aviary attendant and returned to its cage. Lou immediately thoroughly dusted and rearranged his luggage display and must have inhaled the virus in its pulverized form as he dusted. Immediate follow-up studies disclosed widespread presence of the virus in the first floor aviary from which this bird escaped, and proper measures were taken to destroy the suspicious birds and treat those who had not shown any signs of infection with Achromycin. In this instance, we felt secure that we had stopped a potential epidemic of psittacosis in San Antonio and I had the consummate pleasure of having Dr. Shotts complimenting me in diagnosing an extremely rare disease.

*   *   *   *   *

Dr. Shotts asked me, at a later date, to see the pleasant Mrs. Jones in room 240 at the Santa Rosa, who had an unusual lung lesion that he could not define. The attending physician who initially studied her had run all the routine studies for bacteria, virus, and cancer and they were all negative. He was hard put to diagnose this bizarre lesion in her lung. As I entered room 240 my first impression was that Mrs. Jones did not appear to be very sick. She was lying comfortably in bed reading a school textbook. She was a large, robust, healthy looking woman about forty-five-years-old who was constantly sniffing and blowing her nose as we talked. I asked her to *take a deep breath,* and she accomplished that without effort or cough or pain. I then reached for my stethoscope and listened very carefully to her chest. I heard a few insignificant rales at the lung bases. No other abnormal sounds. When

I looked at her x-ray I was totally surprised to see a large circumscribed nodular lesion in the right lower lung the size of a large orange. She did not appear sick enough to have such a large mass. The lesion did not have the characteristics of pneumonitis. Was it a metastatic lesion from a cancer? She had been intensely studied for a primary cancer elsewhere, with negative findings. The lesion was round, nodular, circumscribed and quite dense. The only persistent finding I could obtain on repeated prolonged history-taking was that Mrs. Jones remarked that she suffered from a considerable amount of postnasal drippage from a chronic allergic sinusitis, and that her sinuses would frequently become secondarily infected. The possibility of postnasal drippage into the lung fields was momentarily entertained, but quickly rejected as aspirated material from sinuses would not produce a nodular lesion simulating a tumor.

I requestioned her, "What medication do you use for your sinuses?" Her information elicited a startling revelation. For the past two or three years she was in the habit of using a medication with a petrolatum base that contained menthol. Each night she would apply liberal amounts of the ointment directly in her mouth to her palate. As the warmth of her palate liquified the ointment, she inhaled the soothing mixture, convinced that the vapors would reduce the postnasal drippage lying at the back of her throat. She had used this medication as an inhalant religiously for years, even though the directions clearly stated that it was not to be taken internally. This was the clue to the diagnosis. The medication consisted of, among other ingredients, the base petrolatum (an oil), as well as menthol, a strong chemical. When the menthol was exposed to the tiny little cilia (hair-like fibers) in the trachea and the bronchial tree, it would temporarily paralyze them. Normally, the cilia are constantly busy catching and washing up any form of abnormal debris inhaled into the lungs. However, when the menthol disturbs the function of the little cilia, then the petrolatum lying on the palate would melt and the patient would aspirate this oil. Over the years the petrolatum was slowly accumulating in the right lower lobe of the lung. The bronchus to the right lung is straighter than the one to the left lung and because of gravity, accumulates most of the drippage. Therefore, the right lower lobe accumulated the paraffin material producing a pseudo tumor or granuloma identified as a paraffinoma. To diagnose this lipoid granuloma it was necessary to obtain sputum studies and stain the cells for fat. There are important cells in our first defense immune system known as macrophages. When abnormal irritants or antigens enter our lung spaces (alveoli), then the macrophages gather and gobble up these abnormal particles. The macrophages studied in Mrs. Jones' stained sputum specimens were loaded with fat. These cells gathered together to produce the ball-like tumor (the granuloma) in her lung. When I called Dr. Shotts to tell him of my diagnosis he was impressed and complimentary. I could not refrain from jibbing him and said I was going to call this the "Cooper tumor."

It was still necessary to remove this large foreign body by surgery. This rare case was presented by Dr. Shotts at his weekly symposium and, of course, he called the tumor a "Shotts' granuloma!"

Dr. Shotts continued to refer many of his patients including members of his family for my care. I became the physician for his charming, dynamic, volatile wife, a noted night club entertainer. She, in turn, sent her mother to see me with her arthritic and cardiac problems. She resided in Manhattan and owned a large Chinese restaurant known as "Ruby's." She also started a large industry of canned Chinese food found in all supermarkets and grocery stores known as "Ruby Foods."

*   *   *   *   *

Prior to meeting his wife, Jeanne, Larry dated a fascinating wealthy, sensual French divorcee. He would refer to his girlfriend Laurie, as "Shotts' sexy Frenchy." After his marriage, they remained good friends. She lived alone in a large mansion at the top of a hill overlooking the Japanese garden in Brackenridge Park in San Antonio. One morning Larry asked me to see Laurie inasmuch as she was having one of her severe migraine headaches. This one, he said, was intractable and not responding to the usual ergot preparations that he had sent her, and that she had nausea and vomiting with the attack and needed relief.

I was greeted at my arrival by two large black barking Dobermans. After subduing the dogs she greeted me at the door wearing nothing more than a black, lacy, diaphanous nightgown. She ushered me into the flounced, chintz-filled living room and although it was only 10:00 A.M. offered me a drink. I politely refused and proceeded to question her thoroughly about her migraine. I noticed the bottle of scotch close by and a half-empty tumbler. She told me her headache had become unbearable that day. Her descriptions were typical. She said that they had started during childhood, got progressively worse during adolescence. The attacks were provoked by tension, certain foods, fatigue and between the episodes she was essentially normal. She said her attacks usually occurred on awakening in the morning, sometimes later in the day and she claimed she often had a vague premonition (aura) of when they would occur. The aura consisted of a disturbance of vision, bright spots, or dazzling zigzag lines, and although the headache was on one side of the head, the visual effects were seen by both eyes. She said, as the headache progressed it became throbbing and was usually on the left side of her head. After an hour or so of this severe headache, she became troubled with nausea and vomiting. But if she caught the headache early, using her various ergot prophylactic preparations, she could abort them. She reported that she had had x-rays and CAT scan studies were done, to rule out brain tumor and other abnormal neurological problems, and that it was not necessary for her to be restudied. All she needed was immediate relief! Would I be good enough to give her an injection, a small one, of morphine, which could relieve the pain and break the prolonged migraine attack? Otherwise, the headache would last a day or two and leave her quite washed out for days afterwards. She said her headaches would not respond to lesser pain killers such as Tylenol, aspirin, or codeine.

I tried to proceed with a quick neurological exam, but this proved to be awkward for me because of her state of dress, or should I say undress. I questioned her twice if she were not chilly and perhaps should have a bathrobe on. She smiled infectiously and said, "Doctor, do you think it is really necessary?" Of course, I did not confess to her that it was necessary for "my" state of tranquility.

I believed her story and it looked like she did need help and, although reluctant to give opiates, I gave her a small 25 milligram tablet of Demerol. She told me that she usually had an injection of morphine for these severe headaches when unabated. I did not ask her who her previous doctors were, but wondered if Shotts administered her help. I stayed for another twenty minutes making sure that the medication took effect. She said she was relieved and told me that she would like the privilege of calling me later in the day should the headache recur, and that perhaps she might need another tablet of Demerol since usually she required morphine for relief.

On the way back to the hospital I thought, is it possible that Laurie is addicted to morphine? Although the description of her headaches was classical and she seemed bright, it struck me that she did not seem to be in as much pain as she described. Two nights later I received a phone call from her saying that her migraine headache had recurred and would I be a good friend and come to the house to give her an injection of morphine for relief. I then knew I was on solid ground in suspecting Laurie's addiction. I told her I was unable to come out that evening and suggested that she go to the local emergency room at the Santa Rosa Hospital for medication for her relief.

I called Dr. Shotts the next morning, explained my reaction to our initial meeting, and the additional call last night. I asked him whether he suspected that Laurie might indeed be on the way to becoming an addict. We discussed her condition at great length and decided that she should have psychiatric attention for her possible addiction. I decided to call her and tell her that I was going to refer her to a doctor who was especially interested in headaches, and that he would approach it as a psychological problem. I called a psychiatrist I knew, explained the situation, alerted him to her addiction and suggested that his primary attention be to the addiction rather than the migraine headaches per se.

*   *   *   *   *

Aneurysms of blood vessels are out-pouchings of weakened areas in the walls of blood vessels, and they are prone to rupture. One of the early problems we cofronted were aneurysms of the aorta, the large vessel arising from the heart, and particularly aneurysms of the abdominal aorta. A rupture of this aneurysm has an extremely high mortality. Ralph Kline, a forty-three-year-old shoe salesman, was admitted to the Santa Rosa Medical Center in the early morning hours with excruciating pain in his lower abdomen and back, and had loss of pulsation in his lower extremities. They were cold, pale and very painful when moved. On examination I determined that he had probably suffered a rupture of an abdominal aortic aneurysm. He was in shock and failing rapidly, and if not corrected within a few hours his condition would be fatal. The apprehensive family was apprised of his precarious condition and pleaded with me for a solution. Dr. Shotts was not only interested in thoracic surgery but intensely involved in the new cardiovascular surgical research. As yet, there had not been developed any true prosthetic grafts that could effectively replace a torn abdominal aorta. Dr. Shotts was working with a group at Brooke General Army Hospital experimenting with Orlon grafts in animals for the replacement of blood vessels. I called him in consultation to see this patient at 4:00 A.M., and we both realized that unless we quickly repaired or replaced the ruptured abdominal aorta, this patient was going to die. The tear was so extensive that surgical repair was impossible. We explained the situation carefully to Mrs. Kline and asked her permission to try an innovative experiment. We told her about our animal use of artificial aortas, that they had not as yet been used in human beings, and that we did not know the full prognosis of the duration of this graft, and the surgical technique had not yet been fully developed.

Having obtained permission from the tearful, anguished wife, we rushed to the Brooke General Army Hospital and brought back one of the grafts we were testing on sheep and goats. As far as we knew at that time, no prosthetic artery graft had ever been used in a human being. The patient was rushed to the OR, the abdomen was opened, the large pools of blood were evacuated, treatment was rendered to overcome his shock, massive transfusions given to replace the lost blood, and deftly and carefully, with great skill, Dr. Shotts rapidly replaced the torn ruptured aorta with the graft. The next morning the patient's prognosis appeared, although guarded, somewhat favorable. The blood pressure had stabilized, circulation had returned to the legs and kidneys. There was still evidence of oozing at the suture line of the graft, but it held. We all prayed that it would continue to hold until the body produced a new intima (a new inner lining) to grow over the lining of the graft. For the next forty-eight hours the patient seemed to be doing quite well. Blood pressure normal, legs normal color and warm, patient pain free, and the family was exhilarated, as were the doctors. Then, at 2:00 A.M. the following night, Ralph once again had excruciating lower abdominal and back pain, his legs became pale and pulseless and it was apparent that the prosthetic graft suture line had ruptured! The patient expired within an hour, despite all heroic measures. It was dramatic, revolutionary, but unfortunately unsuccessful. Today graft replacement is an everyday successful procedure and the new grafts made of dacron have been known to last for well over twenty years.

*　　*　　*　　*　　*

Dr. Larry Shotts, the dynamic, compulsive, extrovert, at the age of forty-two suffered a severe attack of pain beneath the breastbone, radiating into the neck and left upper arm as he was making rounds early one morning at the Santa Rosa Hospital. It became immediately apparent to him that he was having an acute coronary occlusion and he reluctantly allowed himself to be admitted to the coronary care unit. His condition was stabilized, the usual program initiated, and his response seemed quite good. He complained daily about his inactivity, the oxygen, the injections, the inability to use the commode, the slowness of the nurses' response to his bell ringing, the temperature of the room, and the mattress on the bed. On the third day after his occlusion Dr. Shotts told the nursing staff that he was pain free, had no congestion and since he had no complications, it was wrong for him to continue to lie in bed. He felt his prognosis would be better with a bit of activity, and demanded to be allowed to leave the bed. Reluctantly, the nurses helped him out of bed and let him sit in the reclining chair beside the bed. Blood pressure, pulse and EKG monitoring all seemed stable. Without being observed he put on his robe, stealthily removed the monitor equipment and quietly stole out of the room and marched down to the surgical section to check the progress of the patient he had operated on the morning before his attack. It was a disastrous move on his part, because within twenty minutes the pain in the chest recurred. He became breathless and collapsed on the floor of the patient's room. He was carried back to his own room by the orderlies. He finally permitted us to treat him like any other coronary patient. He stayed in the hospital approximately two more weeks without any complications and then decided that he could continue his convalescence at home under close supervision.

Since he was to be seen daily at home and as he had good recognition of premonitory problems and symptoms, and especially since he was so obsessive and compulsive (the typical Type A), we felt it was best to allow him to proceed with his suggested program. He did very well and a month later was back again doing surgery and making his rounds with his entourage, demanding obedient attention, and lecturing masterfully, as only Shotts could do. Two weeks later, while arguing with the head nurse on the surgical floor, he was once again gripped with severe chest pain, collapsed and in spite of aggressive cardiorespiratory resuscitation died.

While many years have passed since Dr. Shotts died, he is still keenly remembered by the staff of the Santa Rosa Hospital, the nursing staff, the hospital nuns, and his associates who still talk about this dramatic impressive figure in San Antonio's medical history.

Dr. Snow

After practicing for twelve enjoyable years in the New Moore Building, it was time to move. Downtown had grown increasingly busy, traffic was a problem, parking was impossible, the area sprouted a class of drug addicts and winos, and it became scary for many of my patients to come to the office. A realtor patient called my attention to a beautiful old stately two-story colonial mansion across from a park four miles from downtown that was for sale.

While I debated the purchase of this $17,000 bargain, Dr. Randy Snow, an ophthalmologist, saw the beautiful house and purchased it for his offices, and invited me to share the building as a renter. He was short, stocky, had an abundance of reddish brown curly hair, a square shaped head and had a strong resemblance to the actor Claude Rains. His resonant baritone speaking voice had been compared to the singer Jan Pearce.

One afternoon, after we had settled comfortably into our new surroundings, Dr. Snow called me to say he had returned recently from one of his horseback riding trips in upper Colorado and had not been feeling well. He had diarrhea and bloody mucous. He asked if I would send him a prescription for Lomotil and paregoric to correct the diarrhea. I replied, "Randy, I do not prescribe until I diagnose." Reluctantly, he came as a patient. I took a detailed history and did a complete physical exam. I found that he had a good cardiovascular system but his abdomen was distended with gas and tender throughout. The following morning I proctoscoped him, although he tried to no avail to discourage the test. I was disturbed to see the mucous membrane in the region of the sigmoid, and as high up as I could see, the colon was slightly mottled and inflamed and edematous and had spotty petechiae, that is, small little bleeding areas. I told him that the mucous membrane seemed to suggest a possible parasitic infection and I was particularly concerned whether he might be harboring the Entamoeba histolytica which could be producing amoebic colitis. Cultures were taken and blood studies were done for agglutinations, etc. X-ray studies of the entire bowel were then taken. The cultures came back with a profuse abundance of growth of a parasite known as Giardia lamblia. On further checking, we discovered that this parasite had infested several of the drinking wells in upper Colorado, exactly in the area where he had gone horseback riding. The treatment was very simple. The antimalarial drugs Chloroquine or Atabrine were both very effective against the parasite. The Giardia lamblia is a microscopic parasite that gains entrance to the stomach and then seeds itself down through the entire intestinal tract producing mucous and blood and both upper GI symptoms as well as colon disturbances. Under the microscope the organism is uniquely characteristic — it looks like the face of an Englishman with monocles and a walrus mustache, and it wiggles quickly from field to field.

One week later, following treatment with Atabrine, Randy Snow was completely cured of symptoms, and repeated stool exams and aspirations of stomach contents for the Giardia were negative.

Dr. Snow was an unusual physician. In addition to his skill as an ophthalmologist he was an excellent pilot and had purchased a plane to fly to Mexico to perform ophthalmological surgical procedures for the Mexican physicians who consulted him. His knowledge of flora and fauna was outstanding and wherever he travelled on his many horseback riding trips he promptly learned all about the flowers, the shrubs, the trees, the birds, and the other animals. He was well-read in classical literature, was extremely articulate and respected throughout the state for his surgical ability.

Randy and I cultivated an excellent relationship as professional men, consulting freely with one another in our respective fields. As it turned out, our lives took similar turns quite coincidentally through the years. I leased my section of the 505 Howard Street offices from him for about nine years and when he had fully depreciated his investment he in turn sold the building to me and became my lessee for five years. One year after he moved out to an office in the Physician's Plaza building at the Medical Center, I sold 505 Howard to a family practitioner, and decided to move my office to the medical center. The only office that was available was directly beneath that of Dr. Snow in the same professional building. When he invested in a residential lot in Oak Hills, by sheer coincidence I had also bought a lot on the same street, two months earlier. Later he decided not to build his home in Oak Hills and instead bought a townhouse near the medical center on Songbird Lane. One year later, I was looking for a townhouse near the medical center and found one available across the street from where Dr. Snow lived, and so we once again became neighbors both personally and professionally.

About four years after the episode of the Giardia lamblia, Dr. Snow called me to tell me that he had just finished riding through the upper Pecos Mountains in New Mexico, and that he had a recurrence of the diarrhea, almost exactly as he had had four years previously, with blood and mucous. "Would you be good enough to send me another prescription for the Atabrine" he requested. Once again I declined, with the usual, "Randy you know me better than that. I do not prescribe unless I diagnose. I have not checked you in the last few years, come on by and we will do a complete physical." He was hesitant, but knew I was adamant. This time the exam was again mostly negative. However, his abdomen was not distended this time, nor were there any areas of tenderness as with his previous parasitic infection.

I scheduled him, as he apprehensively concluded I would, for a proctosigmoidoscopic exam the next morning. Viewing through the scope, I was greatly disturbed to see a polypoid lesion arising from a stalk at the lower portion of the sigmoid (colon) with a fragile mucous membrane. I took a biopsy and sent it to the pathologist. The report came back positive for carcinoma of the colon. Two days later Dr. Snow was operated on, a small segment of the colon was removed, and fortunately the cancer was localized and had not invaded much beyond the mucosa. There were no lymph nodes and the liver was negative. We had a chance of a complete cure! I was very happy that I had not sent him the medication he had requested because, had I sent it and the symptoms abated, he might have gone on for months before his cancer would have been recognized.

This was an early diagnosis and I believe a cure, because over sixteen years have passed as of this writing and there has not been any recurrence of his lesion.

My experience with Dr. Snow and his early cancer again reminded me of my old professor, A. J. Carlson, who questioned me during my freshman year about the theory of coagulation, and said to me, "Young man, you cannot take anything for granted. You must prove your diagnosis. You must have evidence." And, of course, this is the approach that probably saved Dr. Snow's life!

My Brother

My father died at the early age of fifty, leaving my brother, thirteen years my junior, for Sally and me to raise and support. Harold, much like my mother, was a born comedian. Had he decided to go into theater, he would have had Alan King, Milton Berle, and Benny Hill running to their writers for more material. But I coerced him to study medicine.

After his internship he opened his first office around the corner from my office to do industrial medicine. Among his comic antics was his unusual ability to mimic. He was particularly capable of mastering languages and accents. He could pose as a Mexican-American, an Irishman with a classical brogue, a Bronx Jew, an Oriental, a Scotsman, a

Russian, a Southerner, a cockney Englishman, or even a Southerner from the Carolinas.

Early in his practice he had plenty of time for capricious activity and he took great delight calling my office and speaking to the secretary in one of his various dialects. He would call and with a heavy Mexican accent say, "This is Ramon Rodriguez from Mexico and I need to speak to the doctor at once." Two days later he was Charles Jones calling from the East end of London and again he would fool my secretary. The following week he would be Boris Stanilovsky from Moscow, a history professor, and with a thick Russian accent told the secretary he was a relative and wanted to talk to me immediately. And so on for several years; my brother enjoyed his antics to my secretary's chagrin and my annoyance.

I soon became suspicious when my secretary would buzz me and tell me about a Scotsman or Russian, a Mexican-American, or South Carolinian who had to talk to me immediately for one reason or another. When the call was transferred to me, I was usually quite busy, would have my laugh and then complain, "Harold, enough is enough. I'm tied up now and I'll talk to you later!"

One morning, after a difficult time on rounds, I had just entered the office when my secretary breathlessly called me on the intercom to report that Robert Kennedy from Washington had to talk to me immediately. He was the Attorney General at that time. When the caller got on the phone with his broad Boston accent, I listened for a few minutes, "This is Robert Kennedy. I understand that you are doing research in cholesterol-metabolism. I need an expert witness in Washington, D.C., because of research problems involving human beings and pharmaceuticals." I allowed him to go on for some time, explaining in detail what he wanted me to do, and telling me that I would get a $10,000 stipend for coming and all my expenses paid, and that it might be an opportunity to meet his brother, Jack, the President. About that time, I'd had it with my brother and said, "Harold, cut the 'crap'. I've had enough of it already. And I'm tired and irritable." A bit taken aback, Robert Kennedy said, "I'm sorry, sir, but I do not seem to understand your reply." It dawned on me, to my deep chagrin, that it *was* Robert Kennedy talking to me! I apologized profusely, and explained my reaction by telling him about my brother. "Mr. Kennedy, I have a crazy brother who keeps calling on the phone, mimicking various personalities and interrupting my work. I thought he was pulling another one on me." Robert Kennedy's answer was a chuckle and a laugh. "You know," he said, "I have a crazy brother too, who pulls all sorts of stunts on me!"

Thereafter, whenever my secretary buzzed me to report an unusual caller on the phone, I found myself checking by saying, "Are you sure you are who you say you are?" This always befuddled them and many hung up on me!

Dr. Smith

During our senior year at the University of Chicago clinics, we came under the tutelage of Dr. William Smith who was one of the brilliant department chiefs. One of the finest teachers at the Clinics, he was always well-prepared, well-organized, and presented his material in concise, informative, comprehensive fashion and with great clarity. All of the students loved to attend his classes. His memory was phenomenal and he could lecture for three hours without one written note. He could discuss clinical cases freely without referring to the charts, recalling the history, present illness, physical findings, and discuss in detail all the lab findings, x-rays, EKGs, and various invasive determinations without referring to a memorandum. Dr. Smith was indeed a whiz kid.

After practicing internal medicine and cardiology for approximately twenty years, I was honored by being elected into the American College of Chest Physicians. It pleased me a great deal as I was particularly interested in diseases of the chest. And, as everyone knew who associated with me in medicine, I was a great exponent of the so-called *take a deep breath* approach with all of its findings. I received my letter of congratulations with a notice that there would be a convocation in Chicago one month hence where we would be formally admitted into the honorary fraternity.

Sally and I flew to Chicago, met many of our old friends and attended the convocation that evening. Dressed in cap and gown, I sat in the front row in the church auditorium waiting for the ceremonies to begin. I looked at the program and was thrilled to see that Dr. William Smith, a director of the organization, was the commencement speaker. I couldn't wait to renew acquaintance with my former brilliant teacher. And then I was suddenly taken aback to see Dr. Smith approach the podium, clad in cap and gown, shuffling along, not striding as I remembered him doing. He climbed the three steps, stood behind the lectern, reached into the pocket inside his gown and pulled out a written speech. He looked at the audience and then began in a hesitant, shrill voice, entirely unlike the former strong, vibrant voice that I remembered, and proceeded to read the address. After the first paragraph, there was dead silence in the room. "Now that you medical students have completed your four years of medicine and are getting ready for your internship . . ." We were all dismayed. It became apparent at once that Dr. Smith was now a confused elderly gentleman who was unaware that the material that he was reading was not appropriate for a group of practitioners who had been practicing for fifteen to twenty years, and were now being elected as honorary members of the American College of Chest Physicians. Instead, he was reading an address prepared for a medical school graduating class. We were all embarrassed, but indulgent and introspective. I looked at Dr. Smith's face, now furrowed by wrinkles and drooping tissue, sagging mouth, dull eyes, sparse scalp hair, and thought to myself. "This is reality."

Frank Green

Frank Green and his brother operated a large plant in San Antonio, manufacturing military uniforms. Frank was the good padre for his 300 plus employees. He made sure they had good working conditions, listened to their problems, loaned them money when needed, referred them as necessary for proper medical or legal attention, and frequently accompanied them to the doctor or lawyer's office or hospital. He was of average height, early balding, ruddy complexioned, moderately obese, friendly and always optimistic.

After I treated his mother for her intractable sciatica due to a partial disk, Frank asked me to be his personal physician. I was happy to do so as he was a delightful, interesting, well informed man. He was very compassionate, sociable, extremely charitable and politically active. He was president of a local synagogue, and organized and helped build and finance one of the better non-sectarian nursing homes in San Antonio. He played a mean game of poker every Thursday evening and always lost. One Thursday evening he saved the life of a local obstetrician, one of the card players, by using successfully the "Heimlich" maneuver. He then chided the OB doctor saying, "I shouldn't have saved you, you only delivered girls to my family."

His hobby was fishing and he was a superb fisherman. He fished trout streams, lakes, rivers, tanks, and deep seas, deftly and very successfully. Frank caught when no one else could. And when they did, he caught twice as many. He fished throughout Texas, Wisconsin, Colorado, Alaska, Panama, Canada, and Mexico.

He often invited me to accompany him on his fishing trips to the Gulf Coast 150 miles south of San Antonio. We would leave either Corpus Christi or Port Aransas and race with his small motor boat some fifteen to twenty miles out to catch trout, flounder, pompano, and redfish. Occasionally, we went deep-sea fishing for marlin, tuna, and swordfish.

His other hobby was practicing medicine without a license. He was a frustrated amateur practitioner. He loved to accompany me to the hospital and make rounds with me, listening intently and observing carefully as I examined and discussed my patients. He would often spend hours with me in the emergency room and enjoyed the excitement and the experiences there, often adding his unsolicited diagnoses.

Unfortunately, on more than several occasions Frank attempted to practice medicine on his friends and family without my help or consultation. He would prescribe cough syrups for coughs, antihistamines for allergies, antipyretics for fever, aspirin and Tylenol for pain, and hydrocortisone for skin conditions. He would also treat minor burns, sprains, corns, and callouses. If his so-called "patients," as he termed them, presented problems that were a bit beyond him, he would reluctantly refer them to my office or call me for consultation.

One afternoon I was consulted by my friend and patient, Leonard Ross, for an extremely painful swelling in his left cheek. He was in absolute agony when he presented himself, with a markedly distended swollen parotid gland (the salivary gland), in the left cheek area. As it was only on one side and as he had already had mumps, this diagnosis was discarded. After careful examination I found that his condition, of twenty-five hours duration, was due to a chemical erosive action on the opening of the "Stenson's" duct, which led from the parotid gland into the mouth. As a result of this erosive chemical burn, the opening was markedly swollen and it closed the duct completely. Therefore the saliva could not enter the oral cavity and instead continued to back up into the substance of the parotid gland, inflaming and distending it, causing excruciating pain. I tried to elicit from Leonard what chemical it was that provided this obstruction. Half-embarrassed, Leonard admitted that he had complained the day before at lunch to Frank Green about his sore throat. Immediately, Frank's diagnostic acumen was challenged. He looked into Leonard's throat and said, "Yes, it's quite red. And I know exactly what 'we' should do. Come with me to the pharmacy." At the pharmacy, he obtained a dozen sulfonamide tablets and told Leonard to hold one in his mouth and suck on it until it dissolved and this would reduce the inflammation of the sore throat. He was to repeat this procedure every two hours. Unfortunately, sulfonamide is an extremely irritating chemical to the oral mucous membrane. When swallowed, it is digested by enzymes and mucous in the stomach and small bowel and effects very little irritation, but in the mouth it is extremely caustic. Leonard took all of the tablets as prescribed by his buddy, the unlicensed physician, and allowed each one to dissolve in his mouth, holding it in his cheek, unfortunately against the opening of the salivary gland duct and the damage was done.

Leonard and I decided once and for all that we had to teach Frank a lesson: to stick with the business at which he was really successful, manufacturing military uniforms, and let the doctors practice medicine. I told Leonard to go into one of the examining rooms down the hall and to lie quietly on the cot with a white sheet pulled over his face. I went to the phone and called Frank, whose place of business was just one block from the New Moore Building. "Frank," I said, "I need your help immediately! They just brought Leonard Ross into my office. He is semicomatose, with a terribly swollen gland on the left side, and he keeps pointing his finger into his mouth and all I can get out of his mumbling is, "Frank did it. Frank knows all about it. Frank Green did it."

Six minutes later Frank came rushing into my office, breathless, having raced up the five floors by foot. "Where is he? I can explain it all," he exclaimed! I directed him to the room where Leonard was lying. He rushed into the room and when he saw Leonard lying there motionless with the sheet over his head he cried, "Oh my lord! Oh my Lord! What did I do?" Leonard could no longer contain himself. He threw off the sheet and sat up, laughing hysterically, forgetting momentarily his severe cheek pain. I then explained to my alarmed friend what had happened with the sulfonamide he prescribed. He was relieved but very embarrassed and said, "I guess I went a bit too far." I said, "Frank, I am going to revoke your medical license and I hope you won't ever practice medicine in my area again!" He laughed sheepishly and promised. Even after this incident, Frank was unable to resist treating friends, relatives and employees, but confined his "practice" to sprains, abrasions, corns, callouses, and psychotherapy.

Frank was, relatively speaking, healthy, although a bit obese, and complained frequently of so-called "heartburn." I diagnosed a large diaphragmatic hernia and hyperacidity and treated him accordingly. His family was notorious for elevated cholesterol and there were many instances of strokes, heart disease, and hypertension in the Green family. As I was intensely interested in cholesterol metabolism research, Frank Green was one of the 120 people I early on placed on a program of a bile-acid sequestrating agent known as colestipol, commercially put out by Upjohn as Colestid. This bile-acid sequestrating agent, when taken orally, removes bile from the intestinal tract. When this happens, the liver recognizes that there is a deficiency of bile, and it gets busy using the precursors of cholesterol to produce more bile. When it does this, of course, there are less chemical agents available to produce cholesterol as such, and the total cholesterol pool drops. Frank Green's cholesterol studies, taken on several occasions prior to starting colestipol, averaged between 350 and 400. After six weeks on the drug regime, his cholesterol dropped to 180 and remained in the range of 180 to 200 for years. Of course, he cooperated in other areas. He ate very little butter, no bacon, cut down on egg yolks, removed the fat from his meat, and ate very little cream cheese or ice cream. He was not a smoker and we felt that if he continued with pharmaceutical measures to reduce his cholesterol, his longevity would definitely be increased.

Although Frank was a very ethical and responsible citizen, he had one pernicious fault. Whenever he went fishing in the Gulf, he loved to steal crabs from other peoples' crab traps. He would rapidly approach other fishermen's traps identified by buoys, look about to make sure no one was around to observe, pull the trap aboard his boat, empty the traps of their crab catches, and then place six or twelve bottles of beer into the trap to pay for his stealth and return the traps to the water. I was sure that he would get caught one day and be brought to Corpus Christi or Port Aransas under citizens' arrest or be shot. People just don't like to have the contents of their traps, which they carefully, skillfully, and with great effort placed in the ocean, stolen. This, in Texas, comes under the category of "horse thief." It is a very serious crime in the eyes of a fisherman.

One day while fishing out of Panama, Frank and a friend from San Antonio spent the night at a fishing camp. They retired peacefully after a successful day of fishing. Around daybreak they were rudely awakened by cries in Spanish, their locked door was forced open, and four ugly bearded dirty terrorists, escapees from the local prison, came rushing into their room with pointed rifles. In Spanish, Frank and his friend were ordered to get out onto the wharf where two other fishing couples were huddled together, also held at bay by another gunman with a rifle. They told the six innocent victims to lie down on the pier, hands outstretched. They searched their pockets, took their money, and removed their watches and rings. They snarled in Spanish that the six would be hostages, that they were confiscating their fishing boat, and would leave immediately. They said that they had just broken out of prison ten miles north of the camp, and would tolerate no deviations from their orders. They meant business, and they looked it.

The six terrified fishermen, rifles pointed at their backs, apprehensive and sweating, marched as ordered down the pier toward the boat. With that, there was sudden clamor, confusion, shouting, and six military men appeared on the scene with pointed rifles and started shooting. Frank and his friend and the other couples stealthily and quickly slipped out of the grasp of the terrorists and jumped from the pier into the water which fortunately was only neck deep at that point. The terrorists fired wildly, missing the soldiers. The military men returned fire, striking all five terrorists with multiple bullet wounds, blood streaming from the many shots as they dropped, fatally wounded.

The harrowing experience played havoc with Frank's diaphragmatic hernia. He developed severe pylorospasm: the stomach was unable to empty its contents into the intestinal tract and filled with fluids, enzymes, and retained hydrochloric acid. He continued to eat for the next day and a half, until he reached the States, not realizing that his stomach was not emptying. I was called to his home the night he arrived home from his ordeal in Panama and found him with a markedly distended abdomen and realized that he was in serious trouble, with gastric dilatation, which has often been known to be fatal. The stomach becomes so dilated that it loses its tone and can rupture, producing peritonitis. I hospitalized him that night, inserted a tube into his stomach, and placed it on low suction to gradually deflate and remove the contents of this markedly over-distended stomach. During this time it was necessary to correct his fluid and chemical electrolyte imbalances. He was terribly nervous and apprehensive from his frightening experience and his gastric complications and so it was also necessary to sedate him. Forty-eight hours after suction it was safe enough to take x-rays of his intestinal tract and we found that the diaphragmatic hernia was present, and distended with retention products, but the stomach had finally partially opened and fluids were now beginning to enter the small intestine. I kept him in the hospital for another twenty-four hours, but with reduced sedation, and then discharged him. I thought that perhaps he would not go fishing for several months until this unbelievable experience had faded somewhat from his memory. But no! The following Sunday Frank went down to the Gulf Coast to do some relaxed trout fishing.

One beautiful May week, two years later, Frank Green called inviting me to join him and a cousin at the Coast. His cousin was also an expert fisherman, and I certainly wasn't in their league, but they often enjoyed having me along because I told jokes and always brought lots of food. However, Frank never would take time to eat while fishing and would be furious with us for putting down our rods and reels and taking time out to eat. "How can you eat at a time like this?" the fisherman would say. "The water is full of trout." Or pompano or redfish. "Don't waste time eating. You can always eat later." We would sometime fish for seven hours without stop, except for quick snacks. But Frank wouldn't stop to join us to eat, and often I wondered how he handled his other bodily functions.

The boat he used was small, only nineteen feet long, a kind of skiff, with very low sides, and one had to stand to pilot the small craft. On the highway, he would be extremely careful never to exceed fifty-five miles per hour. He rarely passed another car and always looked both ways on the rare occasions when he did. However, when he got into his boat he was a demon. He would accelerate to the utmost capacity, thirty-five to forty knots per hour in his haste to reach the "best fishing spot." That particular May weekend when Frank invited me to join him and his cousin, I had planned to join them but my daughter, Patty, pleaded with me to come to Lajolla instead to celebrate her birthday and have a family reunion. We left for California on Friday evening, and had a wonderful time celebrating the birthday.

On Sunday morning, while in Lajolla, I was awakened at 6:00 A.M. by the maid who called me to the telephone saying there was a call from San Antonio. I had signed out to my associate in the office and could not understand why any of my patients would be troubling me so early on Sunday morning when my associate was on call. I was about to receive tragic news. It seems that Frank and his cousin had wandered some twenty miles out of Port Aransas when their small boat was struck by a sudden violent squall. The boat overturned and both men were thrown into the water. Although they both wore life jackets, only his cousin survived. Frank had hung onto the boat for an hour waiting for help from the Coast Guard who usually patrolled the area, but ultimately he became exhausted, slipped into the water and drowned. Twenty minutes later, a helicopter approached the scene and saved his cousin. It is small consolation, but I think Frank died the way he would have wanted, with his fishing boots on. His death was a tragic loss to his family and friends and to the community.

It was necessary to have an autopsy after the drowning and I read the report very carefully. Death was due, of course, to drowning. The pathologist did find the diaphragmatic hernia, but his heart was normal size, and the blood vessels were those of a man some twenty to thirty years younger. There were absolutely no cholesterol deposits in the coronary vessels and his large aorta was completely devoid of atherosclerotic cholesterol plaques. Frank Green had been taking his colestipol religiously for the past twelve years. Here was a man with a family history of coronary heart disease and strokes, who did a beautiful job cooperating on a cholesterol lowering program and had such beautiful coronary blood vessels, and died of accidental drowning at age sixty-six. He would surely have lived another twenty years with that improved cardiovascular system. It was indeed a sad paradox.

Dr. Bilson

Leonard Bilson was an old-time family physician in San Antonio, but his primary practice revolved around obstetrics. He delivered almost as many babies as the obstetrical specialists. Dr. Bilson gained a reputation for collecting almost one hundred percent of his fees for deliveries. The average collection in the city was about eighty percent. He devised a unique way of guaranteeing payment. A customary procedure done to facilitate delivery is to make an incision, called an episiotomy, in the vaginal wall. Immediately after the delivery, the incision is repaired, and all doctors use sutures which will be absorbed by the body naturally within a week, without complication. But, Dr. Bilson used unabsorbable wire sutures to correct the incision in the vaginal wall. He told his patients to return about one week after delivery to have the sutures removed. However, there was a catch. If the patient hadn't paid for the delivery, he refused to remove the wire sutures. He then gave them another week to return for removal when the bill was paid completely. He maintained that by the third week, the husbands came running into the office with cash in hand, saying, "For God's sake, please take the wire sutures out!"

Dr. Bilson enjoyed telling the story of the man who came to his office to pay Mrs. Martinez' bill. He received the payment, shook the gentleman's hand and said, "Thank you, Mr. Martinez. I appreciate your bringing in the money and I will remove the wire sutures this afternoon." The gentleman replied, "I thank you for your help, but I am not Mr. Martinez." And with that, he walked out of the office.

Dr. Bilson also had a well-deserved reputation for being a very greedy physician and something of a bigot. When he approached me after I was elected Chief of Medicine, his remark was, "You guys sure know how to get the best positions in the hospital." I was sure I knew what he meant by "you guys." When I purchased my first Cadillac after ten years of practice and drove up to the parking lot of the Santa Rosa Hospital, Dr. Bilson had just parked his shabby old Volkswagen. He looked at my Cadillac and promptly walked over to me. Once again, "You guys know how to make a lot of money in medicine. The rest of us will never make the kind of money you guys make." I felt this was more than I could tolerate in a friendly fashion, and decided to give him a taste of his own medicine.

"Dr. Bilson," I said, "I didn't make my money in practice. I made it in the stock market." As usual, he replied, "You guys sure know how to make money in the market." I began, "Leonard, I am going to give you a tip and allow you the same opportunity I had." Greedily, he asked, "What is it? Please tell me." And I told him about a stock on the American Exchange called "Dreck," listed under the initials DRK. Of course, since he didn't know Yiddish, he couldn't know that "Dreck" is the vernacular for feces. I told him, furthermore, that I had been buying a good deal of "Dreck" from my stockbroker at Rauscher Pierce, and suggested that he call him and ask to purchase some of the "Dreck" that he had been selling Dr. Cooper for the past several years.

That afternoon I had a frantic call from my stockbroker. "Dr. Cooper, what have you done? A Dr. Bilson called me and wanted to buy some 'Dreck' which he said was on the American Exchange and gave me the identifying initials DRK. He said that I had been selling you a lot of 'Dreck' over the past few years and he wanted some of the same." I retorted, "He's right. Most of the stuff you have sold me has been nothing but 'Dreck'." Then I explained what I was doing with Leonard Bilson. He enjoyed this situation as much as I did, but asked me how he was going to get around it. I told him to tell the doctor that he was all out of "Dreck" at the moment, but the next time some

"Dreck" became available, he would be sure to call him first on his list. What a pleasure it was for "us guys" to get even just a little with "that guy," Leonard Bilson.

Mr. Bennet (Cry Wolf)

"Go to Mr. Bennet's office!" The words sent shivers up and down the spine of the terrified student unlucky enough to be the target of that command. For Mr. Bennet was no ordinary "principal." He was the Director of Education of one of San Antonio's largest religious congregations and his rages were legendary. A unique individual, he was at times frightening, at times an object of ridicule by his students, often witty, but always fair and always demanding that a student be the best person he or she could be. His voice was a rare instrument and could rise from a whisper to a harsh screech in seconds. His anger was like a force of nature, but when it passed, it was over, and the object of his wrath was made to realize that he was loved. Students feared him above all other teachers. But they revered him even as they trembled at his displeasure.

Small of stature, erect, frail, but with piercing gray eyes and a grip like iron, he looked far older than his forty-two years when he arrived in San Antonio in 1947 to assume his duties. He was precise in dress and speech, always wearing a black suit, white shirt and black tie. I never saw him dressed otherwise, even after we became good friends and enjoyed one another's company at intimate dinners. Often, his impeccable diction made him the butt of students' derision. Every syllable was exquisitely pronounced. He was a master punster, famous for frequent referrals to "The Muddle East." "A communist," he said, "is someone who publicly airs his dirty Lenin." Long after finishing their religious studies, former students sought him out — for advice, for comfort, for witty intellectual discussions; all of which were unquestionably forthcoming.

Probably the most erudite educator in San Antonio and holding doctorates from two prestigious universities, Bennet shunned titles, preferring to be addressed as "Mister" or occasionally "Reverend." Some of us who were close friends knew him simply as "Matthew." He was comfortable with college presidents, musicians (he had been a child prodigy pianist and later music critic for a New York newspaper), religious leaders of every faith, and business and political luminaries of the city. His interdenominational lectures and adult study sessions were "standing room only" affairs. But his greatest love was reserved for children, and to them he directed seemingly limitless energy and attention. Childless, he was ready to stand "in loco parentis" to every student who came under his aegis.

With his wife, Dorothy, a sweet, small, moonfaced woman, he lived in a modest, book-filled apartment near the religious school. Dorothy hovered over her beloved husband like a doting mother, constantly fluffing the pillows of his chair, brushing away a speck of lint on the impeccable black suit, or bringing a footstool to elevate his legs. She called him "my baby" and he referred to her as "my darling."

Sally and I were invited with a small group of friends for a Sunday night supper in their home. Books and periodicals had been removed from the chairs, tables and sofa and placed, for lack of other space, on top of the magnificent Steinway grand piano that almost filled the small living room. After a simple, but delicious vegetarian dinner, Dorothy solicitously brought Matthew his pipe and slippers, and we all settled in for an evening of stimulating conversation.

Suddenly, Matthew jerked upright, clutched the left side of his chest, flexed his left arm, became pale, and whispered, "It's my heart again." He looked at me beseechingly. As the only M.D. in the group, I naturally took charge.

"Dorothy," I said, "call an ambulance. We'll get him to the coronary care unit of the Santa Rosa Hospital and I'll contact his doctor."

"No," pleaded Matthew as he winced with pain. "I just need an injection of morphine and the pain will subside."

"Yes," agreed Dorothy, "he gets these attacks often. Nitroglycerine doesn't help. But morphine gives him relief right away. Surely you must have some in your medical bag."

Sally had brought my well-worn bag from the car when the attack began. After taking his blood pressure and listening to his chest and finding no significant abnormalities, I again insisted that he be taken to the hospital for oxygen, EKGs, chest x-rays, and medication for the pain. And again, the two of them were adamant, insisting he only needed a little morphine for the pain. Reluctantly, I filled a syringe and administered the injection. Just as he had predicted, five minutes later, Matthew was pain free and calm.

Again, I tried to convince him he belonged in the hospital, and again he refused to go. Within thirty minutes, he was his delightfully urbane, talkative self, discoursing knowledgeably about the various theories surrounding the mystery of the "Black Hole."

His cavalier attitude toward what could be a life-threatening situation left me totally confused. I had long accepted his eccentricities along with his brilliance, but this had me worried. Before leaving, I urged him to call his internist, John Taylor, in the morning. He readily agreed.

The next morning I called Dr. Taylor and asked how Mr. Bennet was doing. He was surprised by my call. Mr. Bennet had not reported the incident, nor had he made an appointment for examination. But, he told me, the Reverend had been having a series of these attacks. EKGs, stress tests and x-rays of the esophagus were all normal and he could make no definite diagnosis of heart disease. Bennet had refused to have a coronary arteriogram.

Two weeks later I was awakened at 2:00 A.M. by a frantic call from Dorothy. Her husband was having another attack. They could not locate Dr. Taylor and he refused to go to the hospital. "Please," she begged, "come give my baby some relief. He's suffering so." Of course, I responded to her plea and gave him an injection of morphine, to which he responded immediately!

Stopping in the doctor's lounge for a cup of coffee the next morning, I placed a call to the Bennet home to check on his status. The conversation was overheard by a general practitioner, Dr. Howard Shenker, who said, "You too!"

It was then that my suspicions were confirmed. This brilliant, pious, compassionate human being had become addicted to morphine! No one seemed to know how or when the addiction started. But almost every Sunday he would invite a small group of friends, always including one doctor, for an intimate evening of supper and conversation. And at almost every one of these soirees he would have an "attack" and plead for morphine for relief. During the week, he called one of his many doctor friends in rotation in the middle of the night, pleading extreme pain and inability to locate Dr. Taylor. Always, he resisted hospitalization, claiming he had promised to lecture at the "Institute of Texan Cultures," or one of his students was having problems, or he had an important conference with the president of the university the following morning.

Those of us in the medical profession who were his friends decided that the only way we could help him was to confront him with our knowledge of his addiction. With his and Dorothy's cooperation, we would help him with rehabilitation therapy. After many long talks and a little coercion, he admitted his drug dependency and agreed to accept professional help.

Fortunately, he made rapid progress and had a remarkable recovery. The dramatic "attacks" and middle of the night calls ceased. The Reverend was stable after a month and once again he was the recipient of student's admiration despite their dread of his wrath. And again colleagues and friends were exposed to his wit and pithy analyses of cultural and political events.

One Sunday evening, after another delightful vegetarian dinner with Dr. and Mrs. Lorrimer and other friends, the Reverend suddenly became pale, clutched his chest, flexed his arm and collapsed, pulseless. He died before his startled wife and Dr. Lorrimer could reach him. All attempts at resuscitation were futile. Mr. Bennet, feared by some, but revered by all, was gone.

Given his wry sense of humor, if Matthew could have written his own epitaph, it would have read. "They didn't believe me."

Dr. Mena

Dr. Frank Mena's life was a disaster and provoked many perplexing questions. He was a young, energetic, enthusiastic, bright, well-informed family practitioner with the largest Hispanic practice in San Antonio. I was his internal medicine consultant for many years, but never recognized that he had serious psychological problems. At the age of thirty-four he was married to a handsome nursing supervisor at a local hospital and they had three lovely children. He drove a Mercedes, had a large home in the nicer neighborhood, with swimming pool and tennis court. He owned a large sailboat, kept at Canyon Lake, and on weekends would sail with his family and friends. He was a member of an exclusive country club and reputed to be quite wealthy from a combination of a large practice and a substantial family inheritance.

A large apartment house on Myrtle Street was the home for many single working girls. Reports began circulating that the girls were aware of a Peeping Tom and they became very apprehensive. One girl spotted the individual late one night with a black wool knit cap pulled down over his forehead, wearing a black mask, black sweatshirt, and black pants. On two other occasions he was noticed by the girls who screamed for help, but he eluded capture.

He not only peeked in first floor apartment windows, he also climbed fire escapes to the second and third floors for his voyeurism. One night, while peeping through a partially open window observing one of the occupants undressing, he apparently tried to reach in to grab the panty hose she had dropped as she undressed. She heard the noise, spotted his intruding arm, and violently closed the window on his right wrist. He hastily withdrew, yelling in pain, but once again, was not apprehended.

As the overworked police failed to give the apartment frequent night surveillance and the owner of the apartment claimed he could not afford a security officer, the girls banded together and decided to have relatives and boyfriends help with this problem. They were to have alternate assignments during the early part of the evening when the Peeping Tom usually appeared. These vigilantes would hide behind the waste disposal bin in an attempt to spot the intruder. On the second night of the watch by these "Angels of Mercy," they caught him, and after a violent struggle, held him securely for the arrival of the police.

The next morning the newspapers were ready to defame the culprit who was none other than Dr. Frank Mena. After lengthy sessions with lawyers, judges, psychologists and psychiatrists, the decision was made for Mena to be put on probation and to refrain from medical practice for six months, during which time he was to have extensive psychotherapy treatment.

Mena returned to his practice, apparently a reformed and remorseful individual. But he chose not to continue with psychiatric treatment. A year later, while examining a sixteen-year-old female for premenstrual cramping and tension problems, he elected to do a pelvic exam. His nurse was on sick leave that morning and the mother of the young lady was sitting quietly in the reception room, unaware of his decision to do a pelvic exam on her daughter without the attendance of his nurse.

Aroused and uncontrolled, the doctor raped the girl on the examining table. He explained to the frightened and naive patient that he was checking her ovarian function. He also cautioned her that she was not to tell anyone of this experience as he would deny it and then he would report that she wasn't a virgin, inasmuch he had found out that she'd had prior sexual experience. Being a devout Catholic, and most anxious to hide her earlier sex experience, she decided to keep that one a secret.

She was told to return for another appointment in two weeks after taking the prescribed hormone. This time when she came to the office, he dismissed his nurse from the examining room claiming he wanted to have a confidential talk with his patient. Once again he tried to have sex with this cowering frightened patient, but this time she yelled and fought and the nurse and mother came charging into the room, horrified at what they saw. The police were called, the girl was subjected to the usual studies for rape, the doctor was found guilty and given a seven-year prison sentence.

Mena fared poorly in the detention facility. He was unable to tolerate his confinement. He became increasingly depressed, went on frequent hunger strikes and one morning was found by his jailer dead, hanging by his belt from the overhead steam pipe.

How could all of this have been prevented? Candidates for admission to medical school are not subjected to psychiatric evaluations. They are selected on the basis of academic grade attainment surveys and personality interviews. It was not until after his conviction in the rape case that it was learned that during his pre-medical training he was charged twice with exhibitionism at the school yard of a local high school.

Should he have been allowed to re-enter practice after this initial problem with the voyeurism? Why did he not continue with the program of psychiatric therapy when he did return to his practice? Why didn't probation officers demand the continuation of psychiatric treatment? These unanswered questions will torment his wife and children for the rest of their lives.

Homosexuality — Neuro Endocrine?

When Walter McFarland's secretary called me for an appointment, I wasn't prepared to meet such a charismatic lady. Walter was a hard-driving, successful Austin business man who ran a large investment company. He was dynamic, aggressive, and skillfully controlled his company. Though graying of the temples, he looked much younger than his sixty years, and his energy decried it. His wife was a quiet, tiny, obese, mousy, apathetic individual who was completely dominated by her over-powering husband. There were rumors that the couple had marital problems and that Walter had a young mistress.

When his secretary, Ella Mae Watson, was filling out her history forms, my secretary quietly buzzed me on the intercom and said, "Doctor, you're in for a real treat. Wait until you see this gal!" "This gal" turned out to be a slow-talking, delightfully pretty, South Carolinian thirty-five-year-old strawberry blond. She was fascinating and the essence of femininity, with her slow southern drawl, high cheek bones and full lips. When she told me she was Walter's private secretary and had been in his office for the past six years, I immediately suspiciously concluded this must be Walter's alleged mistress. Her chief complaints were vague intestinal problems which fit into the category of "functional bowel distress." She had a beautiful curvaceous body, firm well-pointed breasts, smooth white skin, undulated when she walked, and presented a totally sensuous appearance.

Ella Mae was a delightful conversationalist and I was happy to tell her at the end of the examination that her problems were simple and could easily be corrected by diet and medication. While we were discussing her medical regime, my secretary buzzed to tell the patient that her friend, Wilma, had just arrived in the reception room, apologized for being late, and would wait for Ella Mae to complete her exam. I led my patient out to the reception room. Her friend Wilma greeted her at the door, embraced her, and then introduced herself, in a gruff voice, "I am Wilma Jackson, Ella Mae's best friend." And elbows locked together, they walked smilingly out of my reception room. Wilma was about five-feet-eleven inches tall, thin, rigid, straight of spine, with sparse coarse black hair, a square chin, mild acne, and a characteristic masculine gait, swinging her arms widely as she walked.

Ella Mae returned a month later to discuss the results of the diet and medication. She was accompanied not only by her friend Wilma, but by a third female who sat in the reception room, engaged in close quiet conversation with the omnipresent Wilma.

I discovered that the three girls lived together in the same house and had been exceptionally close and constant companions for the past seven years. My patient insisted on introducing me to their third friend, Lucy Newman. Her habitus was of a type intermediate between the highly sensuous feminine Ella Mae and the overtly masculine Wilma. Lucy was quite affable and talkative. She had short curly brown hair and smiled constantly. She sat exceedingly close to Wilma in the reception room, constantly peering into her eyes as they engaged in conversation. All three laughed and giggled like elementary school girls.

Soon Wilma, who had mild essential hypertension, became a patient, and during the examination I was further impressed by her masculinity. She had a strong broad body, a mesomorphic type of chest, small underdeveloped breasts, wide hips, brawny arms, and a faint mustache. When Wilma had completed her examination, Ella Mae was in the waiting room, and greeted her as she came out with a huge hug and embrace and a peck on the cheek and purred, "Darling I hope all is well." When Wilma reported that her blood pressure was not a problem and the electrocardiogram revealed no heart strain, she became the recipient of a large enthusiastic kiss.

Lucy Newman, the third friend in this unusual trio, was an aggressive, bright independent sales lady employed by AT&T who spent a good deal of time on the road demonstrating the equipment to high school classes in various towns and setting up computers in small retail stores throughout Texas. None of these girls had boyfriends and never went out on dates. They were an inseparable trio.

One day Wilma and Ella Mae brought Lucy to my office to become the third patient among the "Three Graces." It seemed that in the past two years Lucy had developed severe intractable classical left-sided migraine headaches characterized by the premonitory "aura," which is the tip-off for an oncoming headache. Her "aura" consisted of seeing a series of zig-zag light spots. Untreated, her headaches would last for four or five days and this, she confided, was a disaster to her ever-loving, ever-comforting friends. On physical examination, her body build was somewhat midway between the feminine Ella Mae and the masculine Wilma, the so-called "tomboy" type, lean and wiry. She joked a lot and some of her stories were off color. She was a typical "good-ole boy" girl who could drink beer and slap you on the shoulder and tell "hee-haw" jokes.

It soon became apparent that Ella Mae was not Walter's mistress but indeed was part and parcel of the threesome that made up the "Three Graces." They held hands in the reception room, embraced frequently, sat with arms about one another's shoulders, and were terribly concerned about one anothers' health status. They would call me frequently requesting detailed information on the health status of one another and it soon became obvious, and rumors were rampant, that the inseparable friends were intimately involved in a lesbian relationship.

While society has accustomed itself to homosexuality as expressed by two individuals, this love relationship between the three women was a revelation for me.

*   *   *   *   *

He slowly and timidly approached the receptionist in my office and quietly told her he was Timothy Green and that his mother,

Louise, had scheduled his appointment. He filled out the questionnaire, stating that he was eighteen-years-old, a high school graduate, was working presently as a package boy at the A & P Grocery Store and his mother was an LVN nurse working the night shift at the hospital. He stated further that his father had not lived at home since he, Timothy, was four years old, and he had no brothers and sisters. His mother thought he had a hernia and therefore requested the appointment. He reported also that he had no specific hobby. He was not athletic, did not play baseball or tennis or football, but preferred to cook and sew.

He sat crouched in a small chair in the corner of the reception room nervously and jerkily crossing and recrossing his legs and sweating perceptively. He picked up a copy of *Good Housekeeping* magazine and became engrossed in the recipe section.

Shortly afterwards, Jonathan Harris, a severely obese seventeen-year-old with a loose, pendulous abdomen, strolled confidently into the reception room, announced his presence, and asked how soon he could see the doctor. His parents, the wealthy Harrises, had been patients for years. His father, George, was a very successful banker with extensive oil and ranch holdings. He was socially prominent and headed a number of welfare organizations. The youth had four older brothers and one younger sister and a delightfully family-oriented, loving mother. The older brothers were involved in the bank and cattle interests. All the members of this family had a very close family attachment to one another. They were always together and all the boys were quite fond of their younger sister. The father and brothers were all graduates of the University of Chicago, and Jonathan was to enter as a freshman in September.

Jonathan plumped his fat frame down and squeezed it into the chair next to Timothy, looked at him and said, "Hi," and then reached for a *Vogue* magazine. Being talkative, secure, and friendly, he soon established an easy rapport with the quiet, shy Timothy. He told him he was seeing the doctor before going to college in Chicago because he needed to lose considerable weight. He said he loved to eat and although he was very active playing touch football with his older brothers, and tennis with his sister, father, and mother, he just couldn't lose weight regardless of how much he exercised!

Timothy admitted that he didn't like sports but preferred to cook and wanted to take art courses at night because his mother could not afford to send him to college. He told Jonathan that his father ran away from home with a young waitress many years ago and his mother supported him. She worked twelve-hour shifts at the hospital and he respected her for her efforts. Since she wasn't home during the day, Timothy cleaned the house, did the cooking, learned to sew, and was secretly crocheting a large bedspread cover for his mother's birthday.

When Timothy undressed for the hernia part of his examination, I checked his genitalia and I noticed that he had an unusually large penis but very small testes. Each testicle was no larger than a small acorn. During the examination he began to blush and became embarrassed as he developed a sustained erection which failed to subside even at the conclusion of the examination. He did have a right inguinal hernia and he was scheduled for surgery on the following Tuesday. Timothy left the examination room, sat down in the reception room and whispered to the receptionist that he would just sit there and wait for his new found friend, Jonathan.

Jonathan had the appearance of a classical case of Frohlich's syndrome, which is a form of hypopituitarism (deficiency of pituitary hormone). He had large flabby breasts, an enormous, pendulous fatty abdomen, with stretch marks. His genitalia were underdeveloped, he had a very small penis which seemed to be embedded in fat and, as in the case of Timothy, very small testes. For therapy he was placed on a regime of 800 calories, exercise, and a trial regime of injections of pituitary hormone. When he re-entered the reception room after the completion of this initial examination, he was greeted by a widely smiling Timothy and the two of them left together.

After Timothy had his surgery for the hernia, I stopped in his hospital room to check on his postoperative course. I found him just coming out of his anesthesia and there, sitting at the foot of the bed, was his new friend, Jonathan, holding his hand.

Two weeks after the surgery I had a frantic call from Jonathan's mother to see her on a personal, confidential matter. She was embarrassed, hesitant, and tearful and finally told me a very unpleasant experience she had had the previous afternoon. It seems that her bridge club was cancelled and she came home two hours earlier than expected. She surprised Jonathan and Timothy nude in bed, actively engaged in sex. She was overwhelmed with grief and surprise, and she and her husband had a long intimate, disturbing talk with Jonathan that evening. Their son disclosed to them that he had known for several years that he was gay, and since his fourteenth birthday had had several homosexual experiences. He declared furthermore that he was terribly fond of Timothy and decided not to go to school in Chicago in the fall.

For the following six months Jonathan was subjected to extensive psychoanalytical sessions with no improvement or change in his homosexual preference. The psychiatrist concluded that he could not explain or alter Jonathan's homosexuality.

Timothy had never been happier, as his close relationship with Jonathan continued. He was less moody, less withdrawn, and no longer felt he had to be a secretive loner. He knew what he was and could accept it now without self-incrimination. His mother never understood this development in her son, but decided to accept his behavior lest she also lose a son.

Although Timothy's father deserted them when he was a child, there was no special abnormal attachment to an overbearing omnipresent mother. His reluctance to engage in rough and tumble athletic activities and his preference toward cooking, sewing, and housekeeping were probably part of his differential choices due to his neuro-endocrine makeup and not due to the abnormal family background. Jonathan's social background was close to ideal. A loving mother and father and a harmonious brother and sister relationship existed in the family. Was his problem neuro-endocrine?

*   *   *   *   *

Homosexuality is a term that should be used for persons with exclusive or predominate "same sex preference." Epidemioligcally, we have learned that it constitutes a substantial portion of the adult and adolescent population. It is estimated generally that approximately four percent of males are exclusive homosexuals throughout their entire lives, while thirteen percent have predominate "same sex preferences" from ages sixteen though fifty-five. The statistics for female homosexuality is approximately one-half that of men. Since the same social, familial and cultural conditions exist for both the male and female, it is difficult to explain the lower incidence of homosexuality among females, unless endocrines are involved.

Homosexuality is the mode of behavior that concerns a form of sexual behaviorism wherein the affective "love romance obsession" and "genital interests" are directed toward a partner of the same sex. Within this realm, how do we classify and what do we classify, the position of the person who is deprived of heterosexual activity (as in prison or in the military, for example) and then experiences an occasional same sex preference? If he could be labeled, should he be considered one who has just engaged in a "transient" homosexual act or is this an expression of latent homosexuality? The etiologies of homosexual behaviors are enigmatic and extremely controversial even today.

Myriads of social and cultural relationships have been explored in an attempt to explain homosexual expressions. There are numerous theories describing a weak, apathetic, inconsequential mother and the strong, overbearing, hostile father; or the opposite: the strong mother who emasculates the weak unimportant father. And where do the absent mother or absent father or the presence of the stepfather or stepmother fit into the jigsaw puzzles? As one goes through the literature, one finds many well written, well documented papers indicating disturbed social cultural backgrounds as etiological factors for homosexuality and an equal number to conclusively obviate these theories. And, of course, there is the classical documented study of dizygotic (fraternal) twins, living far apart from each other in an entirely different social cultural background, and yet each showed homosexual tendencies. Also, it is important to recall that there is evidence that many, if not most, animals sometimes express same sex preferences. And they never heard of Freud!

In the '80s the American Psychiatric Association accepted documented conclusions that homosexuality is not a mental disorder, nor an illness, nor a personality disorder, nor a psychopathic personality problem. The psychiatrists were at a loss for a logical definition of its causes!

The homosexual is not a psychopathological person. Those who seek out the psychiatrists are "troubled" and seek him out, as do all troubled personalities. And it is easy to understand why homosexuals would be even more troubled, because they are bait for the criticisms that are directed towards them. They have to endure the social and cultural stigma of public rejection. The sexual practices of homosexuals are the same as the sexual practices of the heterosexual, with the obvious limitations imposed by anatomy. Homosexuals, like heterosexuals, show individual preferences that may involve kissing, fondling, oral-genital sexuality, manual-genital manipulation, anal intercourse, as well as the occasional female use of the dildo (artificial phallus). There may be either or any type of particular pattern of sexual expression. They are well stereotyped and are only influenced by the preference of the individual partners. None of these sexual behaviors are the sole activities of the homosexual or of the heterosexual.

One must take cognizance of the fact that at various stages of embryonic development, both male and female organs appear in every fetus. Ultimately, there is an ascendancy of one sex or another. But each, even at maturity, has vestiges of the other. For example, the clitoris in the female is the homologue of the penis of the male. The labia majora of the vaginal introitus are the embryonic remnants of the components of the male scrotum (the sacs into which the testes migrate). "Also, the male has vestigial breasts as homologues of the female's well developed breasts. Where do we fit the hermaphrodites who have both male and female sexual organs?

Why is it that within a given family, there may be several children, all of whom are subjected to the so-called disturbed parent-child complex that some psychoanalysts consider etiological agents for the production of abnormal sexuality, yet only one of the children may develop homosexuality?

It is becoming necessary for us to discard many of the theories of maladjusted family upbringing as being causative factors for the production of homosexuality. More and more studies are published that disprove rather than reinforce this previous impression of social maladjustment at home. We must look for more logical, more scientific, more acceptable theories for the explanations for the development of homosexualities. These answers may possibly come from further finite scientific research findings in neuro-endocrine make-ups. Intense, detailed, thorough study of the hypothalamus of the brain and the all-important pituitary gland and the relationships of their interactions may afford clues. A wealth of information is being pursued and gathered by neuroendocrinologists with new technological methods in the detection of "minute" quantities of sex steroids, and pituitary hormone isolations.

Studies in all of these areas have ushered in a new challenge to learn about neuro-hormonal differentials and their possible role in effecting homosexuals.

Soon, perhaps, we will be totally comfortable in recognizing homosexuals as being no different from so called normals than those who have endocrine changes and develop diabetes or Addison's disease, or Cushing's disease, pituitary dwarfism, or thyroid insufficiencies. Once we identify the specific differences in the neuro-endocrine make-up in the homosexual, then those who prefer treatment could possibly be modified to the so-called normal. Until that time, in this large bizarre population of ours, there is no reason to consider the homosexual an oddity. Studies have shown no differences in their longevities, general illnesses and intellectual capacities.

Me and My Hat — Challenging Clinical Experiences

The Mafia

When members of the Mafia or their families immigrated to the USA, they retained their Sicilian ethics, morals, codes, ideals and, above all, their male chauvinistic attitudes. When Tony Hellini came to see me about his numerous complaints, he referred primarily to his intestinal tract, describing nausea attacks, gaseous distension, burping, diarrhea, and colic. Years earlier I was taught by Dr. Palmer at the University of Chicago Clinics that after ruling out organic bases for gastrointestinal complaints, it is important to delve deeply into the personal history. I learned that although he identified himself as a produce man, Tony also had two bars, an Italian restaurant, a cocktail lounge, and a large poolroom on the west side of San Antonio. He was reputed to be one of the leaders in the "numbers" game, and largely controlled horse race betting in San Antonio. Tony's father, a former patient, had had severe hypertension for many years. I always suspected that he was involved in shady enterprises, although he too told me he was in the produce business.

Tony was short, five feet five inches, with thick, black curly hair, squinty, menacing, deep-set brown eyes, a large scar over his left cheek, and snake tatoos on his left arm. He walked with a slight left-sided limp, and spoke in sharp terse sentences. Tony was a perfect example of Hollywood's portrayal of a lesser member of the Mafia consortium. He told me during the interview that he felt the managers of his bars and the cashier of his Italian restaurant were probably ripping him off and this bothered him tremendously. "Not so much," he explained, "the loss of the money, but for saving face in front of my compatriots." If they knew that his workers were cheating him, they would think less of his abilities to control his henchmen. Since all studies were negative, I placed him on a low residue diet, curtailed his alcohol intake, prescribed mild GI antispasmodics, and gave him a lecture on what his paranoia was doing to his GI tract. I suspect he paid little heed to my explanations and suggestions. Tony had to be what he was expected to be by his family and friends and his employees — tough!

His wife Alexis was a pretty blond, quite sensuous in appearance, who came from a small Polish community known as Falls City about forty miles south of San Antonio. When she first came to the office she wore much too much make-up, the eyelashes were beaded with mascara, the rouge too red, lipstick too bright, and her long tapered fingernails were painted green. She also had other colorations of the face: namely, the right eye was closed with swelling and black and blue. There were also many bruises on her left arm. She did not consult me for these evidences of a recent brutal beating. She was concerned with palpitations. Her heart rate was not rapid or slow, but she was constantly aware of the forceful heartbeat. She had a classical anxiety syndrome with a moderate elevation of blood pressure. She explained that Tony was very difficult to live with, was suspicious of all her activities, extremely jealous and beat her frequently during his rages. He would be demanding and continue to embarrass her in front of their new friends. He claimed that she no longer loved him, and despite the fact that they had no children, she was fearful of leaving him. It seems that no wife of a Mafia member dares leave her husband, as this is too humiliating for him. Tony had threatened to kill her on several occasions, if she left him. She had repeatedly reported these incidents to the local police, but they were unable to make any charges unless he threatened her in front of witnesses.

Tony had ordered an employee from one of his bars to discreetly follow Alexis as, in his paranoia, he was convinced she was seeing another man. But no untoward incidents were reported. Alexis soon became aware that Ben, the henchman, was sloppily "tailing" her. She confronted him and they had a good laugh about it and soon became somewhat friendly. In spite of her sensuality, she behaved with him and he was afraid to attempt any shenanigans. She found Ben to be more intelligent than the usual type that worked for her husband and on occasion they would discuss Italian opera and exchange recipes. He, having recently visited Rome, would describe the museums, the galleries, and the fountains in the beautiful city. Now Tony, suspecting Ben, ordered Gino from the other bar to follow Ben to determine what was going on between these two. Gino was quite ignorant, poorly educated and subject to the same paranoia that governed Tony. Misinterpreting the few talks he observed between Ben and Alexis, he reported to Tony that he was sure they were involved. Tony accused Alexis and expressed his paranoia with the worst beating he had ever given her. Afterwards, he took her to the county emergency room for treatment to the cuts and bruises, explaining that they had been in an auto accident. The following morning Alexis packed her bags and moved in with her mother, a divorcee who lived alone in a small two-bedroom home on the westside. She reported the beating incident to the police, but once again they were unable to help her. She told them she was sure Tony would kill her. The most they promised was to patrol her area and see that an officer surveyed the house four or five times daily. This gave her some comfort, but she was still terribly fearful and apprehensive.

The following morning Tony drove up in his red Cadillac convertible, exited rapidly, stopped at the fence at the mother's small cottage, gently called through the open window, "Alexis, I came to apologize. I talked to Ben and I know nothing was going on between you two. I realize I lost my temper and I promise never to do it again. But please come back with me. I will never strike you again. If you come with me, I'll buy you that mink coat I promised you." Reluctant and fearful, Alexis went down the small sidewalk to the fence. Now, face to face, he no longer pleaded with her but instead abruptly seized her right arm and pulled her through the small gate, breaking its lock. "Damn you, you have humiliated me and made a fool of me in front of my people, and I'll be damned if I'll let you." With a sudden urge, Alexis withdrew her arm from his grasp, turned and tried to run back to the house. With that, Tony whipped out a large pistol and shot her in the back, hitting her twice at the base of the brain. Alexis dropped and died instantly. After assuring himself that she was pulseless, he placed the pistol to the right side of his head, and discharged it, falling grotesquely at her feet. All of this was tragically observed by Alexis' mother through the open window. Although in total shock, she managed to call the police who came promptly. When they arrived, Tony was still partially conscious, mumbling, "No one, but no one, is going to make a fool of me in front of my family and friends." He was bleeding profusely from his left ear according to the police and, when the ambulance rushed him to the county emergency, he was also dead on arrival.

I was asked by the coroner to identify the bodies, inasmuch as the family named me as their physician. It was a gruesome, nauseating sight to view these two bodies. As I identified Tony, I couldn't help saying in front of the medical residents accompanying me, "You bastard, Tony, you had to prove in the only way you were taught that you were a man."

My contact with the Hellini family brought to mind some of my earlier experiences with the Mafia in Cleveland. We lived on the East side in a tough multiracial neighborhood made up predominantly of Italian, Polish, and Jewish first generation immigrants with their American born children. Although we were all quite poor, the Italians fared better through various enterprises circumventing the restrictions of prohibition.

Geraldo was the friendly young opera-singing, cheerful barber whose small two chair shop was on the corner of our street. He had the characteristic striped pink and white barber pole at the entrance, but the inside of the shop looked like it had been transferred intact from Italy. Artificial grape clusters hung from the ceiling. Small ceramic sculptures of "David" and "The Pieta" stood on tall pedestals. The walls were painted red and green, and third rate paintings of the Venetian Bridge of Sighs and of Florence's Ponte Vecchio completed the Italian decor.

I was eleven-years-old and it was time for my monthly Friday afternoon haircut and mom gave me the customary twenty-five cents for the haircut and the additional nickel tip for Geraldo. And Sonny, as I was called, marched into the barber shop. There was a customer sitting on the second chair, a hot towel covering his face, and no one else in the shop. I jumped up on the first chair, greeted Geraldo, and was surprised at his uncustomary silence as he kept replacing the hot towels. My barber was not smiling, was not singing and seemed very nervous. Suddenly he came over to my chair, pulled off the lap sheet, whispered agitatedly into my ear, "Sonny, get out of the chair as fast as you can and run like hell down the street." Startled, I obeyed. As I was running, I saw Geraldo running after me and then, head turned, I saw a large black sedan pull up in front of the barber shop and was horrified to hear the loud staccato barking of rapid fire machine guns pointed from the lowered car window at the plate glass windows of the barber shop. The glass shattered, stifled shrieks were heard from the shop, and then as suddenly as it started, all was silent. The car turned the corner and sped away. Geraldo and I were safe but it was quite apparent my barber was involved in the set-up for the execution of the towel covered patron. And inadvertently, I almost became an innocent victim of the crime.

Death of a Salesman

In the practice of internal medicine, there is great satisfaction derived from the solution of diagnostic puzzles and the challenges in the care of patients. At other times the joys, pleasures and satisfactions come from the interesting personalities that one meets as a practicing physician. Bobby Goode was one of the most amusing, interesting patients that I had the pleasure of attending during many years of practice. He was a bright, effervescent personality, in his early fifties, who had mild hypertension due primarily to his ebullient personality. He was a classical successful salesman who had an enthusiastic persuasive approach to his work and the same attitude towards the people he met.

He was tall, good-looking, with a leonine head prematurely graying at the temples, and his very clear blue eyes sparkled with merriment. He was an especially elegant dresser, as befitted the fact that he was the representative of a popular name brand line of men's suits. His "territory" covered Arizona, Texas, and New Mexico. He carried his samples in his car and drove all through his southwestern route, making many friends in the retail business. Bobby always knew the latest jokes, some off-color, but acceptable, and he laughed heartily as he was telling them. He had a great repertoire. The first ten minutes of every office visit was occupied by, "Have I told you this one, Doc?" And off he would go with one of his latest jocular stories.

He had no children; his wife, Lucille, who also became a patient of mine over the years, had a mild diabetes and an obesity problem. She was a sweet apple dumpling of a woman, short, plucky, plump, smiling, with violent red hair and bright shiny eyes, who laughed constantly. She also had a repertoire of jokes, but none off-color. Both Lucille and Bobby seemed to enjoy life and one another tremendously. They had many friends, were constantly on the go, and were continually kidding one another. It was a pleasure to have either one or both in the office at any time.

Bobby called me from El Paso, saying that he had not completed his tour but had been suffering recently from considerable headaches, and some blurring of vision, which he attributed to his hypertension and thought perhaps he should come in earlier for re-evaluation. On examination the next day, he described his headache as being constant, with very little let-up and aggravated whenever he coughed, sneezed or strained in any fashion. The blurring of vision that he described actually consisted of a visual hallucination in that he would see flashes of light which were quite disturbing. His initial examination was essentially negative. His blood pressure was well controlled by his medication. There was no sinusitis, nor evidence of glaucoma, that is, increased eye pressure. His description of visual disturbances, plus the constant headache, aggravated by any form of increased intracranial pressure, i.e., coughing, sneezing or straining, concerned me. I also noted that his usual explosive personality seemed to be slightly duller. My other concern was his bradycardia (slower heart beat rate). His pulse was down to 55. I questioned him again as to the duration of these symptoms, whereupon he admitted that they'd been going on for almost a month, increasing gradually in intensity. It was then that his wife volunteered some further information. She said that she had noted that Bobby had been misusing words in the past several weeks, and on occasion, he didn't seem to understand some of her spoken words. Furthermore, he would come home from his trips and sit around in his comfortable chair going into a dreamy state, which was most unlike him.

With this additional information, I conducted a complete, thorough neurological exam. Peering into his eyegrounds with the ophthalmoscope, I noticed evidence of slightly increased pressure, producing the so-called choked disk. And there was some weakness in the muscle strength and control on the right side of his body. On further detailed history-taking, he admitted that he had recently experienced some unpleasant tastes and noticed unpleasant smells, none of which made sense to him as he had not partaken of any food or been exposed to any unusual odors. He said that these unpleasant tastes and smells recurred several times daily. There was no history of trauma, so head injury with hemorrhage (subdural hematoma) was ruled out. The blood pressure was not out of control and his carotid circulation to the brain was normal by ultrasound, and that eliminated the possibility of a small stroke. Did he have a brain tumor, or a brain abscess? Since there was no fever and no evidence of infection in the body, my differential diagnosis leaned toward the tumor.

While I was doing this detailed history, suddenly Bobby began to cry with large tears rolling down his cheeks. I asked him if the headache had become very severe and he said, "No. I don't know why I'm crying. I've noticed that for the past several weeks I suddenly begin to cry without any provocation." My concern about his status continued to mount. With this additional history and my clinical findings, I now had firm grounds for suspecting a brain tumor!

I sent Bobby down to the lab in the hospital for an electroencephalogram, x-rays of the skull, a CT scan, and a magnetic nuclear resonance imaging of his brain. The report came back the next day, and the Goodes came to the office for consultation. The x-ray interpretations all indicated evidence of a raised intracranial pressure, secondary to a tumor of the brain which was localized to the left temporal lobe.

As the couple entered my office, I experienced once again the pangs of frustration and insufficiency I felt whenever I had to disclose a diagnosis for which the prognosis is very uncertain and most probably irremediable. Bobby and Lucille were stiffly seated in the armchairs facing my desk. They both looked very pale and apprehensive. Bobby was trembling visibly. "You know, I just remembered I had another symptom I forgot to tell you. I had some episodes of vomiting without nausea." He was describing projectile vomiting that comes rapidly and with great force. This was additional evidence of raised intracranial pressure. "Bobby, I have an unpleasant task ahead of me. I'm afraid I have to tell you that you are showing signs, symptoms, and findings of a brain tumor. It is not a very large one," I lied, "and seems to be in the area that is amenable to surgical approach. I have consulted with a neurosurgeon, and I would like you to meet him. If you feel confident with him, then I think we should operate, and the sooner the better." Lucille rose from her chair, put her arms around Bobby in a comforting posture. "Bobby we've gotten through everything else up to now, and I know we're going to get through this." Then I added, "With that wonderful attitude, we're going to have a good outcome." He accepted the diagnosis with eyes downcast and once again tearing, but this time with provocation. He allowed me to make the appointment with the neurosurgeon.

Surgery was set and he survived the procedure, but the diagnosis of the removed tumor was disheartening. It was classified as a glioblastoma multiforme. This is a highly malignant tumor which grows very rapidly, occurs in people over the age of forty, and constitutes thirty-three percent of all brain tumors and has a very bad prognosis. Characteristically, it may be found in any of the cerebral hemispheres, and as suspected from the symptoms, it was located in the temporal lobe. It was impossible to remove all of the tumor as it was larger than demonstrated on x-ray, and showed considerable signs of necrosis, that is, of destruction and hemorrhage, and it was highly invasive, expanding into adjacent brain areas. To remove all of the brain tumor would have left him a total, complete vegetable. The surgery was followed by a course of radiation therapy. After he left the hospital, it was necessary to have a number of office meetings with him to bolster him psychologically. From the effervescent, boisterous, overt, happy personality, Bobby Goode was now changed to a mentally depressed, dull individual who continued to have headaches, weakness of the right arm and leg, and experienced daily series of convulsions which I was finally able to control by the use of large doses of sodium dilantin (an anticonvulsant). After completion of his radiation therapy, Bobby seemed to improve somewhat. There was increased strength on the right side of his body and the headaches abated. He seemed to show some improvement in his general personality and he no longer had the usual sensations of strange taste and smell. He had stopped vomiting and did not experience any convulsions. When he came to the office and started out with, "Hey Doc, did I tell you about . . .?" then I knew he was in remission and I was slightly encouraged!

After a month, however, all of the symptoms recurred. The convulsions several times daily, the abnormal taste and smell, the mental obduration, the befuddlement, the blurred vision, with headaches pronounced and very difficult to control with the usual analgesics. I continued to give him supportive therapy, and when the condition became hopeless, he was hospitalized to receive twenty-four-hour injections of demerol for pain. As he was unable to take nourishment, he was placed on intravenous therapy, gradually lapsing into coma which became deeper and deeper. He expired one morning, with Lucille at his side holding his hand and embracing his inert body.

Texas' Will Rogers

Although he didn't chew gum or twirl a lariat, he constantly wore a large Texas Stetson which he never removed, even during complete physical exams and hospitalization. He always wore a light blue cowboy shirt, blue jeans, a wide Texas belt with a silver buckle depicting a black stallion, and highly polished lizard boots. He was slight and wiry, smiled constantly, was very likeable, and had one of the finest senses of humor that I've ever encountered. He was a political satirist. He enjoyed making good humored political fun of his mayor in Gonzales, the Texas Governor, the President of the USA, and occasionally, the leaders of other countries as well. Unquestionably, he was a clone of Will Rogers. Clarence Wood was loved and admired by all of his friends in his home town and became a favorite patient of my office personnel. The nurses and technicians were extremely fond of him.

He had been referred by friends in Gonzales who had been my patients. His main complaint was of generalized weakness which had progressed for the past year. He knew he was extremely allergic, and being a rancher, that presented considerable problems. He was the owner of several large ranches in the county, had extensive cattle holdings and two of his ranches boasted three deep, free flowing oil wells. He loved his land, his fishing tanks, his cattle, and his horses, and the bankers loved the income from his oil wells. Although he had considerable help maintaining his ranches, Clarence loved to personally ride his horse over the terrain to check his cattle and their feed. Whenever he was in his fields, the heifers caught his scent and when he whistled, the cattle would promptly come running to him.

It was difficult to obtain a complete history from this gentleman without breaking out in laughter repeatedly, as he continued to crack his quick, spontaneous jokes. He adamantly refused to remove his hat until I told him it was necessary to go over his scalp as part of the physical. He grudgingly allowed me five minutes to check the scalp and then once again "clunk," back went the Stetson. The physical examination revealed a low-grade chronic allergic sinusitis, but with an additional disturbing finding of a low-grade anemia. Not only was there an anemia (depressed red cell count), but there was also a depression of his total white cells and platelets. He did have a slight pallor, which is unusual for a rancher constantly exposed to the sun and wind. On repeated inquiries and examination, there was no evidence of blood loss. He did not have a diaphragmatic hernia, which is notorious for leaking small amounts of blood. He did not have bleeding hemorrhoids. There was no bleeding ulcer. There was no blood in his urinary tact. Stool studies were negative for blood and on scoping the lower bowel, it was found to be normal. His vitamin B-12 concentration was normal, he had normal hydrochloric acid in his stomach, and his reflexes were intact. Pernicious anemia was ruled out. His anemia was not the result of a lymphoma or leukemia, or overt cancer.

I explained to Clarence that it would be necessary to do a bone marrow study to define the anemia because his spleen was questionably enlarged. He agreed to have the bone marrow tap done, signed the necessary permits, turned on his stomach, exposed his iliac crest, the bone of the pelvis from which bone marrow aspirations and biopsy are done, and allowed us to proceed. But he still wore his Stetson hat. Two days later, after consultation with a hematologist and the hospital pathologist who studied the bone marrow slides, a diagnosis of "agnogenic myeloid metaplasia" was confirmed. This is a condition wherein the bone marrow is gradually replaced by fibrosis occurring late in life and is predominately a male disease. On review of x-rays of his pelvis, the upper portion of his femurs and iliac were indeed osteoblastic. That is, they were more dense than normal as there was a greater activity of fibrosis resulting in a greater deposition of bone and calcium. These findings are characteristic of this type of anemia. His treatment, as recommended by the consulting hematologist, consisted of a trial of androgens and blood replacement as needed. For, unfortunately, there is no definitive therapy.

When Clarence learned that I loved to fish, I was invited to try my skill at his various tanks. They were all well stocked with bass and he was a delightful host and guide. After pulling in four small bass, I had the good luck of hooking a three-pounder and we quit. He drove me over a good deal of his ranch until he reached a special vista under a large spreading oak tree. Here he said he loved "to watch the glorious western sunset." It was 6:00 P.M. and the view was unparalleled. We returned to his warm house in Gonzales. His wife had prepared a Texas fried chicken dinner and as I listened to "Will Rogers' " rapid fire spontaneous humor, I laughed until the tears flowed. Texas style pecan pie concluded an interesting and relaxing day.

He called for an appointment approximately three months after my last fishing trip, came to San Antonio in his new four-door Lincoln Continental and limped into the office. For the past two weeks he had suffered excruciating pain along the course of his right sciatic nerve. He walked with a slow deliberate spastic gate and tilted to the right. At examination, he was unable to bend forward to touch his toes because of the severe low back spasm. Flat on his back on the examining table, he was unable to extend his right leg in a elevated position due to the sharp pain, as this maneuver produced stretching of the branches of the sciatic nerve. Routine x-rays and CT scan proved the suspected diagnosis: Clarence was suffering from an intervertebral disk syndrome.

He then admitted the reason for his disability: It seems that a small calf became enmeshed in one of the barbed wire fences. Clarence, who was seventy years of age and weighed only 155 pounds, decided to disentangle the calf and lift him to the other side of the fence. He accomplished what he set out to do, but at great personal loss, for he had been unable to stand erect from that day on, almost twelve weeks ago. His usual home therapy of hot baths, oil of wintergreen, and a few old Texas Indian herbs were to no avail, and he called the "big city docs," as he referred to us, looking for help.

The orthopedic consultant put him to bed at the Humana Hospital. He was put into Buck's extension, given the usual anti-inflammatory nonsteroidal type sedation and considerable ultrasonic diathermy. The nurses complained that he never removed his hat. After five days of complete bedrest, the symptoms had not abated to any appre-

ciable degree. The orthopedic surgeon decided to use epidural cortisone block injections. This was given under partial anesthesia and afforded considerable relief. The injections were repeated again in five
days. At the end of that time, Clarence was symptom-free and decided to
go home. He was told to return once a week for repeated injections of
cortisone in the epidural spaces, which he did on two more occasions.

When he returned to his orthopedic doctor for the last series of
injections, his wife pleaded with him to allow me to re-evaluate his
physical status, as she was convinced that he looked paler and discovered he was running a low-grade fever. On re-evaluation, I found that
his anemia had increased and he did have a 102 degree temperature.
He freely admitted that he was very chilly, had a slight cough and had
been sweating profusely at night for the past several weeks. He had lost
eight pounds in weight. His disk symptoms had disappeared completely. He walked erect, and all the signs of irritation of the sciatic
nerve seemed to have disappeared. I admitted him to the hospital for
further study. His blood counts had receded by at least ten percent
from the last count and his sedimentation rate was elevated. X-ray of
his sinuses disclosed low-grade chronic sinusitis, which was expected
as he had a chronic sinusitis history. The EKG was normal. When he
took a deep breath, I heard some fine crepitation, little crinkly, leathery
rubbing type of rales, indicating air mixed with slight moisture, in his
left upper lung lobe. An x-ray was taken and disclosed a faint hazy,
lacy, infiltrate in his left upper lobe. It was not characteristic for any
specific lung lesion. Sputum studies were done for bacteria and fungi
and for acid-fast organisms (the tuberculous organisms). The bacteriologist reported, in twenty-four and again in forty-eight hours, that all
of the smears showed the usual routine bacterial flora, but none of
them were pathogenic; none could be blamed for his present pulmonary pathology. The immediate smears done on concentrated sputum
with special dyes for TB organisms were negative. But this did not rule
out TB and cultures were taken for longer term studies. He became increasingly sicker as the days passed with no definite diagnosis. The
fever was elevated; the night sweats were horrendous and at times the
fever was so high that he became irrational. But he always wore his hat
and his boots. Repeated x-rays of the chest indicated that the slightly
hazy lesion was spreading across the upper lobe. Because his anemia
had progressed, I thought it advisable to give him several units of
blood to help fight this as yet undetermined infection. By the end of
the first week the patient was acutely ill. Although all the bacteriolog-

ical studies to date were negative and all studies of cultures showed no growth, and all skin tests, for various molds and fungi, and all serum complement fixations were negative, we decided that we had to make a tentative empiric diagnosis of acute fulminating tuberculosis, while awaiting the culture report. It frequently takes four weeks before the positive growth appears.

He was placed empirically on a regime of antituberculosis medication. We were forced to use all guns because of the severity of his illness. He was started on Rifampicin, an antibiotic for the acid-fast TB organism. He was given large doses of Isoniazid and Ethambutol to compliment this therapeutic approach, and I also decided to administer intramuscular Streptomycin. For the first seventy-two hours the patient showed no improvement, actually becoming increasingly dangerously ill. We were fearful that he would succumb to this infection before we had a positive diagnosis or before the therapeutic trial against tuberculosis showed any improvement.

On the fourth day, however, he had a massive sweat and his fever began to subside. On the fifth day, the temperature dropped to 100 degrees, the night sweating had ceased. He had an appetite for the first time in weeks, and admitted that he felt considerably better. The cough had abated somewhat. All of the tuberculin skin tests intradermally were reported as negative, but that is not unusual during "acute fulminating infection of TB." As he continued to improve, the jokes started to reappear. He sat in a rocking chair in his hospital room, boots and hat on, wearing pajamas and a flannel bathrobe, telling his stories. Nurses, technicians and physicians loved to come to his room because of his sparkling personality, and the great store of humorous anecdotes.

By the tenth day of hospitalization, he showed definite clinical improvement. Although there was still considerable inflammatory involvement in the left upper lobe of his lung, his cough had abated, the sputum had decreased, and there was no fever. He was placed on a continuous oral medical regime and sent back to Gonzales and told to do absolutely nothing for the next two weeks, and then to return for a check-up.

The patient's anemia did not improve, it stayed persistently low. The infection in the lung was clearing and eventually we did receive a "positive" lab result of cultures indicating that this indeed was a TB infection. We felt gratified and justified that we had started the therapy early! I then placed members of his family on treatment to prevent cross-infection. He continued on the treatment for TB for well over a year, as did the family members, with smaller doses.

The x-ray of his chest finally cleared completely at the end of the year, and there were no residuals. His chief problems, however, concerned the continued anemia which slowly progressed. It was now necessary for him to have blood transfusions at monthly intervals. As his condition began to deteriorate hematologically, it was soon necessary to transfuse him weekly. He was finally hospitalized as the blood counts continued to drop in spite of the weekly administrations. He was given transfusions daily without effect, as his immune system destroyed the dispensed blood and his bone marrow failed completely to produce sufficient cells. Sadly, he experienced a continued downhill course, his jokes became fewer and further apart and one early morning as the nurse was making hospital rounds, he was found sitting in his rocker, his hat on, cold and pulseless. It was sad but fitting, just as Clarence would have wanted it, to die with his hat and boots on!

The Schlemiel

Robert Samuels was a short, thick-necked, obese, comical-looking man. He had a large nose, blotchy, speckled skin and spoke in a raspy resonant voice, further complicated by a slight stutter. He had been under treatment for hypertensive cardiovascular disease. A clever, successful businessman and well liked despite his physical unattractiveness, Samuels was the most accident-prone person I ever encountered.

He was justified in asking, "Why me?", for if anything untoward were to happen, it would happen to him. In April of 1976, for example, while standing shoulder to shoulder with a policeman, watching the Battle of Flowers parade during San Antonio's Fiesta commemorating the heroic Battle of the Alamo, his wallet was stolen by a pickpocket. When his wife Mary insisted that he must exercise to reduce, he bought a ten-speed bicycle, fell the first day out, and broke his left wrist. Both radius and ulna were fractured and required setting under general anesthesia. When it snowed in San Antonio for the first time in twenty years, Robert took the trash out to the curb, slipped, fell, and tore a cartilage in his knee, and ended up on crutches for three weeks. When his wife invited his friends to a small party in their home, he offered to pour the tea, dropped the kettle and suffered second degree burns on his left arm.

One night while he and Mary were having dinner at a very exclusive restaurant, Mary, who had attended a luncheon that day, wasn't hungry, and could not eat her filet mignon. Robert suggested they take it home in a "doggy bag," and put the package carefully into the pocket of his new suit. One evening, while dressing for the theater, he reached into his left pocket for his tickets and found the steak exactly where he'd left it — three weeks earlier.

Two days after he bought a new Jaguar XJ6, he took his wife and child to a local theater, carefully parked in the lot, making sure there was plenty of room on both sides so the doors would not be scratched. When they came out of the movie, the car had been stolen.

His closest friends were aware of his propensity for disaster and had considerable fun at his expense whenever one of these unfortunate accidents occurred. Soon he was so embarrassed that he made sure his friends did not hear of these bizarre occurrences.

One weekend, Robert and two friends decided to go to Mexico City to get away from it all! They checked in at the new Hilton which had just been completed, but the grounds had not yet been landscaped. Feeling uncomfortable after a late, heavy meal accompanied by three glasses of wine, Robert excused himself and said he would take a walk alone outside. It was a lovely night, but dark. He wandered off into the unlit, unfinished garden area where he was unable to see his surroundings. He tripped over a board and plunged into a deep hole that had been dug in preparation for a tree, cracking his back against the rim of the hole. Covered with slippery mud, he found it difficult to extract himself from this precarious predicament. He was stuck in the hole. He called for help and after an uncomfortable fifteen minutes, a watchman heard him and helped pull him out. He was aching badly and stumbled back into the hotel and stole quietly up to his room, too embarrassed to tell his friends. He washed the mud off thoroughly, quickly changed clothes and returned to the lobby to meet them, claiming he had had a wonderful invigorating walk. They noticed, however, that he was limping and that it was difficult for him to *take deep breaths* as he was now grunting with each respiration. Since he volunteered no information, they did not pursue it further.

The next morning, the watchman approached one of Robert's friends, and asked: "How is your friend this morning? Did he tell you how he fell into the hole behind the hotel?" The friends realized that Robert had been too ashamed to report the incident and allowed him the luxury of being secretive.

The discomfort in Robert's back continued unabated. When he returned to San Antonio on Monday morning, he made an appointment to see me in my office. What he didn't know was that his friends had already had breakfast with me, before my morning hospital rounds, and told me the entire story and I had agreed to disclaim any knowledge of the accident. During the examination, Robert told me he had a painful condition between his rib and spinal column. The area was badly bruised, and he had difficulty *taking a deep breath*. I asked him if he had hurt himself and he denied any trauma. I examined him carefully, finding blood pressure and heart rate under control, and then solemnly gave him my diagnosis: "You have vertebral ribitis dropus holus syndrome." "What's that?", he asked concerned. I explained, "It is a special condition that occurs when one of the ribs tears slightly from the vertebral column and only occurs when somebody suddenly falls into a deep hole." Startled, he exclaimed, "You won't believe it, doctor, but that's exactly what happened to me!" And he proceeded to tell me the whole story.

I could not contain myself any longer, broke into laughter and admitted that I had been told the story by his friends, who had been alerted by the security man in Mexico. With analgesics and diathermy, he was well within three days. Two months later, he was involved in an auto accident and ended up at the Humana Hospital with a broken pelvis. The prototype of the proverbial "Schlemiel" (Yiddish for "sad sack"), Robert Samuels was justified in his plaintive query, "Why Me?"

Rabies at The Santa Rosa

The 1,200 bed Santa Rosa Medical Center in downtown San Antonio claims to be the largest Catholic hospital in the Southwest. The Sister-Nurses of the hospital are dedicated, energetic and tireless. They approach their nursing duties like their religion, with a supernumerary zeal to approach perfection. Until the new medical school, University of Texas Health Science Center (UTHSC), was established in 1970, the emergency rooms of the Santa Rosa were by far the most active, and by virtue of its wealth of clinical cases, the hospital became the center of medical training.

For twelve years I volunteered services twice weekly for the charity clinics. One Thursday afternoon after an especially heavy load of cardiac and diabetic patients, Sister Theresa motioned me aside. The nurse was remarkable for never shirking responsibilities and extended her duties until late in the evenings. Her problem was becoming too attached to her patients. This short, young, Irish woman with ruddy, freckled cheeks had an infectious smile that revealed perfectly even white teeth, and spoke with a charming Irish lilt. "Dr. Cooper, we have a real difficult problem on the third floor in the charity ward. And we would certainly appreciate your diagnostic help." She described a sixteen-year-old girl, Frances Rainey, referred to the Santa Rosa from one of the smaller Catholic hospitals in Harlingen, Texas. She had fever for several days, but her major problem seemed to be some form of "hysteria" which baffled the intern, resident and staff men.

She was now in the seventh day of her illness. For hours at a time she seemed to be relatively normal, with the exception of fever. But suddenly she would have a temper tantrum, throw things in all directions, curse the nursing staff, and refuse to eat or drink. Then she developed a series of clonic and tonic muscle spasms lasting for five to ten minutes. After these subsided, she would become hysterical, and scratch and bite the attendants, yelling, cursing and spitting on them. As suddenly as these paroxysms appeared, they would dissipate, and she would become lucid, smile cooperatively and lie quietly in bed. Many of the staff people thought she was malingering and considered seeking psychiatric help.

I read her chart and noticed she was described as being hypersensitive to light, noise, and touch. Also that she had excess salivation and, because of the difficulty in swallowing, appeared to foam at the mouth! The entries in her chart noted that she had increased tendon reflexes, and that a spinal tap was considered, but not completed because of poor patient cooperation.

Requesting sterile gloves, mask, gown and cap, and with the help of an attendant, I did a quick spinal tap on Frances, during a momentary lucid period. The spinal fluid pressure was increased, and a microscopic exam revealed the fluid to be heavily contaminated with lymphocytes. A blood specimen was then sent to Austin for serological analyses.

"Sister Theresa," I said, "I'm afraid that we are contending here with a case of 'Rabies!' And I prefer that you do not wait for the three-day serum report from Austin. You and the other attendants have been heavily contaminated by her saliva through her biting and scratching, and are at great risk!"

Sister Theresa was horrified, but calm. We then called Mother Superior to the ward. After listening to my conclusions, Mother Superior agreed that all those who had been exposed to this patient should start immediately on passive immunization of the antirabies serum. The regime of fourteen daily injections of the duck embryo derived vaccine into the abdomen is not uncomplicated. The injections are very painful and there is always the risk of an anaphylactic reaction or serious delayed neurological complications. However, the alternative is death, since untreated rabies is 100 percent fatal!

Sadly, in the case of this sixteen-year-old girl, the diagnosis came too late, and she died after a convulsion. Her brain at autopsy had the characteristic diagnostic "NEGRI" bodies. It was heartbreaking to meet the grieved family. Their daughter, they said, had always been an inquisitive outdoor girl, who loved to hike through woods and pastures, and wade streams, always exploring. They recalled, after the diagnosis was confirmed, that Frances had found a bat cave about three miles outside the city limits, had entered and been attacked by the bats. She had run to her home screaming from this frightening experience. Unfortunately, no one in the family or staff had elicited this vital information before the development of her irreversible state.

The antirabies treatment for the staff was uneventful and satisfactory. They all had sore abdomens from the injections, but were saved. Although it was extremely painful to witness the agonizing death of young Frances, the successful treatment of the nursing staff reinforced my respect for the brilliant scientist, Louis Pasteur, who developed the immunization for this vicious virus.

The Frustration of Alzheimer's

The thin, short, freckle-faced girl ran to the podium of the high school auditorium to be presented with her diploma. She was valedictorian of her graduating class and she was barely fifteen years old.

Fifty years later, presented with a pencil, she attempted to comb her hair. Given a comb, she placed it in her mouth. When offered a toothbrush, she tried to write with it.

My sister Molly was born three years before my arrival. Apparently she resented my appearance on the scene as an intrusion on her domain, for one day our mother found her approaching my crib with a hammer. We were never sure whether she intended to vent her frustration on the crib or on my skull. As we grew up, Molly gradually began to accept me and the hostility faded.

She was an exceptional student and became the school's spelling champion as well as number one on the debating team. Upon graduation, she won a scholarship to a local business school, where she completed eighteen months of study in seven. Until she married and started her family, Molly served as executive secretary to a prominent manufacturer. When her marriage dissolved, Molly came to work for me as receptionist and secretary, and managed the office most efficiently for the next fifteen years. When I entered into various complicated research projects, she was immediately able to comprehend the essence of the research, in spite of its biochemical complexities, and was able to assist the technicians.

She later took a job with an insurance company and in short time, became a department head. She retired at age sixty, and being active and alert, donated her services to the arts and crafts department of a local nursing home. She also held a volunteer position at one of the large hospitals in San Antonio, as a receptionist in the information area. My offices were in a building attached to the hospital and Molly would often come up on her lunch hour to visit with the office staff.

One Tuesday morning, while I was busily examining the heart of a male patient stripped to the waist, the door to my examining room was opened abruptly and Molly entered unannounced. Taking no heed whatsoever of the patient on my table, she blurted out: "Al, I have some bad boils that I want you to see immediately." She proceeded to undress in front of the patient. I was startled and called my nurse, Mary, to put Molly in the adjoining examining room. As she was ushered out of the room, she continued to complain to me about the boils. I completed the examination of the patient, and then went to examine Molly. My receptionist called me aside to let me know that my sister had come running into the office, excited and disturbed. She said that she had to see me immediately, and before they could stop her, she ran down the hall into my examining room. I talked to Molly quietly, checked her and found no boils. I asked her why she had rushed into the examining room without knocking. Her answer was a silly giggle, and grimacing, she said, "I just don't know."

Molly's strange behavior that day concerned me. The next morning I phoned the head of the volunteers at the information desk of the hospital and asked if Molly had any problems, and was told that she had been behaving peculiarly for the past two weeks. On one occasion, she sent a patient to the wrong room, and once directed a patient's husband to a different hospital.

Every Thursday evening she was a dinner guest at our house, as we always immensely enjoyed her wit and sense of humor. One Thursday, when I returned late from the hospital, my wife told me that

Molly was there, but had gone into my den. I found her sitting at my desk reading my personal mail. Unwilling to embarrass her, I told her that dinner was ready and ushered her back into the dining room. She seemed perfectly normal throughout the meal, and talked intelligently. Then she reported that she had lost her purse in a restaurant the day before, but could not remember the name of the restaurant. I mentioned several that I knew she frequented, and she finally recalled the name. When I phoned, the hostess acknowledged that they did have the purse. She said they had called earlier in the day and told her they had found it. Molly said she had forgotten all about the telephone conversation. After dinner, she bid us goodnight, and left to return to the restaurant to retrieve her purse. Ten minutes after leaving, she rang the door bell to report she was having difficulty with her car. "It just won't go." I joined her at the car, and started it immediately. "Yes, it starts, but it won't drive" she said. "OK, let's drive around the block," I suggested. She put the gear into neutral, raced the motor and said, "See, it won't go." "But Molly," I protested, "you are driving in neutral. It has to be in 'D' for Drive." "Oh yes, this car sure does behave strangely," she said. Reluctantly, I let her drive to the restaurant.

The following week, I received a call from the hospital's coordinator of volunteers, who told me they could no longer tolerate Molly because of her peculiar behavior.

After detailed examinations, studies, electroencephalograms, CT scans, x-rays, and lab studies, it was our conclusion that Molly was suffering from Alzheimer's disease. Various treatments were attempted with medicines, nutrition, vitamins — all to no avail. She went steadily downhill, becoming totally incompetent, including loss of control of her personal hygiene. In six months, it was necessary to place Molly in a nursing home, where she continued to disintegrate. Ironically, this was the same facility where she had been an arts and crafts volunteer. Within a few months she was no longer aware of who she was or where she was, nor could she recognize friends, loved ones, or hospital staff. She needed total hygienic care. She could no longer speak or comprehend. She developed an unusually rapid progression into advanced Alzheimer's within two years.

With advancing age, there is always some degree of shrinkage of the brain, known as atrophy. Often this has little significance and one may remain alert, perceptive, and keen for an entire lifetime. On occasion, the degree of atrophy may be very severe and then it is associated with some degree of dementia. If this dementia occurs early in life, it is termed pre-senile dementia and often is a form of Alzheimer's disease. In contrast to the natural senile dementia due to atrophy, Alzheimer's disease is characterized by a microscopic widespread loss of nerve cells in the brain. In addition, there is diffuse spread of a silver-staining plaque which contains a protein known as amyloid. In the cytoplasm (body of the nerve cells), there are abnormal fiber-like twisted strands.

Most often Alzheimer's disease presents itself later in life. It may occur in families and possibly may have a hereditary aspect. It usually starts insidiously and subtly, with defects in memory for recent events, and gradual decrease in mental activity. Progression of the disease is usually slow and gradual, and may continue over a period of ten years or more, depending on the age of onset. It is often characterized by severe aphasia, manifested by loss of the power of expression, by speech, writing, or signs. Also, the aphasia may demonstrate a lack of comprehension of the spoken or written language. Alzheimer patients also have a defect known as "apraxia," manifested by the loss of ability to carry out purposeful movements, especially the inability to use objects correctly. As the condition deteriorates, the patient has a total loss of ability to perceive, think, speak or move and terminally succumbs to intercurrent disease, overwhelming infection, or cardiovascular breakdown.

As the diagnostic acumen among neurologist and physicians increases, so does the diagnosis of Alzheimer's disease increase. People are living longer and getting better medical care, and more cases are brought to the attention of the physician for diagnosis. Unfortunately, although considerable active research is being done on the disease, there is no known successful therapy at this time. The emotional and physical aspects of this frustrating disease have a devastating effect on families contending with the patient. It is depressing to the physician to stand by helplessly and observe the decline of a previously normal individual to a state of vegetation.

San Antonio's Lucretia Borgia

The administrator of a successfully run nursing home in San Antonio asked me to see his father because of advanced cardiac failure due to uncontrollable blood pressure. The patient, Boris Lambrowski, was brought to my office by his wife who gave the history, barely allowing Boris to answer any of the questions. It was immediately apparent that she was the prima donna in this combination. They were Russians who came to the USA in the 1970s and retained their heavy Russian accents. Boris had wide shoulders, no neck, was barrel-chested, had a wide slavic nose and sported a bushy unkempt mustache. He was poorly shaven, had a deep scar on the right side of his face, and presented a dull, open-mouthed appearance. He seemed befuddled and confused.

His wife, Katrina, was a chain smoker and as she spoke agitatedly, I detected a heavy odor of alcohol on her breath. She was ten to fifteen years younger than her husband. They were accompanied by a young man whom she introduced as her cousin, George Katapos, from Athens, who had been living with them for the past two years. He was virile looling and swarthily handsome and about ten years younger than Katrina. She told me that she felt her husband was going rapidly down hill as a result of his severe blood pressure and heart condition and was certain that not much could be done to improve his health. Only on the insistence of their son did she bring Boris to my attention. She was flamboyantly attractive with black curly hair, large brown, penetrating eyes, heavily pigmented eyelashes, overly rouged cheeks and bright red lipstick carelessly applied. She kept referring to her husband disparagingly as the "blotnikov," meaning carpenter in Russian. In describing his diet, she said she gave him Russian pancakes each morning. These thin buckwheat pancakes, which she called "blinis," were filled with sour cream. She said that on occasion, since he was such a poor eater, she added some inexpensive caviar. At this time he interrupted, in his slow languorous manner, "Yes, and it's too salty, and after breakfast I am nauseated and unable to eat the rest of the day." I learned from his history that the deep scar on the right side of his face occurred when his wife threw a frying pan at him in a fit of temper.

During the examination, I asked her to please extinguish her cigarette as it was difficult for Boris (or me) to breath with the heavy smoke of the European cigarette permeating the small examining room. As I continued questioning her about dietary regime, she told me that she drank a bit of Ouzo and that he joined her nightly. She explained, "I am very depressed about his illness and the alcohol helps me. Boris is so boring and dull since his illness. He carries on no conversation with me, and I am especially lucky that my cousin lives with us as he is very animated and young and lively. Otherwise I would be even more depressed."

On physical exam, and after obtaining more detailed facts, there were certain elements that proved disturbing. The cardiac failure was not as advanced as she had suggested. EKG and x-ray of the chest and blood pressure and physical findings were noncontributory. The liver was enlarged, however, and there was a slight degree of jaundice. His nails were discolored and brittle and showed a white horizontal stripe above the lunula. Boris reported that his hair was dry and falling out in clumps, especially in the past three months, and the hairs would split whenever he combed. Although she claimed to have given him the prescribed medication on time, she did not, however, adhere to a low-salt regime. I recalled Boris telling me how strongly "salty" his breakfast was, and especially when she put caviar on his blinis. Katrina's critical attitude toward her husband was in sharp contrast to her flirtatious approach toward this so-called cousin.

Because of the presence of the slight jaundice and slight enlargement of the liver, the hyperpigmented bluish gray discoloration of his skin, the condition of his nails and hair, and the laboratory findings indicating liver and kidney injury, I became uncomfortably suspicious. Quietly and furtively, I clipped some of the hair and nails and sent them, along with his urine sample, to the laboratory for possible "arsenic concentration." I re-adjusted his medication, suggested she put him on a very low-salt diet, and questioned her again as to why she was using so much salt on his food, especially the caviar in the mornings. She maintained that she used artificial salt that she bought in the local grocery store but could not remember the name, and said she used it freely since Boris has such poor appetite after breakfast.

Katrina told me she also would like to consult me medically because she was terribly depressed, and was taking too much Valium and the antidepressant Elavil without relief. She admitted that she was a chain smoker and drank too much vodka and Ouzo in the evening with Boris and her cousin.

On the third day after their visit, I received the laboratory's chemical report on the nails, hair and urine. As suspected, there was an extremely high concentration of arsenic present in the hair, nails, and urine. It was now apparent that the so-called "caviar" in the blinis each morning may very well have been a bit of caviar sprinkled with a heavy dose of arsenic. I now faced a dilemma. It was a sordid situation! Apparently, she was involved with the young "cousin" and was attempting to get rid of her sick husband by poisoning him gradually. This would explain the condition of the hair, nails, the liver damage and the marked anorexia that consistently presented itself after breakfast each morning. Also her so-called inability to identify the kind of salt she was using was very suspicious.

I agonized over what approach to take and finally decided to call the priest of her church in confidence. I discussed the story. He suggested that we call the son and apprise him of this serious problem. The son was distraught. It was the consensus of opinion, after our meeting, that we should confront Katrina with our knowledge, but not press criminal charges. I assured them that with proper treatment and discontinuation of this toxic element, Boris would improve.

We met in the chambers of the priest; the son, the mother and I, and confronted her with our knowledge. She broke down, cried hysterically, and admitted her guilt. She justified her crime by claiming she was so depressed, she could not continue living with her domestic situation. She was certain that he was going to die soon anyway because of his cardiac state, and that this was her way out of a desperate situation.

The priest told her he would absolve her of guilt if she promised hereafter to pay extremely devoted, careful attention to the health of her husband. She was to consult with me freely, follow my orders on all medications, and that no criminal action would be taken against her. She was also told that it was necessary for her to immediately send her younger "cousin" back to Athens!

Boris began to improve over the next few weeks. Measures were taken to correct the condition of his liver and to remove a good deal of the already ingested arsenic. Soon he no longer had the open-mouthed dull, bored appearance we had previously noted. His jaundice cleared and the small amount of cardiac failure disappeared. Before long, he was the healthy one, while she became increasingly depressed with the turn of events. She continued to imbibe large quantities of vodka and Ouzo, and according to Boris, became increasingly dependent on various sedatives and mood elevators, and smoked incessantly. Since she was not my patient, there was nothing I could do.

Approximately seven months after our dramatic confrontation, I was told of a tragic sequel to the story. Retiring early one evening to read, Katrina fell asleep while smoking. A fire started in her mattress, and heavily sedated by Valium, Elavil, and alcohol, she did not recognize that the bed was afire. When her husband smelled the smoke emanating from the room, he rushed across the hall to pull her off of the burning bed, sustaining extensive burns to both hands. However, she already had second and third degree burns over her entire body. She was rushed to Medical Center Hospital for emergency treatment and was then referred to the Burn Center at Brooke Army General Hospital, but she succumbed within three days, never regaining consciousness. Ironically, the book found half-burned and opened under her bed was *Dr. Zhivago*. It would have been more fitting had she been reading Dostoevski's *Crime and Punishment*.

Breast Cancer in a Male

He lives, loves, lauds golf and lies about his score. Although he owned a large ladies clothing business downtown, he spent more time on the fairways than in the corridors of his store. Jack Anderson was fifty-three, youthful, tall, lanky, and had a marked resemblance to the actor Fred MacMurray, the then current star in a TV series called "My Three Sons."

His problem, he said when he consulted me, was that a sore on his left breast failed to heal. He was certain it was an infected mosquito bite incurred on the golf course three weeks earlier. "Why has it not healed?" he asked, "I'm strong and healthy and can drive a golf ball 275 yards." I was disturbed at the excoriated purulent granulomatous appearance of his "mosquito bite," which his antibiotic ointments failed to heal.

"Jack," I said, "this lesion on your breast is worrisome and needs to be biopsied." I also examined his left axilla (armpit) and felt three enlarged lymph nodes. They could possibly have been enlarged because of the breast inflammation — but I was concerned. The biopsy report was startling. "Infiltrative lobular carcinoma." A rare situation, a cancer of the breast in a male. He was shattered at the diagnosis, but said, "If that's the 'score' what do I need to do?" "You will need to have the breast tissue and the glands of the armpit removed surgically and this will be followed by megavoltage radiation," I reported.

Before his surgery, I performed a thoroughly complete check-up including chest x-ray and ECG, which incidently were excellent for his age. I had been curious for some time as to the effect of radiation to the heart when treatment was directed to the left breast, and decided to take weekly ECGs during his therapy. I discovered, as anticipated, that there were marked ECG changes during the irradiation to the left chest which occurred during the x-ray therapy and worsened for six months after completion of the treatment. The changes were profound, with prompt development of T-wave inversions in the precordial ECG V2, V3 and V4 leads and flattening and varying inversion of T-waves in limb leads I, AVL, and V6. These changes suggested organic my-ocardial effects to the anterior wall of the heart.

Stimulated by these new findings, I studied and published the re-sults in the *Texas Medical Journal,* December of 1967, a study of thirty patients, male and female who had postoperative radiation to the left chest for breast cancer and found the same ECG changes in each in-stance. When the right breast was removed and treated by the same megavoltage the changes were minimal, as the distribution of the ra-diation was much less concentrated on the heart and the myocardium is spared. I reported my findings of radiation damage to the myocar-dium at the following meeting of the American College of Cardiology.

Jack did very well after his therapy and showed no signs of cardiac disability despite the pronounced ECG changes. Back to the golf course in three weeks, and as the years rolled by, the memory of his cancer became less and less distinct and we thought perhaps we had a complete cure. His ECG, as in all the other cases, improved but never reached their preradiation normals.

Initially, he would come for yearly physicals and then three years elapsed without a follow-up; and suddenly there he was in the office. "No complaints," he said, "I just broke my 78 golf score on Sunday, best ever, and thought this was a good time to check my luck and have my overdue physical."

His 78 on the course was luckier than the findings of his exami-nation. His x-ray disclosed a lesion in his left chest the size of a golf ball, situated close to the mediastinum (center of the chest). It was twelve years since his initial treatment for the carcinoma of the breast. A mediastinoscopy was done and biopsy obtained through an anterior midline incision above his thoracic (chest) inlet. It was a positive re-currence of his earlier cancer, a metastatic chest lesion!

We pondered and pondered about the approach to therapy at this stage. I met with x-ray therapists and oncologists (cancer specialists) and no definite consensus for treatment was derived. The cancer spe-cialist urged the use of massive doses of toxic chemotherapy. Jack re-fused. Further radiation was considered but not urged because of his previous large dosage, and it was questionable as to whether it would be effective.

Having been a student of Dr. Huggins, the Nobelist who con-ceived the theory that many cancers are hormone dependent, I began to meditate on the therapy for prostate cancer — namely orchidectomy (removal of the testes). Already in 1979, the deleterious effects of fe-

male hormones on breast cancer was known and bilateral oophorec-
tomy (removal of ovaries) was being practiced. We had not yet learned
the tests for determining presence of estrogen and progesterone recep-
tors in the breast cancer tissues, but the attack against female hormone
production by surgery was popular. Today, instead of surgical oopho-
rectomy, the use of the drug Tamoxifen is widely prescribed in those
tumors that are estrogen receptor positive.

I came up with the approach that perhaps Jack's cancer was an-
drogen reactive and could he be helped by the same established therapy
for prostatic cancer, namely orchidectomy (removal of the testes). I discussed my theory with the San Antonio oncologist and called the
Breast Cancer Section at M.D. Anderson Hospital (cancer research hospital in Houston) and exchanged ideas and opinions. We concluded it
was a worthwhile approach to Jack's problem, as he was now living
with the sword of Damocles overhead.

After lengthy consultation with Jack and his wife and complete
explanation of the experimental approach to the therapy, and the resulting side effects versus the unquestioned fatal results in six months
if untreated, the couple decided to go ahead with the experimental surgical approach. In two months the chest lesion was twenty percent
smaller. In four months eighty percent regression was the x-ray report.
In six months the lesion was unrecognizable. At this writing, ten years
after the orchidectomy, there has been no recurrence of his tumor. His
present score on the golf course is 82 for the eighteen holes, but he has
"won the tournament" on his therapy response!

Out of the Closet — I.B.D.

It is extremely frustrating to treat a disease that is not fully
understood, and whose etiology (cause) is unknown. So we can only
cope haphazardly with treatment that is empiric (not specific for the
etiological factors).

One such disease is referred to as I.B.D. (inflammatory bowel
disease). Because of their marked similarity, two bowel disorders have
been grouped under this term. One is popularly known as Crohn's disease and the other as ulcerative colitis. These diseases have been correctly diagnosed for the past half century, studied and researched, and
there still remain many unanswered questions. As difficult as it is to
diagnose, it is more difficult for the patients who have to cope with
their symptoms. There is no widespread knowledge about these diseases, and even today many physicians remain ignorant about this

chronic disorder which is characterized by inflammatory symptoms of the digestive tract. There are a total of 500,000 people in the USA who suffer chronically from I.B.D. and 40,000 new cases are diagnosed yearly.

Ulcerative colitis is an inflammation and ulceration of the inner lining of the large intestine and the rectum. Crohn's disease is an inflammatory disease that attacks the lower small intestine (the ileum), and often the first part of the ascending colon (large bowel). The symptoms of each disorder are nocturnal diarrhea, abdominal pain, rectal bleeding, fever, decreased appetite, and loss of weight.

Present day treatment does not cure. We merely control the inflammation and the symptoms. No specific bacteria has been found. No virus has been identified as being implicated in this disease. The onset of the disorder is slow and insidious. Often the disease goes unrecognized for months or even years. Occasionally, it first appears as an intestinal obstruction due to the marked narrowing of the lumen (canal) of the bowel secondary to the inflammation. On occasion, the disease may mimic acute appendicitis.

Twenty percent of the patients who have this disease have family members or relatives who have one or the other of the disorders. Surprisingly, the disease is predominantly found in developed countries, especially the USA, England, Scotland, Scandinavia, Western and Central Europe, and Israel. It has particularly high incidence among the Jewish population. With the exception of Japan, it has not been found in Asia, Equatorial Africa or South America. It is strange that it is not found in areas that are characterized by poor sanitation and poor nutrition.

The disease may start at childhood, but then accelerates to the age of thirty. A second wave of cases appears in the fifties or sixties. I.B.D. is characterized by remissions, periods in which the disease is quiescent for months or years, and then exacerbations, with symptomatic flareups due to increased inflammation.

Some current researchers believe the inflammation is due to a type of toxic protein or chemical, but this has not been proven. The pathological changes are not unlike those of TB of the bowel, but the tuberculous organism has never been isolated. One researcher feels he has isolated an aberrant form of the tuberculous organism, but this remains to be proven.

Both of these I.B.D. disorders are associated with abnormal immune responses. Either the problem lies with the host who has an ab-

normal response to the antigen that is the inciting factor, or perhaps
the etiological factor itself produced the abnormal immune response.
These abnormal immune responses also produce extra-intestinal symptoms, such as skin rashes, arthritis, eye inflammation, and frequent
episodes of severe canker sore involvement of the mouth and throat.

In Crohn's disease, an indurated (solid) tender mass is often felt in
the right lower quadrant of the abdomen, which is the thick and inflamed lower portion of the small bowel (ileum). There are often abnormal inflamed areas about the rectum. There are hemorrhoids, fissures, cracking of the skin, and occasional fistulas (pathologically
produced connections of one part of the bowel to the other by penetra-
tion of inflammatory masses).

The diagnosis is usually confirmed by x-rays of the bowel and sigmoidoscopic and colonoscopic exams. These consist of the use of fiber-
optic tubes with a light at one end which are passed through the anus
and allow inspection of the rectum and colon for the characteristic inflammatory pathological specific findings of the diseases.

Therapy today consists of the use of Azuhidine and corticosteroids
and on occasion, Flagyl (the same drug used for the vaginal Tricho-
monas infection). Frequently, immunosuppressants are necessary such
as 6-Mercaptopurine. Lomotil is often prescribed for diarrhea. On occasion surgery is indicated, especially for intestinal obstruction and for
the treatment of fistulas and abscesses. In ulcerative colitis, frequently
the entire colon is surgically removed.

Due to the poorly functioning digestive tract and bowel, impaired nutrition becomes extremely hazardous for the patient and
strains the ingenuity of the attending physician. In recent years, patients with these disorders have come out of the closet to discuss their
illnesses, and interested physicians are training other physicians on
how to diagnose and cope with these diseases. There are many celebrities with this condition who are also presently educating the public.
Rolf Benirschke, the star place kicker for the San Diego Chargers, had
advanced Crohn's disease, which is now in remission after treatment.
He is back on the football field and actively involved in organizations
funding research for I.B.D.

Paul Richards was an immature, eighteen-year-old red head who
came to my office complaining of abdominal cramping, diarrhea at
night, low grade fever, and weakness of several days duration. This
good looking young man was charming and quick-witted. He had an
easygoing appealing laugh, and said, "It must be the pizza I ate three
days ago. I burp and pass gas like Mel Brooks did in the movie *Blazing*

Saddles!" He localized his discomfort in the right lower quadrant and jumped off the table with pain when I examined him.

There was an enlarged tender area, which felt like a ruptured appendix with the development of an abscess. His white blood cell count was high, and he had an anemia. The rest of the physical examination was completely negative. Since symptoms were those of an acute disorder and mimicked appendicitis, I consulted a surgeon who confirmed my findings and prepared for surgery. Upon operation, the appendix was found to be markedly inflamed and so was the lower part of the small intestine (the ileum) and a bit of the ascending colon (the first part of the large bowel). Together, they produced a matted inflammatory mass, granulomatous in character, making us suspect Crohn's disease. Granulomas are masses of inflammatory tissue which have specific microscopic appearances and are characteristically seen in Crohn's disease. The pathological report confirmed the diagnosis.

After surgery, the young patient healed quickly and was back to his capricious behavior, pinching and trying to fondle the nurses. The supervisor requested that he be discharged as soon as possible, since too many nurses were being entertained constantly in his room, and the service on the floor was disrupted. He was sent home on a course of Azulfidine and a high caloric nutritious diet, with no exacerbations of the disease.

Two years after this incident, Paul called, concerned that he had a recurrence of the Crohn's disease. He reported, "I have lost weight, have a low grade fever, am weak and nauseated. I have slight abdominal cramps, but no diarrhea. I am distended, bloated, and have no appetite. These symptoms have persisted for the past two weeks."

On examination, I noted a combination of pallor and a slight degree of jaundice. His abdomen was distended and the liver enlarged and tender. Examination of the urine showed bile, and the blood serum had a marked elevation of bile pigment. Studies revealed that the patient was suffering from acute hepatitis, and not from a recurrence of Crohn's disease.

In the process of examination, I noticed several relatively recent and many old puncture marks along the veins of both upper extremities. When the lab confirmed the presence of Hepatitis-B, which is the type usually spread by needle contamination, I questioned my young patient privately about the use of intravenous drugs. Reluctantly, he admitted it and begged me not to tell his parents, promising that he would go on a course of therapy for his addiction. I told him I would cooperate with him on a probationary period of two months. But if he failed to comply with his program, it would be necessary for me to tell his parents to seek help to control his condition.

Admirably, he complied with his guidance therapist. The hepatitis gradually subsided under treatment and he returned to a full, normal life. He continued to be examined periodically at six month intervals and at no time did he show any evidence of recurrence of his Crohn's disease, nor had he slipped into any bad habits. At the age of twenty-six, having matured, he married an intelligent young school teacher and confided in her about his Crohn's disease and his one episode with drugs. They now have two healthy children and he has become a very successful stockbroker and is in complete remission. Rarely, this disease has been known to burn itself out. Perhaps he will be a lucky one.

*   *   *   *   *

Sanford Horn, age thirty-four, a fragile, thin bookkeeper, consulted me for what he thought was spastic colon. He was nervous, apprehensive, tremulous, and admitted he feared doctors. "I faint when they draw blood from me, so, Doctor, please don't hurt me. You won't, will you?" he pleaded. "I'm so depressed."

His symptoms were those of gaseous distention, gurgling, cramping and diarrhea, especially at night. He had low grade fever, had lost weight, was weak and had tender areas throughout his bowel. His lab work-up revealed suspicion of an inflammatory process.

On physical exam, all the findings were confined to the abdomen, especially to the right lower quadrant, where a large indurated tender mass was found. Sigmoidoscopic and colonoscopic exams of the prepared bowel revealed evidence of numerous spotty areas of inflammation through the entire colon. X-rays revealed irregular areas of narrowing of the small intestine and the large intestine due to inflammatory masses. The area surrounding the lowest part of the small bowel was so inflamed as to barely allow barium to pass through, producing the characteristic "string-sign" diagnostic of Crohn's disease.

Mr. Horn was quite ill and it was necessary to hospitalize him and start him immediately on large doses of cortisone given intravenously to reduce inflammation of the bowel. He was also given Azulfidine orally. To accomplish total bowel rest, he was fed intravenously. The patient's response to the program was poor. The inflammation continued unabated and soon there was complete intestinal obstruction, and surgery was necessary to alleviate this condition. A large part of the small intestine was removed. Pathologically, the diagnosis was characteristic of granulomatous inflammation of Crohn's disease. The patient's course was so poor that it was necessary to keep him in the hospital for several months.

During this time, he developed complicating fistulas, that is, one part of the bowel would adhere to the other, with an abnormal inflammatory rupture. He then also began to experience the "extra-intestinal" symptoms of Crohn's disease due to the abnormal immune response, a severe, painful arthralgia of the knee-joints and ankles. He developed inflammation of the eyes and a red spotty rash about the chest and abdomen. His nutrition was severely impaired because of the marked inflammation of the bowel and it was necessary to continue the feeding by vein. Because of the continued inflammation, the development of the fistulas, and the evidence of abnormal immune responses, he was placed on the immunosuppressive drug 6-Mercaptopurine. Only then did he begin to improve. With the additional continued use of prednisolone, a cortisone derivative given orally, and the Azulfidine and controlled nutrition, many of the symptoms finally subsided, and he was permitted to go home for continued treatment.

After a month he was well enough to return to work. Sanford Horn's remission lasted two years, and then there was exacerbation of all the findings. But this time surgery was not necessary. Hospitalization, with massive doses of cortisone, alleviated the second occurrence. With protein supplementation, vitamins, and the use of Lomotil and Azulfidine, all of his symptoms subsided. For the past three years there have been no recurrences.

It is interesting to note the disparity of the response to this disease by the two entirely different personality types. The young, jocular, optimistic Paul responded favorably and with few complications. The older, apprehensive, fearful, depressed Sanford had a protracted, complicated course. I have often noted in my medical practice that the varying response to treatment is affected by the patient's psychological approach to the disease. The optimist does better than the anxious depressed patient. There is considerable research today studying the relationship of the mind and its effect on the neuroendocrine immunity responses with startling findings.

The Chameleon Virus

While it is true that, for the most part, specific etiological agents produce specific signs and symptoms in a patient, occasionally the varied manifestations of the disease are dependent upon the "host" response to the same agent effecting the disease. It is true that endocrine disorders have typical signs, symptoms and appearances. The rash of smallpox has specific characteristics, as does measles, chicken pox, and diphtheria. Right heart failure is classical and distinct from left heart failure. Different bacterial organisms produce their specific diseases and fungi produce their particular responses in the human body. But for the virus of "Epstein-Barr," this general rule does not apply, for it may produce different diseases.

Several years ago I was consulted by a family who brought their son, age fourteen, to see me. They were from the small town of San Marcos, Texas. He had been ill for approximately eight days. His sickness started with a sore throat, followed by fever, succeeded by the development of a small shotty lymph gland enlargements at the back of the neck, which gradually grew larger. He was weak, anorexic and slightly nauseated, and in the past two days had developed a slight case of jaundice. On examination, it was apparent that he had a slight erythematous rash. The lymph nodes, as described, were enlarged and tender. His throat was red. His liver was enlarged and tender and his spleen was palpable. Normal spleens are difficult to feel. The rest of his physical examination was essentially negative. His total white count was increased, with a marked predominance of the large white cells known as monocytes, so-called horseshoe shaped nuclei in white cells. There was a slight anemia, sedimentation rate was increased and the temperature was a hundred and two. The chemistries indicated there was some involvement of the liver in an inflammatory process, as the liver enzymes were elevated. Suspecting a diagnosis of benign infectious mononucleosis (due to Epstein-Barr virus), I ordered complement fixation tests and a spot test for mono. The spot test, done in our laboratories, indicated evidence of infectious mononucleosis, and the heterophile antigen test was also reported as positive. The patient had a classical case of infectious mononucleosis (the kissing disease) complicated by a slight case of inflammation of the liver. Hepatitis is not uncommon as a complication of mononucleosis. The family was told that he would do well inasmuch as he was, prior to his illness, a young healthy male, and the prognosis was good.

His mother told me that two of his young cousins were visiting from Houston and had spent the summer sleeping in the same bedroom with the young boy. I told them there was a 50/50 chance that one or both of the boys would probably also develop infectious mononucleosis. Two days later, one of the cousins was brought to me from San Marcos. He was acutely ill, with very high fever and marked generalized enlargement of the lymph nodes, not only in the neck, but under the armpits and in the groin. His spleen was markedly enlarged and extremely tender. The liver was normal and there was no evidence of jaundice. Suspecting another case of mononucleosis, a peripheral blood count was immediately studied. We were shocked to find that his total white count was approximately 80,000, over ten times normal, and they were all lymphocytes, most of them young forms of the lymphocytic series, namely lymphoblasts. With this history and finding, the diagnosis of acute lymphoblastic leukemia was confirmed and the patient was referred immediately to a hematologist for further care and treatment. The patient was hospitalized and treated aggressively, but with very little positive effect on his leukemia. He rapidly went down hill and expired within three weeks.

His brother, who also slept in the same room with the cousin who had developed mononucleosis, was brought to the office during the time that the leukemic patient was hospitalized, presenting himself with large enlargement of lymph glands in the neck. They were not the small, shotty, pea size lymph nodes of mononucleosis. They were large lymph glands encircling the neck, almost obstructing the breathing by compressing his windpipe. His peripheral blood count was slightly abnormal, but neither characteristic of mononucleosis nor leukemia. He was very sick and febrile, as were both his brother and his cousin. A needle biopsy of the large glands revealed a startling pathological finding: The patient was diagnosed as having Burkitt's lymphoma. Burkitt's lymphoma is extremely rare in the United States. The disease is well known in children in Central Africa and is also caused by the Epstein-Barr virus and transmitted from native to native by the mosquito vector. There were no vectors involved in this disease process. All of the boys had been exposed to the same virus. The family of this boy, whose home was in Houston, requested that they return to the M.D. Anderson Cancer Institute for further diagnostic and therapeutic help. He was given chemotherapeutic treatment and eventually responded with subsidence of his disease.

A month after the death of the acute lymphoblastic leukemia patient, the grandmother of the three boys came to the office because of a severe sore throat, fever and difficulty in swallowing. Examination of the back of the throat and the palate revealed a shabby fibrinous growth that bled easily when touched. She was also quite ill with this condition. Bacteriological and viral studies were taken in addition to biopsy. A diagnosis was established by a pathologist: Lymphoepithelioma caused by Epstein-Barr virus!

In that same household, the Epstein-Barr virus, produced an array of different diseases depending upon the host reaction to the same etiological agent. One boy developed infectious mononucleosis, the usual standard response in a young male to this particular virus. His cousin developed the fatal acute lymphoblastic leukemia, his brother contracted Burkitt's lymphoma, and finally the grandmother came down with lymphoepithelioma. All were different reactions on the part of different hosts to the same etiological agent. There were two or three other cases of infectious mononucleosis among young classmates of the boy in San Marcos, and then the disease subsided, as quietly as it crept into that family with such diverse, disastrous results.

Too Many White Cells

Henry Stern was referred by one of my patients from Mexico City. Average height, stocky build, he moved gracefully, and spoke with a residual European accent. He had a strong resemblance to Charles Boyer, the French actor. Equally as debonair, but Henry had more hair. He was born in Frankfurt, Germany, and was fortunate to have had an extremely perceptive father. Sensing the course of events in 1932 in Germany, and being Jewish, he managed to emigrate with his family to New York City. Henry was then only six years of age, and went through the entire school system, including college in New York City, but never entirely lost his German accent. He received a Bachelor of Science degree in chemical engineering, and went to work for an international minerals and chemicals conglomerate. After working in New York and Chicago for several years, he was transferred to Mexico City.

When he came to me with his medical complaints, I noticed a definite pallor. For the past six months he had noticed fatigue on the tennis court and while mounting steps rapidly in Mexico City's high altitude. All of his physical findings and history otherwise were negative, with the exception of a definite anemia. He was certainly well nourished, apparently had an adequate iron intake, and had no evidence of bleeding, and no infection anywhere. I found it extremely difficult to classify his type of anemia. He was referred to one of the outstanding hematologists in San Antonio who studied his bone marrow and made an alarming diagnosis. He called it an aberrant type of "sideroblastic anemia." This blood disturbance has a lurking tendency to develop into leukemia. As there was no specific therapy, he was instructed to have a high protein diet. He was prescribed androgenic (male) hormone to stimulate the bone marrow to produce new blood cells, and he was to avoid excessive exertion and to treat all infections promptly and energetically with antibiotics.

Henry and I became close friends. We visited him in his lovely Mexico home, adorned by the many sculptures that his wife, one of the most eminent sculptors in Mexico, created. We played tennis at a modified pace and ate in Mexico's finest restaurants. Over the next several years he came to San Antonio often as our house guest, while I kept a wary eye on his health status.

While attending an American College of Cardiology meeting at the Waldorf Astoria in New York, I received an urgent telephone call from Mexico City. Henry had developed a debilitating intestinal dysentery, and had been treated locally with high dose antibiotics. After the subsidence of all the gastrointestinal symptoms, it was noted that he developed a marked increase in the severity of his anemia. I returned to San Antonio to meet him in my office the following morning. The pallor was frightening. His blood count had dropped to approximately fifty percent of normal. Although he felt sick, his attitude and optimism were great, and his approach to his problem was comforting to his wife and to his worried doctor.

At the hospital in Mexico the hematologist discovered that he had developed abnormal cells in his bone marrow, which were unquestionably indicative of an ensuing acute myelogenous leukemia.

The hematologist was a superb laboratory scientist, but unfortunately, lacked the humanistic approach necessary for rapport between patient and doctor. I had just entered the patient's hospital room in San Antonio. I found both Henry and his wife, Norma, stunned and silent. "Al," he said to me, "the doctor in Mexico laid it on me heavily. He told me I was developing an acute myelogenous leukemia and that I only had a maximum of six months to live!" With that, his wife broke down sobbing, and Henry tried to comfort her. Throbbing with emotion, he exclaimed, "Norma, I do not believe him, and I am going to fight this damn condition!"

I attempted to reassure them after this terribly pessimistic, brutal blow, reminding them that nothing is absolutely certain in hematology. Different hematologists come to different analyses and different interpretations of bone marrow studies. So they venture different prognoses, I told them as I hedged. We were extremely distressed at the abrasive manner with which the hematologist confronted my patient. There are gentler, more compassionate methods of imparting serious prognoses!

I told them that I knew Dr. Roberts, a hematologist in New York, who was an expert in myelogenous leukemia. I would accompany him there and have Henry admitted for his personal supervision. I calmed both of the Sterns and again reminded them the Mexican hematologist was noted for being an alarmist. Regaining composure, Henry facetiously remarked, "I guess he is a 'cold blooded' doctor."

Dr. Roberts, on the contrary, was a delightful man. Personable, attentive, friendly, knowledgeable, he immediately established an excellent relationship with the Sterns and me. I became especially fond of him when I learned that he also loves to ride horses, and rides in Central Park on weekends. He occasionally journeys to Upstate New York and Vermont for longer riding experiences and I was very familiar with the challenging trail rides in those areas.

Henry was studied thoroughly by Dr. Roberts, who reported to Norma and me that his findings were unfortunately the same as those of the Mexican hematologist. However, his approach to Henry was humanistic! He admitted the findings of the abnormal cells, but his attitude was, "Let's fight it together. There is therapy that prolongs life," he said. "One approach," he explained, "is a protracted course of treatment of 'small doses' of chemotherapy with fair benefits. The other approach is to use the 'large dosage' with much more prompt response and greater possible favorable results. The higher dose, however," he warned, "has many side effects, and it is necessary to be especially careful not to allow the patient to be exposed to any infection."

Henry and Norma were given the opportunity to discuss the pros and cons of the two therapeutic approaches. They were to make the final decision as to which course to follow. They elected to take the one that promised the greater benefit; namely, the large dose attack in spite of the increased risk.

For two weeks while the treatment was administered, he was confined under aseptic technique. Everyone who entered his room was advised to wear mask, cap and gown, and not to approach him if they had the slightest evidence of infection.

Henry's attitude was admirable and magnificent. He raised everyone's morale, that of his son, his daughter, his wife, and even his accompanying San Antonio doctor. "I know I am going to beat this," he kept saying, and soon we began to think he just might!

Henry's immune system had been markedly depressed by the leukemia, as well as the strong chemotherapy. On the eighteenth day of his therapy, Henry developed a cough and the respiratory infection developed into pneumonia. This was complicated by a blood stream bacterial infection that overwhelmed him. By the fourth day after the cough had started, he lapsed into a semicoma and expired during the night. Dr. Roberts rationalized that Henry's immune system had been so impaired by his disease and his therapy, that the infection which overwhelmed him did not necessarily have to come from an outside source. We all have bacterial and viral insults constantly within our system and our normal immunity saves us. Henry had a fatal disease, and admittedly the chances were slim that the "strong chemotherapy" would have saved him.

Henry entered New York Hospital shortly after Robert Gale of Los Angeles, a famed hematologist, returned from Russia. He had been called for his input on the "Chernobyl radiation incident." I contacted him and asked about the possibility of a bone marrow transplant. His answer: "They never succeed in anyone over the age of 40."

A week after Henry's death, I received a most interesting note from Norma expressing her gratitude for our efforts. She exclaimed that although her husband died early at age fifty-nine, if his father had not had the insight to leave Germany in 1932, Henry would probably not have survived his tenth year.

Get the Lead Out

Adolpho Rodriguez, a local stockbroker of considerable prominence, was a sinewy, brawny, athletic young man in his early thirties. He played baseball, golf, and tennis, and excelled in all. In high school he studied manual training and later became a teacher of shop and manual training in a high school before he went into his stockbroker business.

At home he maintained a workshop and was constantly constructing furniture. He was also quite busy with metal work, having become quite proficient in welding. After considerable success in the stock market, he and his beautiful wife, Frances, decided to purchase one of the outstanding old homes in the historic King William district, the first residential, flawlessly preserved historical area of San Antonio. These mansions were built well over one hundred years ago, with

stately Doric columns and gingerbread framing around the windows
and doors. The many windows were of lead-lined glass. Each house
stood on spacious, well manicured grounds. These gracious homes
were most desirable possessions. The house they purchased was in a
poor state of repair, but it offered great promise, as it was an architec-
tural delight. Adolpho decided to do most of the repair work. He accepted the challenge of modifying the ancient plumbing and felt competent to do the considerable amount of carpentry needed. Both he and
Frances enjoyed this challenge and worked at it steadily for well over
six months.

For a full month prior to coming to my office, Frances noticed
that Adolpho seemed inordinately fatigued, which was most unchar-
acteristic. He discontinued his baseball, golf, and tennis and concentrated only on the house repairs. He then began to complain of abdominal cramps and developed severe spasms in the muscles of his
abdominal wall. Two weeks prior to coming to my office, he also noticed an aching in the nerves of his hand, and after using his hands for
several hours he developed actual wrist-drop. He had developed an extreme pallor in the past month and, according to his wife, he began to
experience headaches.

On the initial examination in my office, it was obvious that this
well-developed, muscular athlete was moving slowly and spastically,
and was very pale. The physical exam was otherwise essentially noncontributory with the exception of defined depressed neurological reflexes. The lab reported a decided anemia with a hemoglobin of seventy percent of normal. As I examined his throat, I noted a thin
blackish line along both gum margins just below the level of the teeth,
a classical lead sulfide line. I immediately called my technician and
asked her to bring me the prepared slides of his red blood cells. As suspected, his erythrocytes revealed basophilic stippling. The red cells
had the bluish point specks which are indicative of lead poisoning. I
immediately had the lab follow this up by taking his urine sample, and
mixing it with acetic acid and ether. This resulted in the characteristic
purplish-pink color designating increased coproporphyrin #3. The diagnosis was clinched. Adolpho had lead poisoning. For final confirmation, serum was sent to Austin for lead concentration studies. In a
week the returned report showed extremely high lead concentration,
confirming the diagnosis.

On further inquiry, it was discovered that our amateur contrac-
tor-plumber had been replacing and working for months with all the

pipes in the old house, not realizing that they were all of lead origin. Working unprotected with the lead dust for hours at a time, he was inhaling the metal. Frances brought his dinner to him at the new house each evening, and as the plumbing was not functioning, Adolpho ate his dinner without washing his hands. Thus, he ingested more lead. This accumulation of the metal which is unfortunately excreted slowly, produced the chronic syndrome of lead poisoning.

He was hospitalized and given chelating agents which consisted of intravenous calcium, disodium versenate. After seventy-two hours of this treatment, most of the acute symptoms subsided, and he was sent home for continued care and promised not to do any more plumbing and to avail himself of the services of a professional plumbing company who would be aware of the presence of the lead pipes and take the necessary precautions.

Adolpho and Frances have finally completed the restoration of one of the most beautiful old mansions in the King William district. It is freshly painted, with non-lead paints, lead pipes were all removed and replaced with copper, and Adolpho, his reflexes all back to normal, is back playing baseball, golf, and tennis. His blood counts have improved and he has a healthy ruddy complexion. But now he has a "handwashing" phobia.

The Wholesale Examination

I have always found it difficult to understand and accept wealthy people who unnecessarily contrive to economize when it concerns their health. Fred Kramer, a very successful entrepreneur, was one of the finest salesmen that I have ever met. He made a fortune in videotapes. Along with his boyish looks, curly hair, Paul Newman blue eyes, and infectious smile, he was bright, aggressive, and extremely energetic. When he determined to sell, he sold. People found it difficult to resist his sales technique. Not only did he make a fortune in videotape franchises, but he also was extremely successful in real estate transactions, and lived in a beautiful home in a very exclusive neighborhood. Fred never bought anything retail; he thought that was unbecoming and demeaning. He bought everything wholesale. He adhered to this wholesale approach even where his health was concerned. His wife was equally conservative, very arrogant and had difficulty getting along with people. This unattractive woman was brusque, indifferent, and loved to order people around. She referred to her household help as her "servants."

Both Fred and his wife, though difficult, were patients of mine for many years. Whenever a test was ordered he would question whether it was really necessary, and always asked, "Why does it cost so much?" He was in the habit of calling several pharmacies to determine which one would fill a prescription cheaper. Slow in paying bills, he often would use the telephone for medical consultation in an attempt to save charges for an office visit.

When he began to develop suspicious chest symptoms of mild compression, without radiation into neck and arms, and not related to food or effort, but primarily related to tension, he was concerned that he might be developing early angina pectoris or coronary disease. When he called me on the phone with these complaints, I told him to come to the office so I could thoroughly evaluate him. "What does that include?" asked Fred. I told him, "In addition to a complete physical, you will need x-rays of the upper intestinal tract, electrocardiograms, stress tests, x-rays of your chest, enzyme studies, chemistries, possibly a diagnostic Holter (continuous ECG recording) for twenty-four-hours, and if indicated, an echocardiogram." "What do you think that will cost me?" he immediately questioned apprehensively. I reported that the complete work-up was probably about $300, which was the equivalent of about eight or nine videocassettes sold in one of his stores. He yelled into the phone, "That much? Is it necessary to have all those studies? Can't you just talk to me about it?" "Any chest discomfort is too serious and it has to be studied correctly or not at all." I insisted that he come in for a diagnostic study. He said he would discuss it with his wife, Gertrude, and would call me back in a day or two for an appointment. I urged him not to procrastinate, and in an attempt to alleviate his penurious concern, I offered, "Perhaps not every test will be indicated, but I want you to be prepared, in case they are needed." Several days passed with no further word from Fred, and I assumed he was feeling well.

One of my duties as clinical professor at the University of Texas Medical School was to take fourth year medical students, interns, and residents on rounds in the teaching ward of the second floor of the Bexar County Medical Hospital. The nurse in charge of the floor would present the charts of the teaching patient and I would then review the cases with the staff and discuss their physical and clinical histories. The teaching wards were not charity wards, but the cost of a thorough complete work-up was by far less than would be feasible in a physician's office or in a private hospital.

When I entered the room of my second teaching patient that day with my entourage consisting of the resident in internal medicine, the intern, and the usual six medical students, I was amazed to see the name on the chart: Fred Kramer! Here was the multi-millionaire, who was so determined to get things wholesale that he took himself to the medical school and allowed himself to be admitted on the teaching ward to economize. He had already had his EKG, stress test, x-rays of the chest, and enzyme studies done, and fortunately, they were all normal. The complete physical exam had already been done previously by the intern and counter-checked by the resident. Their conclusion was that he was probably suffering from nervous tension and anxiety and that the episodes of chest discomfort were due to symptoms of cardiospasm, that is, muscular spasms of the lower end of the esophagus which often occurs as a result of nervous tension. (I remembered my attacks during my early days of practice.) However, it was necessary to rule out the possibility of heart disease, as the symptoms are frequently confused.

Here was Fred on my teaching service and I decided that he was going to be treated like any other case on the teaching ward. As we entered his room, his wife jumped up with surprise and embarrassment, not expecting me. She blushed freely, and Fred began to laugh. "Doctor, I know you're so busy and I thought I would save you some energy and time, and would have the work-up done here in the teaching hospital and bring the results to your office. What a coincidence. Here I am admitted to the hospital on your teaching service! Isn't it ironic?" Gertrude nervously stuttered her own explanation. "I know you are very, very busy and we plan to leave town next week and I wasn't sure we could get an appointment with you on short notice." Et cetera.

I relieved their apprehension and told them that their choice was not a bad one, inasmuch as a very fine diagnostic work-up had already been done and we were now going to bring the pieces together. "What do you mean by that Dr. Cooper?" Gertrude asked. "Now we have to have the medical resident and intern present Fred's case to the students as I observe, and then each of the six students will do complete thorough physical examinations, and we'll discuss the x-rays, lab tests, etc. Gertrude jumped up hastily and protested, "But it's not necessary to repeat all those physical examinations. They have already been done." "Yes they have been done by my intern and checked by my resident, but since Fred is on the teaching service, he has to submit himself to a complete physical exam by each of the students."

Gertrude protested, "No, I won't have it. He's already been through all of it. And I just won't have it." I calmed her down and told her that she had no choice in the matter. Since he admitted himself and signed himself in as a teaching case in the medical school, he had to follow the rules. And the rules state that medical students have to do a history and physical on each patient who is admitted to the teaching service. It's just as simple as that. I then asked her to leave the room and told the medical students to come into the adjoining classroom to discuss the case before they proceeded with their examinations of Fred. After the six four-year medical students had assembled in the classroom, I closed the door, and told them quietly about this patient of mine who had gone to great lengths to save money and that he should be treated just like any other patient on the hospital service.

"By that I mean," I told them, looking each one straight in the eye, "I want you boys to do thorough, complete, extensive physicals. Take your time and go over him, one by one, over and over again. And don't forget, I don't accept a physical as completed correctly unless a rectal exam is included. When you gentlemen are through, I will be down in the cafeteria having a cup of coffee. I want you to come down and report your findings." But instead of going to the cafeteria, I could not resist entering the room adjoining Fred's hospital room and listening through the thin walls, leafing through a medical journal. As each student tackled Fred, I could hear him saying, "Oh no! Please — not again. No, I just had it done. Please. Not again." This went on for about thirty minutes. I thought to myself, "He's really getting a bargain. Six rectal examination for the price of one. That's really wholesale!"

My Second Hat — Teaching and Learning

Becoming Board Certified

It is a fervent desire of all practitioners of internal medicine to pass the examinations and obtain a certificate of specialization from the American Board of Internal Medicine. The usual qualifications require completion of four years of medical school, one or two years of internship, and three or four years of internal medicine residency. Then written and oral examinations are taken. Since all practitioners could not afford the time for this extensive residency, the board has in the past allowed some minor concessions: completing internship and one or two years of residency, years of extensive post-graduate courses, and practice confined to internal medicine for a period of a minimum of ten years. If the examinations are passed, the ABIM certification is awarded. After internship and residency and extensive post-graduate training in internal medicine at various prestigious hospitals and clinics, and after ten years of practice in internal medicine, I applied for permission to try the exams for certification.

The two-day written exam was given at Brooke General Hospital, Fort Sam Houston in San Antonio. It was a relatively easy multiple choice type, and one could have deduced the answers on guesswork. The following year I applied for the oral exam to be given at the Letterman Hospital in San Francisco. Three diagnostic clinical problems were presented to each of the twelve aspiring candidates. We were al-

243

lowed thirty minutes to take the history, do the physical, study x-rays, lab findings, EKGs, etc., and report our diagnoses.

My first patient was an elderly fisherman with a classic case of "polycythemia vera" (increase in the total cell mass of the blood). He had the typical purplish red flushed face and mucous membranes that seemed somewhat cyanotic (bluish). The conjunctiva of his eyes were markedly congested. There were scratch marks on the skin, as polycythemia vera patients often have severe pruritus (itching). He had a markedly enlarged spleen and liver. There was evidence of thrombosis (clotting of the veins) in his lower swollen extremities. The lab reports were consistent with the diagnosis. He had a markedly increased hematocrit, that is, the volume of the blood cells and the specific cell counts, red, white and platelet, were increased. His chief complaints were visual disturbances, severe headaches, and painful legs. His name was Emil Deutsch, and he spoke with a thick German accent and did not understand English very well.

The doctor who followed next to examine this man had no difficulty in making the diagnosis in approximately three minutes. When no one was in hearing range, he told me that he confidentially asked this German patient, since the doctor was also German, "Vas ist los mit dier?" meaning, "What is wrong with you buddy?" and the patient answered, "Ich habe polycythemia vera." And so the doctor went contentedly on to examine the next patient — diagnosis confirmed in German by the patient!

The next case confronted was Addison's disease. This is the condition that President John F. Kennedy suffered. Adrenal gland deficiency, with the characteristic signs and symptoms, history and physical findings of adrenal hormone inadequacy. The skin changes consist of faulty deposits of melanin pigment in various parts of the body. For example, pigmentation may appear in the palmar creases of the hand, or wherever there are scars. It will often appear around the tongue and gums and the pigment is frequently found in the rectal mucosa. This is due to melanin production stimulated by the adrenal corticotropic hormone while trying to stimulate the adrenal gland to produce more of its deficient hormones. The decrease in the hormone production is usually due to destruction of the adrenals by tuberculosis, or occasionally a tumor. But more often it is idiopathic (occurring without known cause), that is, the gland just doesn't produce the correct amounts of the adrenal hormone. The patient fatigues easily and is often lethargic. The electrolyte studies reported by the lab were low sodium and chloride while the opposing electrolyte, potassium, was quite high. If one attempts to increase the adrenal gland hormone production by using adrenocorticotropic stimulation, the adrenal gland does not respond as it would normally because it is unable to put out the necessary stimulated increased cortisone. On occasion an x-ray of the abdomen will reveal tuberculous calcification in the adrenal glands. The syndrome could also be produced by a deficiency of pituitary hormone secretions (the master gland) that stimulates the adrenals. I felt quite secure with this second obvious diagnosis. He was a classic case of Addison's disease. Incidentally, if not for cortisone, President J. F. Kennedy would not have survived to become the president.

The third patient was an attractive female, approximately nineteen or twenty years of age, sitting on a cot, with her chest totally exposed. We were informed that she would not be permitted to give us any history and that the diagnosis had to be made by virtue of inspection and physical examination alone, confined to the chest. She was a beautiful young woman with blue eyes, blond hair, well endowed in the mammary gland area, sitting erect and smiling at her examiner, but not talking. She moved freely and gracefully without any evidence of pain.

I observed her for several minutes and obtained no immediate clues. There were no bruises anywhere in the chest wall, no cuts or lacerations, no scars, no bulging masses other than her shapely breasts. There were no masses in the neck, and no abnormal pulsation of the neck blood vessels (carotids). I didn't see any enlargement of her lymph nodes, or salivary glands. There was no interference with inspiration, the *taking of a deep breath,* was normal. There were no problems with expiration (the letting out of the breath). The rate was normal, sixteen per minute. She didn't sigh or hyperventilate, symptoms which usually denote anxiety. It was not easy to view this beautiful upper body without some arousal — but doctor had to be doctor and so on with the examination.

There was no evidence of cyanosis (oxygen deprivation), no increased skin pigmentation or rash. She did not cough, hiccup or wheeze. Her well polished, manicured nails and fingers were normal. In certain chronic lung or cardiac conditions, the ends of the fingers become knobby (hypertrophic pulmonary arthropathy). There were no little splinter clots under the nails as seen in endocarditis (inflammation of the heart valves that throw off emboli). The thrust of the heart beat on the left side of the chest seemed well within normal. Both breasts were equal in size. The pigmentation around the nipple (areola) was normal, no fissures, and no oozing. I had no clues indicating any abnormalities in this beautiful young female. She was a delight to gaze at and appeared healthy.

The next step in an attempt to gather clues (a-la-Sherlock Holmes) was palpation (touch). For a moment, I forgot this was an examination for the boards of internal medicine, and anticipated enjoying this part of the diagnostic work-up. I was too young then to be considered a "Dirty Old Man" — maybe a dirty young doctor! So back to medical analyses: no glands, no tenderness in the blood vessels of the neck, no masses in the armpits, and no tenderness. The intercostal areas (the spaces between the ribs) were not tender, and there were no lumps in the chest wall. Mammary gland examination was done slowly, carefully, and proved to be normal. The breasts were not tender as in cystic mastitis, there were no tumors or adenomas. I palpated the region between the scapulae (shoulder blades), and there were no pulsations as seen in one of the congenital heart disorders, coarctation of the aorta. The costosternal junctions (the joints between the breast bone and the ribs) were normal, not tender as with osteochondritis, the "Tietze's syndrome." A condition which repeatedly brings a female to the doctor with the mistaken concern of coronary heart disease. The ribs were not tender, and there was no evidence of sprain, fracture, or invasion by cancer, or leukemia.

Next, on palpation of the heart area, there was normal cardiac thrust. The lungs had normal resonance (air sounds) on percussion. The dullness that was elicited revealed normal contours of the heart. I found no evidence of hyperresonance, as in emphysema. Indeed, this was one of the most normal chests I was fortunate enough to examine. Checking between the ribs for that soreness reminded me then of an incident that occurred during the third year of medical school.

Dr. Peter Buell, chief of neurology and a neurosurgeon of great repute, was making rounds with our group of externs and staff, when suddenly while we were on the pediatric ward he stopped, turned to his resident and called in alarm, "Quick put me in bed! I'm having a coronary! I'm having extreme pain in the region of my heart, and I am sweaty and shaky!" He was immediately put in one of the large beds in the pediatric ward. The resident physician proceeded to examine him and found extreme tenderness between the ribs on the left side. His blood pressure and pulse rate were normal. The heart was not enlarged and there were no murmurs heard. He was not in shock or perspiring.

EKG and x-ray of the chest were normal. There were no cardiac enzyme studies available at that time such as creatinine phosphokinase (CPK) that would have been helpful in determining the presence of a coronary occlusion (myocardial infarction). The staff decided to watch Dr. Buell for two days. A cardiac consultation was obtained, again with negative findings. Dr. Buell was then moved from pediatrics to the coronary care unit and was carefully observed for two more days. At the end of the fourth day, he developed a vesicular (blistery) rash in the region of the painful intercostal nerve (between the ribs). A classic diagnosis of "herpes zoster" (shingles) was evident. What a paradox! A chief of neurology with a classical case of shingles (a neurological disorder) with pain for four days prior to the eruption of the typical rash, and he mistakenly concluded that he was having a coronary. The boss goofed! How often we are too close to make the correct diagnosis for ones' self! A doctor who diagnosis and treats himself is occasionally thought to have a fool for a doctor, but not always!

I failed to get a clue as to what was wrong with this beautiful statuesque female. I obtained no help from inspection, palpation, and percussion. I did not, I confess, find the "touch" part of this examination too difficult. It was then necessary to proceed in physical diagnosis to the "auscultation phase" — the hearing sense. Already we had determined that there were no abnormal breath sounds discernible to the human ear, so I listened with the stethoscope, which intensifies the sense of hearing and simultaneously eliminates extraneous noise. Again, all was normal and I was becoming increasingly concerned — what did I miss? There were no adventitious sounds (abnormal sounds) heard in her chest, no evidence of fluid (hydrothorax), and the windpipe (trachea) was in normal position. I listened carefully to the beat and all the valves and areas of the heart, and found no problems.

I was now completely frustrated, sweating, insecure, and worried. I concluded my diagnosis a bit facetiously writing, "I find absolutely no abnormalities in this chest. I think it is a beautiful chest," and walked out of the room, stymied, irritated, frustrated, and worried.

The final part of my board exam was the oral part, and the inquirer was Dr. Chester Jones of Boston, the editor at that time of the *New England Medical Journal* (one of the most respected medical journals). And he was considered one of the "stiffest" examiners and had a reputation for flunking at least sixty percent of his applicants. When I walked into his room with my little black bag, and put it down carefully by the chair next to the desk, waiting for the inquiry, I noticed that I began to tremble slightly and perspire a bit. How foolish, it seemed to me, to react like a schoolboy before a high school examination. Nevertheless, I had to admit, it did happen to this mature clinician. It was like being on the witness stand, subjected to the lawyers' badgering.

Dr. Jones' first inquiry, however, was a snap. He asked me to discuss all the various diagnoses associated with the increased enzyme alkaline phosphatase, and to list all diseases that have decreased alkaline phosphatase. Having had an earlier experience in medical school with Dr. Bodansky (the enzyme expert) in Dr. Phemister's amphitheater, I became throughout the years, particularly cognizant of alkaline phosphatases. I spouted my bits of information in rapid succession, and he agreed. The next inquiry concerned an x-ray of the chest which he placed on the view box, and asked me to describe the findings. I studied it for several minutes and could see no overt, obvious abnormality (again insecurity). The trachea was in midline, there were no masses. The heart was not enlarged. There were no abnormal contours. The lung fields seemed to be entirely clear. The bronchovascular markings were normal. The hilar regions (central areas) of the chest were negative. There was no abnormal shadow in any of the lung fields, and the diaphragms were at normal levels. There were no calcifications seen in the lung or in the chest wall, and there were no masses seen. I pondered and pondered, becoming increasingly uncomfortable and then I noticed two "tiny" punched out areas in the fourth rib on the left side. They were each no more than four millimeters in diameter. This was the clue. There are rare instances of leukemia in which the only changes in the bone marrow of the ribs present themselves on x-ray as lytic (punched out) areas.

I turned to Dr. Jones and said, "My only diagnosis at this time would be to look for evidence of leukemia." He nodded his head and said, "Very well, Doctor. You may leave!" I shook his hand, and rushed out into the hall, only to find out that I had forgotten my little black bag. Very much embarrassed and blushing freely, I returned to the office, knocked on the door, and when allowed to re-enter, apologized for interrupting him, and said, "I guess you did make me a little nervous. It seems that I left my bag in your examining room." He laughed and handed me the bag and said, "You'll be hearing from me."

After the oral exam, and the three patient presentations for diagnosis, there was a room set up with twelve pathological specimens for microscopic study. At the other end of the room were ten abnormal x-rays on view boxes and on a table ten abnormal EKGs to be diagnosed.

When our group of twelve candidates completed all parts of the exam, we met in the coffee shop of the hospital for the usual post-mortem discussions. None of us had any problems with the Addison's disease or the polycythemia vera case. What confused all of us was the diagnosis of the young lady with the beautiful chest. I heard the various impressions made by the doctors and felt quite uncomfortable as I did not find any abnormalities. One doctor presumed she had a "mitral valve prolapse" as he was sure that he heard a mid-systolic click when listening to her heart. I did not. Another physician said that she had a small area of atelectasis (a small portion of lung collapsed) and he identified it as being in the left lower lobe. My physical exam did not discover this area. One examinee talked about a rare costoclavicular syndrome where the brachial plexus, the nerves to the arm, are pinched by narrowing between the clavicle and the ribs. I didn't even consider this a possibility. And finally, one of the younger doctors was sure that he saw pulsation between the scapula (the shoulder blades), and made a diagnosis of "coarctation of the aorta," a condition due to a congenital band constricting the aorta. He was sure he detected evidence of collateral circulation between the shoulder blades. By then, I felt increasingly uncomfortable, I never concluded any of these diagnoses, nor made any definite diagnosis. I reported her as being a normal healthy robust female.

Several weeks after I passed the Boards and was certified, I had the courage to call Dr. Chester Jones in Boston and asked him what was wrong with the young lady in the third room. He laughed reservedly and reported, "She was a model, a perfectly normal healthy female, who was hired by the American Board examiners with the definite objective of reminding the doctor that one must not make a diagnosis unless one is definitely convinced of the physical findings! "You were correct." he said and I went back to practice with renewed confidence.

Conferences — The Fried Chicken Revolt

I was always enthusiastic about learning, and I was just as enthusiastic about teaching. Before the days of Medicare, Medicaid, and medical insurance plans, there were large charity wards in the hospitals. I was involved with the out-patient departments. This would include teaching the interns who attended at these large free wards. I was enthusiastic in this role for in the process I learned a great deal. Interns and residents consistently loved to challenge the attending staff physicians. They would often pursue the medical literature for obscure facts and then use this information to throw a curve question at the attending physician. This kept us on our toes, and though we may not always have welcomed such questions, they certainly were stimulating. My stock response to the questions I was unable to answer was: "That's a good question, doctor. I'm glad you brought that up. And I think we should pursue it further. Next week when we meet again, I would like you to present the group with a discussion on that subject."

As part of my teaching role, I initiated Thursday medical conferences and luncheons at the Santa Rosa Hospital, and I would select speakers who were experts in their various fields to present papers. These "Lunch and Learn" sessions became extremely popular with the medical staff of the Santa Rosa and the physicians from the other hospitals. The speakers had to be well-versed in their topics, and produced lucid and stimulating presentations, such as the newest research and the latest medical findings in his area of expertise, or an unusual and interesting case history with detailed discussion of the pathology. The Santa Rosa administration was very pleased with these lecture series as it helped to elevate their status.

The Thursday luncheon and conference series continued weekly for twelve years. But one constant problem was there during those years — the menu! Week in and week out it was the same: fried chicken, a small salad, and a small desert. The menu was as predictable as the Texas bluebonnets in spring, but progressively less pleasing. I invited Sister Angela Clare, the hospital administrator, to attend the next session as I promised it to be a particularly interesting one. When she arrived at the meeting, she was greeted with the following announcement printed in large, bold, yellow chalk on the blackboard: "This is the ninth year of our Thursday medical conferences. We have had over 300 meetings. At each meeting I consumed two chicken legs. Over the past nine years I have eaten 600 chicken legs. I am not disappointed in the meeting, or bored or frustrated. The meetings are excellent! But I am fed up with the chicken!" I signed my name to the board, and after me fifty-two other doctors had added theirs. Sister Angela Clare read the chalked board, laughed out loud; and thereafter we had a choice of fish, steak or chicken and vegetables. Shades of the Mt. Sinai revolt incident in Cleveland!

Physician Heal Thyself

Many patients revere their physicians as Gods. And regrettably, many physicians think they are. In the middle of the 19th century, Honore Daumier produced a great body of lithographs satirizing lawyers and doctors. He was especially vitriolic about doctors and medicine. The Boston Book and Art Shop has published a book of illustrations by Daumier depicting doctors as fallible human beings, subject to all the foibles of mankind, who should not consider themselves personally irreproachable. Their methods are not perfect and therefore medical science is not to be considered sacred or holy. It would be wonderful if all doctors study this marvelous collection of lithographs to allow them an opportunity to laugh at their own image. While it is true that the art was inspired by mid-19th century life in France and costumes and language were different, the subject matter is universal. Since we physicians can't as yet attain all of our goals as perfect healers, we must be able to accept ourselves as the subject of humor, whether in story or art.

Several years ago while driving through France, we stopped at an interesting small very old Catholic hospital in Lyons. It was a crumbling rock building, but still active as a hospital for a small area in this province. A kindly old priest showed us through the entire hospital, explaining its history. He then took us up six stories to the attic, to a large cob-webbed room, with ceilings so low we had to stoop to avoid hitting our heads on the beams. But it was well worth it. There was a fantastic collection of old medical memorabilia, antique apothecary jars, obsolete French medical books, instruments used 150 or more years ago, old bedpans, clysters, hypodermic needles, monaural stethoscopes, some of the earliest blood pressure equipment, and hand-drawn charcoal anatomical charts. The priest then selected a portfolio of old medical caricatures. One of these which was particularly delightful depicted the following in four frames: In the first of the series, the patient is seen writhing in painful agony, grasping his abdomen and looking towards the door where a physician enters and is seen depicted as an "Angel." In the second frame the doctor is administering aid to this pitiful patient. The doctor is now depicted as a "God." In the third frame, the patient appears relieved of his discomfort, the doctor is shaking hands with the patient in farewell. This time the doctor is depicted as a "Mortal Human." In the final frame, the patient receives his bill, and the doctor is portrayed as a "Devil!"

Residents frequently, as a result of having completed four years of medical school, internship and years of specialized training, frequently develop large egos. When that occurs, I take great delight in telling them a little story that I have repeated over the years, in which a doctor dies and tries to gain entrance to heaven. As he reaches the pearly gates, he sees a long line of people waiting for entrance and notices St. Peter at the head of the gate. Bypassing this long line, the doctor rushes to the front of the line, stands at the gate, confronts St. Peter and says, "I'm a doctor, let me in first. I'm not used to waiting in line. I always come first." St. Peter looks at this arrogant person, and orders him to the end of the line. "But you don't understand," says the agitated doctor. "I'm a doctor. Don't you see, I always go ahead of everybody else. Let me in, immediately." Once again, St. Peter orders him back to the end of the line. Irritated and frustrated, the doctor, slowly works his way back to the end of the long tortuous line. As he reaches his position in line, he notices a tall statuesque figure clad in surgical gown, mask and cap, wearing rubber gloves, walking up to St. Peter. St. Peter bows to him, and admits him freely through the gate. With this, the doctor is enraged and once again rushes to the front saying, "I saw you admit that doctor through the gates without sending him to the end of the line. How come you let him in and not me?" St. Peter holds his index finger up to his lips and says, "Shh! That was God. Once in a while he plays doctor." That story never failed to deflate a pompous resident.

In the spring of 1952, I was working harder than ever. I had an unusually heavy patient load in the office and a large number of patients in the hospital. In addition, I was involved in the teaching service at the Santa Rosa Medical Center, and busily engaged in my research program on cholesterol metabolism, I found that wearing my three hats was exhausting and beginning to show in the form of fatigue and irritability. Sally recognized these symptoms and said, "It is time for a vacation and I have mapped out a great trip for us. We're going to drive to New Orleans, spend several days on Bourbon and Royal Streets, take in the local sights and foods, and then go on to Havana, Cuba, on a ship which is a combined freighter and cruise liner."

The drive to New Orleans was uneventful, and after three days of exploring the culinary goodies of Galetoir's, Antoine's, Commander's Palace, and other famed restaurants, we boarded the SS *Quirigua*. It was a small ship with space for only 100 passengers, the rest being filled to capacity with industrial cargo to be sent to Havana, and then bring back bananas to the States.

A small storm began to gather just as the ship reached the outlet of the Mississippi into the Gulf of Mexico. The weather became increasingly stormy and the ship rocked and rolled like a toy going down Niagara Falls. Shortly after the ship passed through the river's outlet into the Gulf, the passengers one and all were busy projecting their stomach contents over the ship's railing. It was small comfort for the passengers to discover that the Captain as well as the ship's doctor were also confined to quarters because of "mal de mer."

When we finally arrived at the Havana port we found it to be sunny, bright, and cheerful with tremendous bustling activity and husky singing longshoremen bellowing in Spanish what turned out to be bawdy songs. Havana in the mid to late '50s was a beautiful, clean, sophisticated city. It was lively, bustling and prosperous, with the beautiful Veradero Beach, broad shining expanses of white sand dotted with kiosks offering everything from soft drinks to fashionable swimwear. We stayed at the luxurious Hotel Nacional with afternoons spent lolling on comfortable lounges, reading and soaking up sunshine and atmosphere. The days flew all too quickly. We hired a chauffeured car, went to the Morro Castle, explored it and then drove into the countryside to see banana palms and lush plantations. During the day we drove through the city and were impressed with the wide, tree-lined landscaped boulevards, broad manicured avenues lined with stately well-maintained airy white mansions. The Cubans truly loved topiary gardens and wherever we wandered we encountered busy gardeners transforming trees and bushes into elephants, giraffes and camels or whatever grotesquery their fertile imaginations dictated. Dining in Havana was never a problem. The city abounded in fine continental restaurants and bistros. We often preferred to take our meals in small cafes where we could listen to the ever-present Latin music and observe the Cubans in their natural environment. We enjoyed the Cuban cuisine, which we found to be less piquant than the Mexican fare we knew in San Antonio. We especially learned to enjoy an ethnic Cuban food, which was delicious, thick steaming black bean soup served over mounds of white rice. Our hotel was extremely comfortable, overlooking a popular beach and was crowded with Americans.

At night, the native nightclubs and casinos jumped to a thoroughly Cuban beat. Havana's elite mingled gaily with the free-spending American tourists. Wine and dollars flowed freely. Music and flowers abounded. And if there was any thought of impending revolution, it was beautifully camouflaged behind polite smiling masks.

Our relaxing, rejuvenating vacation was brought to an abrupt halt the day before we left Havana when I suffered a sudden acute precipitous attack of "tourista." The nausea, vomiting and diarrhea prostrated me in a matter of hours. I went on a liquid diet, and took diodoquin tablets faithfully, and various Cuban pharmaceutical preparations. But recovery was slow. The next day, when we boarded the ship, the dysentery had subsided but I was still very nauseated. On board, we watched the Cubans tackle the tremendous cargo of bananas which were skillfully placed in the holds of our ship. Returning to New Orleans was uneventful. It was smooth sailing, and both the ship's doctor and the captain made their appearance freely on deck. We spent two more days in New Orleans before attempting our trip back to San Antonio in our car, which we had left parked in a garage near the pier. Once again, we planned to savor some of the local restaurant fare, but my appetite was not the same, nor was my GI tract ready to receive the famous spicy delights.

Regretfully, the time came to begin the trip home. About seventy-five miles out of New Orleans and three miles from the nearest gas station, our four-year-old Pontiac had a blowout in the right rear tire. We were not concerned, as I assured Sally that I knew how to change a tire. What I didn't realize was that due to my state of health, it was hard to jack up the rear end of the car. I felt unbelievably fatigued! When finally, at the point of exhaustion, I had the car elevated, I found that I was unable to lift the tire from the trunk and had to elicit Sally's help. The effort was overwhelming. I sweated, felt faint, and developed palpitations. Finally, the two of us struggled to get the tire on and, with Sally's help, tightened the lugs. Sally drove the next one hundred miles while I rested.

For the first week following our trip to Havana, I found practicing medicine a difficult physical ordeal. I was constantly fatigued, had sore muscles, a questionable low-grade fever, and found myself holding to the edge of the examining table while I tried to examine my patients. Soon Sally and my family were all aware that I was sick and coerced me into seeing my good friend, Dr. H. L. I told him to treat me as he would any other patient, that I was feeling badly, and I described my symptoms as primarily weakness, low-grade headache, periodic low-grade fever, muscular ache, and intermittent GI symptoms of bloating, watery stool and mucous and occasionally with a bit of blood. On physical exam, the only findings H. L. elicited was a slight tenderness in the right upper quadrant of my abdomen and some distension and tenderness in the right lower quadrant. All of these physical findings were diffuse and nonspecific. The blood count and urinalysis were essentially negative. One stool exam done in his office was negative for parasites. Dr. H. L. felt I had no organic problems, that I was merely showing symptoms of overwork. He was aware of the fact that I had a large practice, a large hospital load, was doing research, and teaching. He suggested that I discontinue research and teaching for several weeks and reduce my office load and hospital practice by fifty percent and come see him again in approximately ten days. As any dutiful patient, I complied with his request, and returned in ten days, not showing any sign of improvement, in fact, I thought my energy had decreased even more in spite of the alleviation of the workload. A re-exam, new x-rays, new studies were all essentially negative. One radiologist's interpretation of this new x-ray brought up the possibility of a small mass near the stomach. After four other opinions were obtained, the result was that two concurred with a questionable mass, and two defiantly reported the x-rays were normal, with just a slight aberrant position of the stomach. Once again, I had no definitive diagnosis. At this time, Dr. H. L. felt that I was still under a state of nervous exhaustion, perhaps I should talk to a psychologist or psychiatrist.

I was unhappy with his final diagnosis and his suggested form of therapy, and confused about the x-ray findings. I decided to go to the University of Chicago GI clinic to be studied by the eminent Dr. Walter Lincoln Palmer. Unfortunately, when I got to Chicago, the chief was on vacation and the department was under the control of the fellows and instructors. They did the usual routine physical and x-rays and this time, because I was tender in the region of the liver, did some early liver function studies, which turned out to be questionable, but still in the range of normal but suggestive of some slight impairment. Their conclusion was that the entire symptomatology and findings fit into the category of so-called functional bowel distress or spastic colon syndrome, and I was sent back to San Antonio with a load of x-rays, pages and pages of lab studies, and no definitive diagnosis!

I returned home thoroughly frustrated and disgusted. I knew this symptomatology of mine was not due to tension. Upon my return from Chicago, Sally said, "Your complexion looks a bit muddy." Then she turned to me and said, "Let's assume that a patient came to you with the history and findings and complaints you have presented. What would you do as the physician for your patient? What would be your potential diagnosis and how would you go about finding it, doctor?" "Physician, Heal Thyself!"

I knew that I had exhausted my local medical resources and had come back from Chicago without a diagnosis which I could accept. I needed a fresh start and followed my wife's suggestion. "Sally, I think I have a form of hepatitis, secondary to colitis, and I think if I were the patient, I would expect the doctor to aggressively look for a potential foci, namely the Endamoeba histolytica."

I called my friend, Col. Sullivan, at Brooke General Hospital, described my problems, told him what I suspected my diagnosis might be, and asked whether he would help with his guidance and the use of the labs at Brooke General to ascertain whether my suspicion was correct. Col. Sullivan was cooperative. He did a complete exam, repeated all the x-rays, and this time, following my suggestion, we decided to study fresh warm stools in the parasitology department. On each of the next three days, the stool specimens were studied microscopically immediately, as they were passed, by one of the expertly trained parasitologists. The diagnosis came back. "Cysts and trophozoites of the Endamoeba histolytica." More sophisticated tests were done on liver function and direct positive evidence of hepatic involvement was discovered. Serum was sent to the Contagious Disease Center (CDC) in Atlanta for the indirect hemagglutination test for amebiasis and the call came back the next day — "strongly positive." Now all the parts of the jigsaw puzzle fell into place. Apparently I had picked up a severe infection of amebiasis in Havana, manifested by the so-called tourist disease.

Untreated, the amoeba was lying there in the colon dormant and then became intermittently active and then produced the diarrhea. The parasite later invaded the hepatic portal vein and settled in the liver. During the two to three months that I was being seen by excellent physicians and in one of the foremost clinics in the United States, and with no therapy directed to the intestinal amoeba, the hepatitis continued to flourish. Fortunately, it had not yet reached the stage of abscess, which potentially could be fatal. Having confirmed the suspected diagnosis, treatment was started: Aralen (known as chloroquine) was taken orally, daily for two weeks. And to be reassured that all the organisms in the liver were killed, I took intramuscular injections of emetine daily for ten days. It was miraculous. Within one week the fatigue began to subside, the energy began to return, the intestinal symptoms began to disappear, and I gradually returned to fulltime practice. However, I decided not to take any night calls for several weeks until I was fully recovered.

On the third night after this decision, a phone call came at 2:00 A.M. from Mr. Alan Gross, a longstanding patient, to come see his wife who was having some problems with her asthma. I explained to the patient I had been ill, was slowly recovering and could not make night calls for another week or ten days. I referred him to another very prominent internist who was willing to help me with my practice at this time. The following morning I received a phone call from Gross, telling me that all went well and he appreciated my sending the doctor out, but he wanted me to know that inasmuch as I was not available when he needed me, he no longer wanted a sick doctor taking care of him. He summarily "fired" me and announced he would continue with the other doctor.

Recalling the four lithographs that the priest of the old hospital in Lyons had shown me, in which the doctor was depicted as angel when needed, God while healing, mortal when patient was well, and finally the devil when sending his bill, I now thought of a fifth illustration: The patient is calling Dr. Jekyll to attend him at night and the doctor reports he is ill and can't attend. At this point the patient's vision of the doctor changes and he sees him as the cursed "Mr. Hyde."

It's Different Now — The Caduceus and the Dollar Sign

In 1967, when the Medicare law was enacted, the large Catholic Santa Rosa Medical Center became the recipient of many financial benefits. I admitted a very colorful patient to the hospital, a member of a prominent old, wealthy Texas ranching family. She was eighty-four-years-old. Her father had operated three of the largest ranches in the Uvalde area, the largest was reputed to encompass 125,000 acres. The family practically controlled the goat industry in Texas. In addition, she owned a local bank, the hardware store, the drug store and a real estate office, and the family developed a large retirement area that sprawled over 200 acres in West Texas.

Mrs. Bromberg had been referred by her surgeon, Dr. Lloyd Ross. Following successful gallbladder surgery, an attendant unfortunately allowed her gastric suction tube to slip back into the stomach

and was unable to retrieve it. Dr. Ross was concerned and called me to
help with the problem in this elderly female. If the tube coiled up in
the small intestine or in any part of the large intestine, it might produce intestinal obstruction.

Intestinal obstruction in an eighty-four-year-old person would be
a real hazard. After checking her carefully, I found her cardiovascular
system to be relatively good for her age. She had been troubled for
years with isolated premature auricular systoles, so-called skipped
beats, arising in the auricles, but these were not important nor detrimental. On several occasions, she had some episodes of premature ventricular beats arising in the ventricles. These were of more serious concern. But as her EKG surprisingly showed no evidence of coronary
disease, it was only necessary to use a simple medication to control her
transient arrhythmias.

Confronted with the problem of the coiling tube in the intestinal
tract, I suggested to the nursing staff that every two hours they feed
Mrs. Bromberg alternately one ounce of mineral oil or two tablespoons
of milk of magnesia. The following morning she delivered the tube intact. It looked like a large round elongated tapeworm, but there it
was, lying quietly and patiently in the bedpan. The nurses congratulated me, and Mrs. Bromberg was relieved as, of course, was Dr. Ross,
her anxious, worried surgeon.

A month later, she was admitted for treatment of a fractured hip.
Elderly women frequently develop osteoporosis, a thinning of the
bones due to decreased calcium, and fractured bones occur with slight
trauma or falls. She had never taken the female hormone estrogen or
large doses of calcium to prevent osteoporosis.

She had a deficiency of the lactase enzyme that digests milk sugar so
she avoided milk products as they produced bloating, cramping and diarrhea. Unfortunately, no one had supplemented her diet with calcium.

Mrs. Bromberg occupied the most luxurious private corner suite
at the Santa Rosa Hospital and had engaged twenty-four-hour private
duty nurses. She was highly educated, a graduate of Bryn Mawr College, articulate, poised, and a very handsome woman. Always beautifully groomed, her hair was attractively coiffed, and her nails trimmed
and tinted carefully. She had a beautiful modulated voice and her
grammar was impeccable. Indeed, most people thought she was English. Her ancestry, however, was Danish. Her father was born in Copenhagen and came to Texas as a young man.

I was particularly fond of Mrs. Bromberg because she was an unusual, elegant lady, who would tell me many stories of her relatives in Copenhagen, especially those who did so much to protect the Jewish people during the war. She had intimate knowledge of members of her personal family who hid and fed Jewish people in their attics and basements during the German occupation, at great personal risk.

The surgery for the fractured hip was successful. There were no cardiovascular complications and there was no evidence of the usual dreaded problem of pulmonary embolisms due to clotting of the veins in the immobile legs. She was maintained on prophylactic small doses of the anticoagulant heparin to prevent thrombosis.

On the fifth day post-op, I received a call from the administrator of the hospital to discuss a very important matter. She said that President Lyndon Baines Johnson, who had just enacted the Medicare Program, wanted to come to the hospital and have a live TV conference about Medicare. He asked that an elderly female patient be selected who was presentable and could handle herself well on a TV interview. He was going to discuss Medicare with her. He requested that her doctor be in attendance, as he planned to interview him also.

As the cameras rolled, Mrs. Bromberg was to be interviewed by the President, who planned to enter her room at 10:00 A.M., shake her hand, and then ask, "Isn't it wonderful that we now have Medicare? Here you are in a beautiful private room surrounded by private duty nurses, and all of this being supplied to you by virtue of Medicare. And it only costs you a very small portion of what it would normally have cost."

He was then going to interview me about my reaction to Medicare. All of this was to be on national TV and was scheduled for the following Friday at 10:00 A.M. The hospital was to be cordoned off by security people with the only entrance via the guarded back stairway. I was to present myself in my patient's room at 9:45 A.M.

The administrator asked if I would be kind enough to discuss the situation with Mrs. Bromberg and have her prepared. It had been decided she was probably the best choice for the interview.

What the administrator did not how was that Mrs. Bromberg was an extremely ardent republican and found democrats totally distasteful. Furthermore, she was very displeased that Lyndon Baines Johnson had become our president. She considered him to be an obnoxious democrat! It also appeared that their families, the Stevensons and the Johnsons, both ranching families, had not gotten along with one another for many years. President Johnson did not know whom he was going to interview.

When informed about what was going to happen Friday morning, Mrs. Bromberg had a good laugh and said, "I can't wait for this interview!" I told her that he would ask, "Aren't you happy that Medicare has been approved? Here you are in this beautiful private corner room with nurses all around you, and it will only cost you a small portion of the entire bill."

Eyes twinkling, she retorted, "I know exactly what I am going to say, Dr. Cooper. I am going to say to the president, "Listen, Sonny, I can buy the whole damn hospital if necessary. I do not need your charity Medicare!"

She was dead earnest. That was how she prepared to answer the president, and she relished the thought.

I was initially taken aback, but it dawned on me that this is a free country with freedom of speech guaranteed. What a sensational response this would be for live TV! It also occurred to me that I probably would become, for the few minutes of the interview, a controversial doctor in the USA, although I might lose my Texas license!

Nevertheless, I told Sally in confidence what Mrs. Bromberg was going to say. She agreed that I had no right to censor anyone's remarks and besides, it would make very exciting television viewing. Sally, our friends and relatives were poised to tune to the TV at ten o'clock on Friday morning!

At 9:45 A.M., as instructed, I approached the security men, identified myself, went up the back stairway to the third annex, down the hall surrounded by guards, and approached Mrs. Bromberg's room. There were the TV cameras, security men, the smiling administrator and the chiefs of staff all crowded into Mrs. Bromberg's beautiful room brimming with fresh cut flowers. All systems were go!

At 9:55 A.M., two security men came over to the TV reporters and cameramen, and started to whisper to them. Then they advanced to the administrator and whispered to her.

It seemed that President Johnson's uncle, Mr. Baines, had suddenly had a heart attack early that morning and died at the Pedernales Ranch. The President had been recalled urgently to the ranch. The meeting was to be postponed!

I guess, all-in-all, it was for the best, because I visualized Mrs. Bromberg re-enacting the John Wilkes Booth affair and Johnson being the contemporary Lincoln. She was sorely disappointed at missing the opportunity to tell the "damned democrats off."

Medicare or "Mal-de-care"

Tremendous changes in medicine have taken place during the span of my practice. Countless lives have been saved and improved by virtue of immunizations, antibiotics, DC cardioverters, cardiac valve surgery, coronary bypass procedures, balloon angioplasties, lasers, pacemakers, and prostheses. Extensive pharmacological drug developments, biochemical controls and gene manipulations promise great developments. And the advances in psychopharmacological approaches in psychiatry have been innovative, impressive and therapeutic. Once considered Frankenstein fiction, organ transplants have become commonplace surgery in the past two decades.

Presently, concentration is directed at radiation safety factors, improved methods of nuclear waste disposal, and measures to keep our waters clear and our agriculture safe from toxic insecticides. Current efforts to control and conquer cancer and the AIDS virus have been frustrating and disappointing. With constant new emerging approaches in biotechnology, it is believed that these diseases will also be controlled in the next decade.

But all this medical euphoria is being tempered today by the emergence of a threat to tranquility. Medical practice is being altered by the evolvement of the third party — the insurance companies, Medicare, Medicaid, hospital administrators, health maintenance organizations (HMOs) and the businessmen who own hospitals, clinics, laboratories and research foundations. And the exorbitant malpractice insurance premiums brought on by lawsuits with their outrageous awards pose serious problems.

The government, with it burgeoning bureaucracy, is affecting how physicians treat patients and ultimately may take over their relationship completely. The federal government pays about forty-two percent of today's medical costs. There are thirty million Medicare patients, and twenty-three million low income Medicaid patients under government control. Sixty percent of medical research in the USA is supported by the federal government. Therefore, for the most part, it is the government that decides which researchers get financial support and how much.

We recognize that the exorbitant cost of today's health care has become a significant challenging issue. Mental health care costs approximately $25,000 per patient. Coronary bypass surgery and balloon angioplasty are priced at $20,000. The entire course of pre-op and post-op care for a heart transplant can amount to $100,000! Bone-marrow transplants for leukemia patients may approach $125,000. And today's battle with AIDS is estimated at well over $125,000 per patient. Many smaller rural hospitals face bankruptcy. And the government sponsored Medicare and Medicaid programs have insurmountable financial problems, and defray only "a portion" of the medical expenses.

D.N.R. or C.P.R.?

It is in light of this astronomical financial burden to the taxpayer and to society in general that we are faced with the moral-ethical-philosophical dilemma of the application of life-sustaining technology. The acronyms DNR and CPR found on patient charts have come to symbolize this problem faced daily in every hospital.

There are ever increasing numbers of instances when the conscientious physician must question whether to preserve life at all costs. Our advances in technology have brought the doctors literally to the position of having to make God-like life and death decisions. Medical treatment must be of demonstrable, or at least possible, benefit to both patient and family. If the quality of life after CPR is unacceptable to patient and family, should the physician persist with heroic measures? Mere maneuvers to impress family and hospital personnel are neither beneficial nor ethical.

Is the decision to write CPR — Cardiopulmonary Resuscitation — on the chart, instead of DNR — Do Not Resuscitate — based solely on the physician's technical ability to do so? Should the physician's commitment to the preservation of life override the possible wishes, to the contrary, of the patient or family? Can our civilization afford to preserve life at any cost? And if not, by whom and on what basis can such decisions be made concerning who shall live and who shall die? The controversy concerning the use of human fetal tissue for scientific research is now plaguing society.

But more worrisome is that the age-old medical symbol — the caduceus (the wand of Hermes) — is being replaced by the dollar sign and, ironically, there is an unmistakable similarity in the configurations of those two emblems.

Entrepreneurship Among Physicians

Medicine today unfortunately suffers from a split personality. It is a profession devoted to "well being of others," and a commercial economic enterprise governed by "self-interest."

As profits from care are threatened, some hospitals have initiated a questionable scheme of attracting physicians to utilize their facilities by paying them bounties. They are buying, and doctors are selling! The practice of kickbacks is widespread and growing. Several hospitals were recently criticized when it was learned that they offered $70 per referred patient.

A new clinic was found to have been given an interest-free loan of $75,000 by a hospital as "starting expenses" and if they admitted a minimum of seventy-five percent of their hospital patients over three years, there would be no need to repay the loan. Recently 400 physicians in a large city were charged with taking kickbacks from a medical testing laboratory. There also exists a sleazy new trend called "self-referrals." The doctor owns a stake in a lab or clinic and refers patients there for tests or treatment. It is estimated that those doctors with vested interests refer their patients for as much as forty percent more services than doctors with no stake in the facility. This, of course, results in increased costs to the patient and milks Medicare for millions.

Another ethical issue has in recent years reared its ugly head. Are there unjustified procedures being performed that are motivated by the magic dollar sign, rather than the magic wand of Hermes (caduceus)?

There is a sense that more gynecological surgical procedures are done than are necessary. Are more arteriograms performed than indicated? Do cardiologists recommend angioplastics and pacemakers too easily? Also, could many of the coronary bypass patients have been controlled by medication instead of surgery? Do neurosurgeons perform more carotid endarterectomies than are beneficial? Are more scopes being entered than necessary?

I believe that prior to initiating a procedure, the physician should ask himself, would I order that approach for myself or my family?

Public opinion polls suggest that the entrepreneurship among physicians has not gone unnoticed and it is anticipated that in the near future, there will be a response from congress and the Department of Health and Human Services.

Over the years of practice, I have noticed a tremendous change in the doctor-patient relationship. The patient no longer sees the doctor as the bearer of the torch of wisdom, with the promise of a cure. Nor does the patient have the sense of security in sensing that the present day technical physicians do care.

The busy, harassed, self-protecting healer has difficulty imparting the feeling that he is dedicated to the welfare of the patient. The patient does not feel important to the doctor, and the doctor does not feel important to the patient.

The age of technology and specialization has displaced the traditional art of the "laying on of hands." The age-old *"taking of a deep breath,"* with all its manifest remarkable signs, has been replaced today largely by the x-ray, CAT scan, the MRI (magnetic resonance imaging machine), the echocardiogram, the ultrasound, the ECG, blood gases, the radionuclide studies, invasive angiograms, and new biophysical instruments.

No longer does a physician have to be physically close to the patient to learn about the chest. The superb technical procedures of today have converted the earlier warm, close doctor and patient medical environments to cold, distant Siberian Gulags. New doctors are unfortunately being deprived of some of the intimate personal relationships and the satisfying memorable experiences that should be part of the practice of medicine.

The mass of new technical knowledge is responsible for major advances and patients do live longer, healthier lives. It seems, however, that a sacrifice had to be made in the course of medical evolution. Our society reveres technical prowess, and with reason, but much has been lost in the transition from the "laying on of hands" to the "laying on of instruments."

I believe that these two approaches should be combined for the benefit of all. In order to achieve this, the study of "humanistic medicine" would have to be put back into the curriculum. Medical education today is unfortunately deficient in teaching the human aspects of care!

Acronyms and the Approach

During internship and residency in hospitals it is often difficult for the young doctor to learn to communicate with a patient or with the family in a comprehensible fashion. I overheard one of my residents talking to a family about their father, who had just been admitted to the emergency room. The young doctor reported to the family as follows: "Your father was A.D. nearly DOA in severe CHF with VF, and although we debated CPR or DNR we decided to attempt to use DC and the A abated, and then we aggressively treated his CF with a good response, but his BUN, CPK and B.P. were very elevated and his U was full of prot. Also, because of the left-sided weakness, we suspected M.I. of the LCA complicated by TIA." Imagine the frustrated family attempting to gain some information about their father after listening to his discourse of acronyms!

There are over 6,000 medical abbreviations and acronyms being used freely — even doctors confuse one another and much is mumbo-jumbo to keep the magic in medicine.

What the doctor was trying to tell the family was that their father was admitted and he was nearly dead on admission. He was in severe congestive heart failure with ventricular fibrillation and he was so far gone they debated whether to use cardiopulmonary resuscitation or not to resuscitate. But they attempted the use of the direct current defibrillator and the arrhythmia abated, and then they aggressively treated his congestive failure with a good response. They did find that his blood serum for kidney function was poor, and that the enzymes indicating the coronary occlusion were very elevated. His urine was full of albumin (protein), and because of his left-sided weakness, they suspected that he already had a myocardial infarction of the left coronary artery, and all of this was complicated by a transient ischemic attack which probably meant a small embolus obstructed one of the blood vessels to an area of the brain. It might have taken approximately two minutes more of this busy resident's time to explain the patient's condition in English, but apparently a certain type of arrogance allowed him to use the abbreviated shorthand used in the medical profession, the "acronyms."

I also preached to my medical students and interns that patients are people, not cases. It is disturbing to me to have a young doctor report to me that the case in room 201, or the case in room 318, or the nut in room 411, has such and such. Certainly, these people have names and identities and can be referred to as persons not room number cases. I also remind them that they can obtain a world of information if they would learn the patient's background, family life, occupation, type of recreation, travel experiences, and occupational factors. All of these are clues in making a diagnosis. Approaching diagnostic problems, the physician should be a Sherlock Holmes pursuing details!

The patient always expects, and should receive, "time" from his physician, not just time with sterile machines and different technicians, and busy nurses. He is crying, "Hear my complaints, alleviate my anxieties, relieve my sufferings." These cries are terribly important! The doctor must not allow scientific studies and details to obscure a regard for human needs. Also, it is extremely important to inform a patient before a consultant is called, rather than springing a new doctor on a patient without proper preparation. The patient must understand why the consultant is needed and what his function will be. I will always return to see the patient in the hospital with the consultant and with proper introduction. This immediately establishes a rapport.

When the consultant suddenly appears unannounced in a room, the patient becomes terrified seeing the strange face of another doctor who says, "I was told to check you," and then proceeds to do his thing. Where is that wonderful doctor who was presented on TV by Robert Young for so many years, and what happened to the young Doctor Kildares? Not all the TV doctors were idealized fiction! A good doctor must be guided by clinical findings and his experience and by intuition, and let the technological areas confirm or disprove the diagnosis. The indiscriminate use of tests to make a diagnosis is very disturbing and unbefitting a good physician.

I have also instructed residents to continue with enduring concern for patients, even if the patient is transferred to another service from their department, or is transferred to another hospital. It is important to follow the course of the problem, even if one relinquishes control of the patient to another discipline. It is in the evolution of a disease that one learns medicine. It is especially rewarding to be attentive to the questions and comments of the nurses. Nurses are very perceptive about a patient's condition, and perceptive about doctors and their abilities. If information is needed about a referring doctor, ask the nurse.

The Nonphysical Aspects of Healing

It is also essential to recognize that there are nonphysical aspects to healing: the spiritual and psychological. Mind, hope, will, attitude toward life, and religion all effect the outcome of illness. These aspects are mediated through neuro-endocrine and metabolic processes which subconsciously affect the patient. The medical student should be able to listen not only to the physical response when a patient *takes a deep breath* but to the patient's "attitude" as he describes his illness, and his approach to the sickness as well.

I was recently invited to take part in a symposium at our Temple in which the topic was "What is Happiness?" The other speakers on the panel were sophisticated and spoke boldly and beautifully on happiness as a social, familial and hedonistic state of mind. As I sat on the podium listening to the others, I realized that I was better qualified to only speak about the "physiological changes" that occur during expression of happiness.

Much to the surprise of the panelists and the audience, I began my talk with church-related jokes. Soon the audience, including the Rabbi and Cantor, were rolling in their seats and holding their sides with laughter. I then proceeded to explain that laughter is an "acute" response of happiness. And during this "acute" episode of happiness, many physiological changes occur.

First, one *takes a deep breath* and has a number of expiration cycles which wash out the carbon dioxide from the lungs. Blood vessels dilate, blood pressure is lowered and the circulation is improved. Coronary blood vessels dilate and this improves heart function. Lacrimal glands are stimulated to produce tears of laughter, and pupils dilate. Sweat glands and salivary glands are activated. Peristalsis of the intestinal tract (intestinal contractions) increase and if one were to listen with a stethoscope to the abdomen, one would hear purring due to this peristalsis. Cats are notorious for indicating contentment by purring when stroked. The skeletal striated muscles will relax, and people have been known to fall out of their chairs during intense laughter. The state of mind has a profound effect on bodily function!

Recent research has documented that laughter increases levels of IgA antibodies which are important immune fighters. Also, humorous situations stimulate the production of beta-endorphins, the same chemical that induces the "runner's high." Conversely, those who are prone to view their illness as catastrophic or who develop depression with illness, impair their cellular immunity processes and physiological responses, and do poorly in recovery.

Hostile people produce excess catecholamines (sympathetic nerve chemicals) which are detrimental to the contraction of the heart, decrease coronary circulation and elevate blood pressure and cholesterol. A recent publication in a California journal followed mortality statistics in thousands of people for over ten years. Those who believed themselves to be in good health had a lower mortality risk than the pessimists.

Every doctor should be aware that in spite of his physical-pharmacological approach to therapy for disease, the patient is a partner in the therapy. And therefore, the doctor must be close enough to the patient to listen while the patient *takes a deep breath,* and determine his emotional approach.

One particularly illuminating example of a patient participating in his own therapy is that of Norman Cousins, the celebrated editor. Cousins had a serious, painful, crippling collagen disorder. During his stay in the hospital, he began to view old Charlie Chaplin films and claims that ten minutes of hearty belly laughter gave him two hours of relief from pain. He now advocates that all hospitals install a "Laughter Room" where patients can view comic videos to help alleviate their distresses. Attitude can be an invaluable adjunct to therapy, but never a total substitute for treatment.

Where There's Smoke

Despite all the persuasion, lecturing, appealing to the intellect, threats of calamities, and statistical evidence, smokers recoil from admonitions to stop. The decision must come from within. The smoker alone must decide. I recall vividly the amusing story of the woman who had just finished reading an article on the harmful effects of smoking in the *Reader's Digest*. The article warned that smoking produced chronic bronchitis, emphysema, cancer of the lung, lips and tongue, bladder and breast, and had pathologist's reports and statistics to prove it. The report further discussed the hazards of smoking to the gastrointestinal tract, producing ulcers and irritable spastic bowel problems. It disclosed that smoking by pregnant women can result in fetal injury, premature birth, and low birth weight. Finally, it explained that smoking raises blood pressure and advances coronary heart disease. The reader became very disturbed, threw down the magazine and there and then swore off *reading* the *Reader's Digest!*

After contending successfully with my first house call, the problem of Mrs. Zentz and her inability to void, her husband Jake decided to have a complete physical evaluation. Upon entering the reception room smoking a cigarette, he politely asked my receptionist for an ashtray. She explained, "There are no ashtrays in the entire office, because the doctor abhors smoking. Would you be kind enough to put it out?" In spiteful response, he blew the smoke in the nurse's face and reluctantly stubbed out the burning ash in one of the potted plants. As soon as he was placed in the examining room and told to strip to the waist, he immediately reached into his pocket for a cigarette and stealthily lit up again. The nurse detected the smoke, entered the room and requested that he please extinguish the cigarette. He was furious. "I'm nervous," he said, "I've smoked for forty-five years, and you people are not being fair." The receptionist and the nurse warned me before I entered the examining room that Mr. Zentz was ready to do battle over nicotine.

During the preliminary interview and history, he coughed and wheezed continuously. "I believe you must be a heavy smoker." I feigned innocence. "Yes, and you don't have a damn ashtray anywhere around here," he wheezed belligerently. Then he noticed the sign on the wall. "Thanks For Not Smoking." He sputtered, "I don't want your gratitude."

I concluded my examination and determined that Jake had chronic bronchitis, some asthma, an enlarged heart, and markedly elevated blood pressure. After prescribing medication for his cardiovascular system and hypertension, I placed him on a low salt diet, and admonished him about smoking. "It is detrimental to your lungs and your heart and your blood pressure." He asked me, "How long have you been so dead set against smoking?" "Since the early '40s when I learned all of the detrimental effects of nicotine on the human body." With that, I unleashed my customary lecture to patients about the many reasons for giving up smoking. After listening to my harangue while dressing, he turned to me and said: "Doctor, unquestionably you are an enemy of tobacco." "No, Mr. Zentz," I replied, "Tobacco is the enemy of people."

Through the ensuing years, I found that I was constantly harping on the dangers of nicotine and whenever I could, regardless of the diagnosis, I was able to somehow interject that nicotine and tars are harmful for whatever condition my patient had. It was especially easy to point guilt to patients with lung conditions, cardiovascular disease, and intestinal complaints. If they were concerned about their skin and wrinkles, I told them that nicotine destroys the elastic tissue in the skin of the face. If the patient was losing hair, I told them to stop smoking because nicotine produces vasoconstriction of the small blood vessels leading to the hair follicles and promotes baldness. Here and there I've had to stretch the deleterious effects a bit to justify my insistence on no smoking.

*   *   *   *   *

I recall a patient who had severe sciatica, secondary to intervertebral disk rupture with compression of the nerves leading to the lower extremities. I sent him home on Buck extension, which is a pelvic girdle with weights attached to effect traction on the pelvis. I gave him nonsteroidal anti-inflammatory drugs, prescribed analgesics and in parting, I told him, "Remember, no smoking." He quickly turned around and asked: "No smoking? What has that got to do with sciatica?" Thinking fast and trying to protect my position, I explained: "When you inhale a cigarette, you depress the diaphragm and increase the lordosis of the lumbar muscles of your lower back. The result of this is greater tension on the spinal nerves and this will aggravate your sciatica." I'm not so sure he believed me, nor did I feel I was on secure ground with this wild extemporaneous explanation. But in any case, he promised he would stop smoking. As he was leaving, I grabbed another straw. "Remember, you will be in bed twenty-four-hours a day. If you fall asleep, you might set the mattress on fire." As he left the office he said: "You sure don't like cigarettes do you Doc?" "Bill," I said, "I'm considered an enemy of tobacco!"

I think I got away with that one, but several days later I went a step too far in my never ending struggle against the evils of nicotine. Carol Dagle, age thirty-five, had severe diabetes. She consulted me for control of her diabetes, and in my examination, I discovered a severe urinary tract infection and a severe yeast infection of the vaginal tract. Diabetics have an unusually high amount of sugar in their urine and in the vaginal tract, which enhances the growth of yeast infections, namely Monilial organism. Frequently, when the diabetes is out of control, women develop persistent Monilial vaginitis. I regulated her diabetes, prescribed alkaline sodabicarb douches, ordered nystatin vaginal suppositories for the infection, and monistat tablets to be taken orally. In parting I added, since she was a heavy smoker and reeked of tobacco, "I want you to stop smoking." She looked at me quizzically and said, smiling: "Doctor, I inhale my nicotine through an entirely different orifice!"

*   *   *   *   *

Robert Kroll, age fifty-six, was referred to me from Alice, Texas, because of severe pulmonary problems. His referring physician did not prepare me for the advanced respiratory insufficiency that he was experiencing. He was brought to the reception room stooped over, gasping for breath, holding on to his wife and daughter who attended him.

He was coughing constantly, bringing up copious, foul smelling mucopurulent (pus-y) sputum. His expiration was prolonged and difficult, associated with severe wheezing, and I noticed that he pursed his lips and grunted with each expiration. When he sat down in the reception room, it was necessary for him to lean forward with his arms spread out on a chair in front of him in order to breathe. He was cyanotic and with great effort was breathing thirty times a minute compared to the normal sixteen. His daughter carried a portable oxygen tank and was constantly applying the mask to his nose and mouth. He was immediately ushered into one of the examining rooms where I found him using a manual isuprel aerosol bronchodilator. He had been a grocer and managed the same store for thirty years. He had not been exposed to any organic or inorganic dust. He was not involved with any cotton industries, nor had he inhaled any of the chemicals used in the plastic industries. He had not inhaled sulfur dioxide or nitrates from car exhausts. But Robert had been a three-pack-a-day smoker for forty years. During the past ten years, he had had severe episodes of chronic bronchitis and as the nicotine destroyed the elastic tissue of his lungs, he began to develop emphysema in addition to his bronchitis. He was trapping considerable amounts of carbon dioxide in his air sacs. Because of the loss of elasticity, he was unable to expel the trapped gases. In addition, the cilia, the tiny hair-like projections of the tracheobronchial tree, which normally bring up mucous and abnormal particulate matter, had been paralyzed by the nicotine through the years and were non-functioning. As a result, all of the debris was collecting in the lower lung sacs. An x-ray exam of his chest revealed large bullae (huge air sacs), since many of the septa, the little elastic membranes separating one sac from the other, had ruptured. Some of the bullae were so large as to threaten the possibility of a spontaneous pneumothorax. This occurs when the large bullae rupture, air gets outside of the lung into the pleural spaces, collapsing the lung, producing an emergency, which requires immediate drainage procedures of the abnormal air collection for survival.

It was apparent that he needed immediate hospitalization. He was severely dehydrated, his electrolytes unbalanced, and severe bacterial infection was complicating his condition. He was placed on corticosteroids as an anti-inflammatory aid and for reduction of the swelling of his tracheobronchial tree. He was placed on the proper antibiotics after the sputum was cultured. Aerosols were used both by hand nebulizer and by intermittent positive pressure machines. He was taught postural drainage, which meant that someone held him while he leaned over the bed, head down. Thus, gravity would produce a certain amount of drainage of the infected material from his bronchial tree. His electrolytes were corrected by various fluids, and he was rehydrated. Because of his heart failure, he was placed on digitalis and diuretics. It was impossible for him to use bathroom facilities as his breathlessness was so severe that he would faint with the exertion necessary to walk back and forth. Therefore, portable commodes were used. His prognosis was bad.

The medications were of some help, but his condition was too far advanced to expect any marked improvement. He returned home confined to bed and with instructions to continue with all the medications that were used in the hospital. In less than ten days he was readmitted, this time as a result of the anticipated spontaneous pneumothorax, in which the bullae ruptured and collapsed his lung. He was treated immediately with the usual air drainage procedures. His sputum was again markedly infected, this time, with an entirely different organism, and a different antibiotic was instituted. He showed further advancement of heart failure. The family and the physician were concerned about his status and he was in the end stages of his emphysema, as a result of his many years as a chronic smoker. He went steadily downhill and in spite of heroic and aggressive measures, expired on the fourth day. His wife and daughter explained after his demise, that they had found it totally impossible to get him to discontinue his addiction to nicotine for the past ten years. I told them that I truthfully thought that discontinuing smoking over the last ten years would not have reversed his condition, 'tho it might have prolonged his life. The damage had already been done.

In Mr. Knoll's case, as in many other complicated diseases affected by smoking, the U.S. Surgeon General's warning printed on the packs of cigarettes: "Quitting smoking now greatly reduces serious risk to your health" was overdue. The NOW should have been THEN. Now is too late for too many. Despite the information on all packs as to the number of milligrams of tar and nicotine in each single cigarette, intelligent people still actively inhale these noxious substances. Smoking is the enemy!

*　*　*　*　*

Nancy Clark was a happy extrovert who loved to sing, dance and act. She was a combination of Liza Minelli and Charlie Chaplin. She participated in every amateur production in San Antonio. She could act, she could sing, she could dance. But she always preferred to be the buffoon. This hyperactive young woman was in her early thirties when we first met. She was our neighbor when we bought a new home. The day we moved in, preoccupied with the turmoil of the move, Nancy came to our front door with a large pot of chicken soup. She introduced herself, welcomed us to the neighborhood, and said: "I knew you wouldn't have the time or energy to make supper." We met her husband, James, and we all became close friends. For the next twenty years we lived on that street, and the two families were inseparable.

Nancy was obviously a chain-smoker and that disturbed me greatly. She was excitable, nervous, smoked rapidly, had a very expressive face, and long wavy blond hair. But all this attractiveness was dissipated in my eyes by her incessant smoking. When one cigarette was almost gone, she used the butt to light up the next.

Nancy had a simple thyroid problem. She had developed a benign adenoma, a small, nonmalignant, lesion, which I detected early in our relationship. I recommended surgical removal as there was a fifteen percent chance that this could develop into malignancy.

When Nancy reached her late forties, I was still unable to dissuade her from her nicotine habit, and she had already developed chronic bronchitis, coughing constantly and bringing up massive amounts of mucous in her sputum. Her other medical problem however, was the development of early osteoporosis. Her bones were brittle, despite a good oral intake of calcium and the use of estrogen hormones, a regime which probably delayed the extension of the osteoporosis, but did not stop the process. Unbelievably, at age fifty-one, she became pregnant, and this added impetus to her ongoing developing osteoporotic problem.

She consulted me, complaining of abdominal distention, maintaining, "At last I'm in menopause, as I haven't had a period for over two months." She was shocked to find out that her abdominal discomfort and cessation of menstrual cycles were the beginnings of pregnancy, rather than the menopause. Surprisingly, both Nancy and her husband were thrilled. They elected to have this baby, despite the fact that both of them were in their fifties, and their other two children were in their late twenties. And after a difficult pregnancy, Nancy gave birth to a healthy boy.

Her osteoporosis continued unabated and soon there were several small fractures of the thoracic vertebra due to minor trauma. Then a fracture of the lower lumbar vertebra necessitated her wearing a support. Her amateur career of singing and acting had come to a halt as she had to be very careful to prevent further fractures. But Nancy continued to smoke endlessly. Her reaction to my constant harassment was always: "When I find that I have symptoms due to my smoking, then I'll quit." I told her, "When you have symptoms that you can recognize, then your life will be ready to quit." She laughed and continued to smoke, but never in my presence.

Nancy called for an appointment one morning, stating that she thought she had another fracture of her osteoporotic spine. She was in severe pain and wondered if I could see her that day. Examination revealed severe tenderness over the third lumbar vertebra. I concurred with her own suspected diagnosis and ordered x-rays of the vertebral spine. The report came back, "osteoporotic compression of the vertebrae." But while studying the films, and comparing them to earlier ones, I became concerned as the x-rays did not appear to show the "typical" compression fracture of osteoporosis. I was not satisfied with the interpretation of the radiologist and referred her back to the x-ray department, recommending CT scans be taken at several different angles. The new report came back as I feared: "Osteoporosis complicated by destruction of bone, possibly secondary to metastatic bone disease." This meant invasion of the bone by cancer from a primary source elsewhere in the body.

Although this was appalling news, it was not unexpected as an outcome of her pernicious habit. It was difficult for me to tell my good friends this news, but they accepted it bravely. My problem was to locate the primary source of the cancer in order to develop a plan of therapy. The most common sites for a primary cancer that spreads to the bone are the thyroid, the breast, the pelvic organs, the kidneys, and the lungs. Radioiodine studies of the thyroid were normal, and all other lab and x-ray studies were noncontributory. We were at a loss to find the primary source. Nancy was referred to oncologists who pursued an intensive investigation, and also were unable to find the primary source of the cancer. In the meantime, radionuclide uptake studies of her skeletal system revealed additional metastatic lesions in the right shoulder and in two of the ribs. The prognosis was bad. Nancy extinguished her last cigarette in my office when apprised of all these findings. But the horse had already left the barn by the time she closed that door. A biopsy taken of the involved vertebra proved to be an adenocarcinoma of a type usually found in the lung, the "Smoker's Cancer." Repeated CT scans and magnetic nuclear resonance imaging of the chest were, however, again negative. We were still unable to pinpoint her primary source, but suspected the lung.

The ravages of her disease were terrible to behold. The formerly active, happy, singing, delightful woman was now a frail, lethargic, dull, apathetic, tearful woman in constant pain. Various chemotherapeutic drugs were given, and deep x-rays were applied to the bones to decrease the pain. But the relentless destruction of Nancy's life continued unabated. She became anorexic, lost weight, became increasingly feeble, lapsing into periodic states of loss of consciousness, and finally expired at the age of sixty-three.

After Nancy's death, I often agonized: Why was I unable to stop this woman from smoking? She knew me and respected me and we were close friends, and yet I failed to dissuade her. And as forewarned, by the time Nancy discovered that smoking was hurting her, it was too late. At autopsy, a small focus of cancer was found in her right lung, which was the primary source of the spread. The cell type was typical of smoker's cancer, and though it was too small to be discovered by x-ray, this was the primary tumor that spread throughout her body, destroying her.

*   *   *   *   *

I always enjoyed treating people raised on ranches. They were honest, respectful, friendly, have beautiful Texan drawls, and ride horses. And riding is my second love. The Dolan family, from Uvalde, a hilly, ranching community in South Central Texas, seventy miles from the Mexican border, have extensive goat ranches and are one of the largest producers of Angora wool in the United States. When a Dolan talks about a ranch, he is not talking about a few hundred acres. Rather, they drawl, "My upper 70,000 acre spread," or "My eastern 54,000 acre sections" or "My small grazing ranch of 32,000 acres." And they're not bragging. Those are the facts.

Emma Dolan, the youngest daughter of Sikes Dolan, who started the family ranches, was thirty-four, married, and had no children. She was slender, vivacious, had long red hair, which she wore tied in back with a violet ribbon. Emma dressed like the typical wealthy Texas rancher's wife, in a fine cowboy hat, pearl buttoned shirt, string tie, blue jeans, and beautiful alligator boots. She was very pretty, with beautiful white teeth, which I learned later were characteristic of the Uvalde area as there is a good fluoride content in their drinking water.

Emma's initial complaint revolved around low grade sinusitis and severe allergy leading to nasal obstruction and postnasal drip. "And occasionally, I think I have a touch of asthma." Emma was a heavy smoker. She admitted to having started to sneak cigarettes behind the barn at age twelve, and had smoked ever since and was now up to two packs a day. I was disturbed to hear this from this beautiful, young woman, and wondered how her husband relished kissing her with the heavy odor of tobacco on her breath. She stated that she'd had allergies since early childhood and had tried several courses of immunizations with poor results. X-rays of her sinuses showed them to be partially obliterated and there was definite evidence of postnasal drip. She had a low grade chronic bronchitis and when she *took a deep breath,* one could hear squeaks and squeals as air entered through the inflamed bronchial mucosa. The chest x-ray revealed exaggerated bronchial markings which I attributed to her high nicotine intake. During the consultation, I admonished her: "The reasons you did so poorly on your immunization programs for your allergy is because of your use of a constant severe irritant to your nasal passages, sinuses, and bronchial tubes, namely the smoking." I prescribed various antihistamines and antibiotics, and gave her my lecture on the hazards of nicotine, tar and carbon monoxide, and the particular problems due to her bronchitis. She promised to discontinue this pernicious habit.

I saw Emma again two years later, at which time she reported she lost twelve pounds, and had an unhealthy anemic color. She was coughing incessantly, had a light cyanosis around the lips, and a grunting respiration, as she exhaled pure nicotine smoke. One look at her and I said: "Emma, you're killing yourself." At that time I didn't realize how accurate my statement was. The x-rays showed a further increase in the densities of her bronchial vascular markings, and a slight suggestive haziness in an area of the right lung, close to the mediastinum (the middle of the chest). She was only thirty-six, and I was quite concerned seeing the dramatic change in the x-ray after two years. I ordered a CT scan of the chest to better define the haziness and sent accumulated sputum to the lab to study for cancer cells.

Both the CT scan and the sputum cell study suggested an early cancer of the lung. For complete verification, I ordered a bronchoscopic exam (a lighted tube enters the tracheobronchial tree) under anesthesia, with suction aspiration of cells for microscopic studies as well as direct look at the mucous membranes. The look was obscured by old blood in the bronchus, but the aspirated cells showed unquestionable cancer.

At the consultation, I discussed my findings honestly and openly with Emma and her husband. I thought perhaps this cancer was early and operable and hoped for a good result. We consulted a thoracic surgeon, who felt that removing the right upper and middle lobes of the right lung might offer a cure. The lower lobe was uninvolved. The patient was prepared for surgery, with control of electrolytes, intravenous fluids, and antibiotics. The operation went smoothly. Emma was left with a residual small portion of the right lower lobe but the entire left lung soon compensated for the decreased aeration areas. I cautioned her again about the increased bronchovascular markings in the left lung and said: "Emma, you must absolutely throw away that weed, as it has already almost killed you." She agreed and her husband promised to see to it that she complied.

After dismissal from the hospital, I walked both of them down to the car, told them that they were indeed fortunate to have had this early cancer removed before it had metastasized (spread to other areas of the body). She was to be scheduled for a course of chemotherapy and deep radiation to ensure that all cancer cells were completely destroyed and was told to return in one month.

I waved good bye, wished them good luck and re-entered the hospital to continue my rounds. A few minutes later, the nurse who had wheeled Emma Dolan out to the car came running to me as I entered the elevator. "Doctor, you are not going to believe this. But after Emma got settled in the car, she reached into her purse, pulled out a cigarette and lit up." I sighed as I responded, "Emma must definitely have a death wish."

She returned for evaluation after completion of her radiation and chemotherapy. As expected, she had lost all of her hair, but regained some weight. Her breathing was improved as the left lung began to fully compensate for the loss of the two-thirds of the right lung. But there were still many rales and rhonchi in the chest indicating bronchial infection and mucous in the air spaces. Emma admitted to me tearfully that she just couldn't stop smoking. I again collected cells for sputum studies, but they showed only inflammatory reaction. There was no evidence of recurrence of her cancer. I lectured again to both Emma and her husband, this time in sterner, more persuasive tones, and callously threatened her with disaster if she continued to smoke.

Emma failed to keep her monthly visits to me for a period of eight months, when her husband called from Uvalde to say that she was quite sick again, and would I please hospitalize her. Upon admission, I hardly recognized Emma Dolan. Only thirty-eight, she looked sixty years old. Even thinner, she was anemic, cyanotic, and coughing incessantly. She was tremulous, complained of pains in her chest, severe headache, and had been unable to eat for the past week. The follow-up exam revealed what I feared I would find, namely, a new large lesion in the lower lobe of the *left* lung. The x-ray had all the characteristics of cancer. This was confirmed by CT scan and sputum and bronchoscopic exam. Emma was no longer a candidate for further surgery. She had had all the radiation therapy that her body could tolerate. Oncologists were consulted in an attempt to use other forms of chemotherapy to attempt to extend her life and give comfort. She failed to respond to any of the therapeutic modalities that were tried. Soon, she became comatose and we suspected a metastasis to the brain, as this often occurs with lung cancer. She expired four days after hospitalization in severe respiratory distress.

I may have been portrayed as an enemy of tobacco, but tobacco is indeed an enemy of the people.

My Third Hat — Research

Clinical Research

After medical school and graduate training, it becomes apparent to fledgling M.D.s that the greatest part of their education has been the absorption of a wealth of information and techniques developed by the many scientists who preceded them. Anthony Leüwenhock, William Harvey, Marie Curie, Louis Pasteur, Albert Sabin, Jonas Salk, Joseph Lister, Charles Huggin, Alexander Fleming, William Osler, Christian Barnard, Thomas Hodgkin, and all the other thousands of geniuses, who propelled medicine forward.

Learning from their cumulative efforts, we assumed the role of practitioners, the middlemen transferring their discovered knowledge to the public, our patients. How profoundly we are indebted to them.

Many of us have felt an innate urge, and indeed a deep responsibility, to express our gratitude and respect by trying to contribute in some small fashion to the advancement of medical knowledge. And what better way than by becoming involved in clinical research!

Research is to "Search and inquire again, investigate, discover, revise, scrutinize, or add to what had already been accumulated." The knowledge, the techniques, and the art of medicine must constantly be subjected to review and modification in the light of newer developments. Besides practicing medicine (My First Hat) and teaching (My Second Hat), I have thoroughly enjoyed wearing a Third Hat, "Research."

280

Research

Overactive Thyroids

When Barbara Bush, the First Lady, was diagnosed as a "hyper-thyroid" (Grave's disease) and was treated by an oral antithyroid drug followed by Radioiodine, I was reminded of my first tremulous, exhilarating experience in clinical research.

In 1945, shortly after starting private practice, I read an article reporting that rats given the drug Sulfaguanidine developed subnormal growth, a decrease in food intake, lowered oxygen consumption, and became apathetic. These physiological symptoms were suggestive of a reduction in the production of thyroid hormones, producing hypothyroidism. Perhaps, I thought, a pharmacological drug could be developed to eliminate the need for surgery for overactive thyroids. Surgery had a ten percent mortality, was too often complicated by hoarseness or loss of voice, and frequently left an unsightly throat scar.

The Lederle Laboratories attempted to find a drug that could depress thyroid hormone production in humans with minimal side effects. The final result was the production of the drug, Propylthiouracil. After its safety was proven, it was released for clinical study. I was asked to be one of the early researchers to test this drug for its efficacy and toxicity. My clinical studies with thirty-seven patients revealed that the drug prevented the uptake of iodine by the thyroid gland, and less thyroid hormone was thus produced. In patients who had overactivity of the thyroid, the rapid heart beat was reduced, the blood pressure brought to normal, tremors disappeared, and excessive perspiration ceased. There was no longer loss of weight, irritability, protrusion of eyeballs or other symptoms of an overactive gland.

After three or five months, the symptoms of the overactive thyroid had abated in eighty percent of the patients, and the drug could be discontinued. Only those who were resistant to the oral treatment were subject to surgery and, if the patients developed a thyro-cardiac condition due to their hyperthyroidism, or in older patients, Radioiodine (I-131) was also used. Today, some forty-five years later, the same type of drug is used for treatment of overactive thyroids.

This initial clinical research taught me how to approach new therapeutic treatments. I learned to be alert to potential side effects, toxic effects, incompatibilities with other drugs, adverse reactions and contraindications. Especially, it taught me the importance of "fine tuned" dosage for individual patients, and never to use drugs indiscriminately!

Hypertension

Anyone whose blood pressure is consistently above 140/90 has high blood pressure (hypertension). This is the leading factor for stroke, and the major contributor to heart attacks and kidney disease. Sixty million Americans have hypertension and only about one-half of them know they have it. Black Americans need to be checked often, as they are thirty-three percent more likely than whites to develop elevated blood pressures.

Ten percent of strokes are preceded by warning events called "transient ischemic attacks" (TIAs), or small strokes. The symptoms are sudden temporary weakness and numbness of the face or limbs, transient dizziness or double vision. It may manifest itself by difficulty in speaking or understanding, or disturbance in mental activity. These symptoms may last minutes to hours and leave no permanent damage. But if not recognized and treated, many develop a major stroke!

It has been recognized for years that increased blood volume due to retention of sodium will produce hypertension. Because of that knowledge, low salt diets were widely propagated, and pharmacologists were busy developing drugs that promote the excretion of sodium by the kidneys. I was involved in the early clinical testing of the diuretics that increase secretion of sodium and chloride (salt) through the kidney. These chemicals were known as chlorthiazides. They reduce the sodium and chloride in the blood, and effectively produce a lowering of blood pressure. It was also learned that in many patients given diuretics, potassium is also excreted, producing the chance of ventricular irritability of the heart — a dangerous complication. Therefore, with diuretics it is necessary to have a high intake of foods containing potassium, such as bananas, tomatoes, and orange juice. If the intake of these foods is insufficient to keep the potassium levels normal, then they must be supplemented by the oral intake of potassium tablets.

It was during the study of the antihypertensive drug, Minoxidel, that the growth of hair, its side effect, was first noted by our group of researchers. Today the drug is used as an ointment to retard baldness.

Beta Blockers

Nitroglycerin under the tongue, and nitrates taken orally do not always abolish the pain and discomfort of angina pectoris. Research was therefore devoted to developing a safe and effective beta blocker drug to abolish the painful anginal effects of catecholamines (Dopamine, Epinephrine and Norepinephrine) on the heart, and also reduce the deleterious, painful effects of sympathetic nerve stimulation. Both chemical catecholamines, and sympathetic nerve stimulation increase heart rate, and increase cardiac contractions and elevate blood pressure. These are the beta effects and affect the heart adversely.

Beta blockers, conversely, lower heart rate, reduce cardiac contractions and arterial blood pressure. Thus, by decreasing the oxygen requirements of the heart, beta blockers would abolish the pain of angina pectoris and would also be helpful in the treatment of arrhythmias.

Fifteen years ago, the Ayerst Pharmaceutical completely satisfied with their preclinical studies of the drug propranolol (Inderal), concluded that this early beta blocker drug was efficacious and safe. A research committee then selected fifteen physicians to do the clinical testing. I was the practicing physician in that elected group; the other researchers were the chiefs of various university cardiovascular sections.

The beta blockers proved to be marvelous additions to the cornucopia of cardiovascular drugs. In addition to propranolol (Inderal), a host of other beta blockers have also been developed.

As our clinical research progressed, we soon learned that beta blockers were also effective in the treatment of hypertension, thyrotoxicosis (overactive thyroids), mitral valve prolapse (a common cardiac disorder), and in some patients relief from migraine headaches. A number of exciting papers have been published recently, proving that beta blockers, given early after heart attacks could reduce mortality!

As in all medications, one must be cautious and watchful when prescribing a new drug. "Do No Harm!", and "Be Alert to Side Effects," are paramount measures in prescribing.

Motrin

This is the era of the nonsteroidal anti-inflammatory drugs. That is, drugs that do not contain cortisone derivatives, but behave as anti-inflammatory medications. I was involved in the clinical research for the drug Motrin (ibuprofen). It is one of the most widely used drugs on the market because of its anti-inflammatory antipyretic (reduces fever) and analgesic (reduces pain) properties. It can be obtained "over the counter" at present and sold as Nupren, Haltran, Medipren, Advil, etc., all are Ibuprofen. Many of their functions are similar to those of aspirin. They work by inhibiting prostaglandin synthesis, which reduces fever, pain, and inflammation. The drugs do not alter the disease, they reduce symptoms. Our original research was confined to rheumatoid arthritis and osteoarthritis. We learned that Ibuprofen does reduce joint swelling, decreases pain, lowers temperature, relieves morning stiffness, and improves functional capacity. Grip strength increased, delay in onset of fatigue, and improved walking occurred in all our arthritic patients studied. Aspirin which is much less expensive, accomplishes some of the same effects. However, its side effects preclude its widespread use in high doses.

Although there are gastrointestinal side effects in three percent of Ibuprofen users, with aspirin there are ten percent who have the problems, such as heartburn, nausea, vomiting, and bleeding, and aspirin may precipitate asthma in the overly sensitive. Although cortisone products have the same clinical applications, their side effects and expense decrease its general use. We learned that it is best to avoid the use of Ibuprofen products in those with peptic ulcer, nasal polyps, and asthma. It is not a safe drug to use in hypertensive and cardiac patients as it causes fluid retention and blocks the effects of antihypertensive drugs. Therefore, caution must be exercised to prevent excessive ingestion of the "over the counter" ibuprofens. They are not innocuous candy mints. The jury is not yet in on the prolonged use of anti-inflammatories!

Cholesterol — Coronary Heart Disease, and Aspirin

My father died of coronary heart disease at the early age of fifty. His brother succumbed to a myocardial infarction at fifty-three. Cousin Eleanor had her coronary at forty-four and her brother developed electrocardiographic evidence of heart disease in his thirties. Naturally, I became interested in research in coronary atherosclerosis in the early days of my practice.

In the middle of the 19th century Karl Rokitansky, a famous pathologist, was one of the first to describe the deposits of cholesterol in the coronary vessels of patients who died of "cardiac seizures" as they were described then. One hundred years later in the middle of the 20th century, Louis Katz and Mildred Pick of Michael Reese Hospital in Chicago "produced" atherosclerosis in the coronaries of chicks by cholesterol diet and then "reversed" the changes by resumption of normal chick diet and the administration of estrogens. The role of cholesterol had been reluctantly and laboriously accepted by physicians and the public. Today, however, the following salient facts are universally believed.

Thousands of people die daily because of ischemic heart disease (atherosclerosis of the coronary vessels). It is well known that over fifty percent of Americans have cholesterol levels that are too high, and by reducing their cholesterol level, it is possible that a quarter million lives could be saved annually.

Those who have cholesterol levels over 265 milligrams percent have an increased risk of heart disease, four times greater than those whose levels are 190 milligrams or less.

Most can substantially reduce their cholesterol levels by diet, decreased tension, reduction in weight, discontinuing smoking, increased physical activity, and control of blood pressure. And for those who are resistant to these measures due to a genetic proclivity, there are many drugs that will help lower cholesterol.

Atherosclerosis is the deposit of plaques of cholesterol and calcium into the lining of blood vessels. This narrows the lumen of the arteries and interferes with circulation. Ultimately, it results in blood vessel occlusions of the coronaries with resultant high morbidity and mortality. And those plaques that obstruct the blood vessels to the brain cause strokes. If the plaques deposit themselves in the arteries of the lower extremities, they produce marked disturbance in leg circulation and, if unalleviated, the obstruction leads to gangrene and loss of limbs.

LIPOPROTEINS — THE GOOD, THE BAD,
THE INFLUENCE OF SEX HORMONES

Cholesterol is an animal product and must be combined with lipoproteins in the bloodstream to become soluble and thus move freely. There are predominantly three types of lipoproteins: the low density lipoproteins (LDLs), the high density lipoproteins (HDLs), and the very low density lipoproteins (VLDLs), known as triglycerides.

The LDLs carry the greatest amounts of cholesterol and are by far the most serious atherogenic type. The HDLs carry lesser amounts of cholesterol and seem also to be beneficial in clearing the cholesterol from the bloodstream, while the VLDLs, the triglycerides, seem to have a controversial mid-position in the atherogenicity. My wife's inelegant, but effective method for identifying the main types of cholesterol carrying lipoproteins is: *H*DL are helpers; *L*DL are losers.

At a recent meeting of the American College of Cardiology, the following conclusion was propagated: "Medical historians will refer to the 1980s as the decade of enlightenment with regard to cholesterol awareness!" One of the more interesting papers reported at that meeting indicated that lowering total cholesterol, and especially, lowering the dangerous LDLs (low density lipoprotein) produced "regression" of coronary atherosclerotic lesions! It appears that we may be able to reverse atherosclerosis!

All of the new research papers were fundamentally correct in their analyses, and their interpretations solid. But for scientific accuracy, it should have been stated that the 1980s was the decade of the "rediscovery" of the effect of cholesterol and low density lipoproteins on atherogenesis.

Aggressive approaches to all of these stated findings had already been researched, proven, described and published initially in the decade of the 1950s. But these findings had, unfortunately, lain dormant for well over thirty years before current generalized acceptance by physicians and the public.

In January of 1958, I published an article in the *Texas State Journal of Medicine* entitled, "Dietary and Pharmaceutical Approaches to Atherosclerosis." In that article, published over thirty years ago, I stated there was a general agreement that atherosclerosis was due to lipid and lipoprotein metabolic defects, and increased serum cholesterol was the culprit.

We discovered in the 1950s the dangers of "beta lipoproteins," which was identified by the use of the "ultra centrifuge." They were the same abnormal group of lipids known today as "low density lipoproteins (LDLs)."

I reported at that time that in the average American home, fat supplied forty percent of the total caloric intake, and in some gluttonous homes, fat consumption reached as high as sixty percent of calories consumed. Minnesotans with a fat intake of forty-one percent of total calories, compared to eight percent in African Bantu tribes, had a fivefold increase in the incidence of coronary heart disease.

Convincing evidence was reported in my article some thirty years ago that cholesterol was reduced by increasing the intake of unsaturated fatty acids, as in vegetable oils (maize, soybean, sunflower seed oils, safflower, cotton seed, and olive oil), and marine animal oil. Conversely, saturated fatty acids found in butter, lard, palm oil, coconut oil, chocolate, cream, beef drippings, beef muscles, bacon, and egg yolks, caused marked rise in cholesterol, and especially increased the beta lipoproteins, the LOLs (the Losers).

The incidence of coronary disease in various geographical areas was compared with relation to diet. Despite the high intake of fat by Eskimos, the incidence of coronary heart disease was low because their diet consisted of seal, fish, and other marine animals which have fat characterized by unsaturated fatty acids, and omega-3s.

Japanese who lived in Japan had very little atherosclerosis because they had a high intake of fish and little beef. This changed when they moved to the U.S. and adapted their diets to local tastes. Latin and Mediterranean people tended to have a comparatively low incidence of heart disease because they use large quantities of olive oil.

Having identified, in the early 1950s, the bad beta lipoproteins, or LDLs of today, the search began for methods favorably changing the atherogenic lipoprotein spectra. The relative differences in susceptibility of the sexes to atherosclerosis was an intriguing area for research.

The following facts became evident: There are fewer atherosclerotic manifestations in premenopausal females than in the postmenopausal. If the ovaries are removed, the woman has an increased tendency to atherosclerosis. Eunuchs have a paucity of atherosclerosis, while the mesomorph, that is, the male with predominant maleness, has a much greater concentration of the bad lipoproteins (LDLs), and therefore, a greater liability for coronary occlusion and strokes and peripheral vascular disease.

I initiated a study in January of 1954 into the effect of hormones upon the lipoprotein patterns. The results of the first thirty-four cases that were published indicated vividly that androgens, the male hormones, aggravated the atherogenic state of the lipoprotein pattern, while estrogen seemed to exert a favorable influence.

The following conclusions were made after two years of study of the effect of hormones on beta lipoproteins, the LDLs:

1) When estrogen was administered to the atherosclerotic male, there was decided "favorable" change in his lipoproteins, changing to the lipoprotein pattern of the healthy young premenopausal female.

2) Castrated males and eunuchs had lipoprotein spectra similar to those of healthy young premenopausal females.

3) A prostatic carcinoma patient who had testicles removed or received estrogen therapy, had a marked improvement in his lipoprotein patterns.

4) Females who had their ovaries removed early in life, developed a profound increase in their beta lipoproteins (LDLs), the bad ones.

5) Finally, when androgens were given to eunuchs, normal males, and normal premenopausal females, there was a marked increase in the bad beta lipoproteins (LDLs).

The experiments suggested early on that hormones are of significant importance in the alteration of lipoproteins. Their exact role in atherosclerosis is yet to be determined!

CORONARY DRUG PROJECT:
ASPIRIN AND HEART ATTACKS

In 1967 the National Heart Lung and Blood Institute funded a nationwide clinical trial known as the Coronary Drug Project. This was designed to assess the long-term efficacy of several lipid lowering drugs in men with ECG-documented myocardial infarctions (heart attacks). I was urged by my colleagues to apply for this grant. As a private practitioner, I questioned how I could possibly compete with the heads of the various university cardiovascular departments in being awarded this nine-year prestigious grant. Hesitantly, I applied and sent all my research studies to the National Heart and Lung Institute.

Shortly thereafter, Sally and I attended an interesting party. For entertainment they had a fortune teller sitting behind a beaded curtain suspended over a bedroom door, inviting those who had the courage to have their fortunes told. I am not a believer in astrology, crystal balls or tarot cards, but felt that at a party the psychic would poke fun at the guests. So I thought I would have a go at it.

Although she wore the usual customary red bandanna and sat behind the table with a glass ball in front of her, I was surprised to find a relatively young, attractive female who looked like a freshman college student. She held her hand forward and I grasped it, thinking she was going to shake hands with me, but instead she turned my hand over and started to "read my palm."

I had never seen her before and yet she looked at my palm and said all in one breath, "You're a physician, and you are going to be surprised on Tuesday morning when you receive a letter indicating that you have been accepted for a very rewarding opportunity. Furthermore, I recommend you accept it as you will have a ten-year involvement in a very exciting and worthwhile project." Then she abruptly said, "Who's next?"

I turned the curtain aside and asked Sally to go in, but she refused. However, I told her what the fortune teller had prophesied, and she said, "I wonder if it had anything to do with the grant?" "Ridiculous," I said, "she was just postulating."

Tuesday morning, after rounds at the hospital, I was told there was an urgent call for me from my home. "You won't believe it," Sally said, "but I want to read you a telegram that was delivered. Congratulations, you have been accepted to be the principal investigator for Clinic 23 for the National Heart and Lung Institute research for the Coronary Drug Project! This will be the clinic for the Southwest region!" I had an eerie feeling when I recalled the prediction of the fortune teller at the party.

In this research project, a total of 8,000 patients were enrolled. Our purpose was to see the effect of various lipid lowering drugs on cholesterol and the incidence of coronary heart disease. The pharmacological preparations that we used in this research were estrogen (the female hormone), nicotinic acid, Atromid S (clofibrate), sodium dextrothyroxine, and a placebo (inert, nonactive preparation) in a double blind study. I enrolled 200 patients in my clinic and studied them for over nine years.

We were unable to continue the complete trial of the estrogen (female hormone) because of the frequent unfavorable side effects. The males who were given this hormone complained of enlarged painful breasts and decrease in sexual potency, and a suspicious increase in phlebitis (vein inflammation).

I recall a young lady who came to my clinic complaining bitterly of the depressed sexual drives in Mr. Abrams, one of our research patients. I surmised he was probably in the estrogen group. When I questioned her, "Wouldn't you rather have your husband live a longer life, even though he had a decreased sexual drive," she answered, "His longevity is not my concern; it's the loss of our pleasures that disturbs me. And besides, Doctor, I am not Mrs. Abrams!"

Perhaps if at that time we had used a smaller acceptable dose of the female hormone, and precluded the undesirable side effects, we might have had some interesting cholesterol lowering effects, and exciting changes in the LDLs, but lipoproteins were not studied then and in retrospect we used too large a dose of estrogen.

Another drug used in the project was Atromid S (clofibrate). The drug lowered the cholesterol slightly, but there were side effects of muscular cramps in many patients and a suggested increase of the incidence of gallstone development. Therefore, this drug was discontinued.

The third drug tested was a nicotinic acid preparation which was quite effective in breaking down cholesterol, but its side effects of flushing of the face, and the associated itching made it very difficult for patients to continue with the treatment, so results were inconclusive.

The final drug that was studied was sodium dextrothyroxine. I had already published earlier in October of 1965, my experience with a four-year study of ninety-one cases with sodium dextrothyroxine. This drug is an analogue of thyroid. It did lower cholesterol, but effected cardiac irritability and was worrisome and therefore discontinued.

Although none of the drugs evaluated in the Coronary Drug Project was shown to significantly prolong life when compared to the placebo, a great many important findings relevant to the management of myocardial infarction patients, and the history of coronary heart disease resulted from this long, large group, nine-year study and all our results were widely published in several medical journals.

In 1975, I concluded and published the results of a two-year clinical study of Upjohn's bile acid sequestrant Colestipol. This drug effectively lowered cholesterol by eighteen to twenty percent. It is an insoluble tasteless powder that binds bile in the intestinal tract and excretes it in the feces. As the bile acids are lost, the liver manufactures new bile utilizing cholesterol. Since the liver and plasma cholesterol are in equilibrium, plasma cholesterol is thus reduced. Conceivably tissue cholesterol may also be reduced and probably atherosclerosis. Gaseous distension and constipation were the minimal side effects encountered in three percent of the patients studied. Many have continued taking this medication with safety to date — more than fourteen years. Both cholesterol and LDLs were lowered. However the medication is a gritty tasteless powder and many patients had to discipline themselves to continue on the program.

Today there are at least three well documented cholesterol lowering drugs that have been well received, Lorelco (probucol), Mevacor (lovostatin), and Lopid (gemfibrizol), but they must be carefully controlled by frequent examinations and lab analysis. They beneficially effect the ratio of the LDL and HDL (the bad guys drop and the good guys increase), but more time has to elapse before the final safety of these drugs can be documented.

Aspirin and Heart Attacks

Early in 1981, the National Heart and Lung Institute completed a four-year study on aspirin and myocardial infarction. As the principal investigator for the Southwest, I had joined with thirty other cardiovascular clinics to complete this double blind study of 5,000 patients.

The research protocol called for the administration of 15 gr. (grains) (3 tablets) of aspirin daily for those patients who had one documented coronary occlusion. It had been already proven that the acetyl radical of the aspirin formula (acetyl-salicylic acid) inhibits platelets from aggregating. This would impair the clotting process. Thus, it was anticipated, it would keep the atherosclerotic vessels from clotting (thrombosing). The theory was ideal. The results proved unquestionably that the incidence of a second coronary occlusion would be decreased by the aspirin.

However, the results would have been much more impressive had we known earlier that the 15 gr. (3 tablets) dose was too large! One tablet daily (5 gr.) would have sufficed. The excessive amount of aspirin handicapped the research by inadvertently blocking the production of an enzyme known as prostacyclin, a normal enzyme that blood vessels produce to keep blood from clotting. Thus, while aspirin kept the platelets from aggregating, which is necessary for coagulation; by virtue of the large dosage (15 gr.), the aspirin inhibited the patients' production of their own anti-clotting mechanism, the prostacyclin. The ultimate result, however, was still efficacious.

In the interim years, other clinical research areas in the United States and abroad published research statistics that proved undeniably that the "one aspirin daily" dose was sufficient to reduce coagulation. This once again proved that, "fine tuning" in dosage is important for best therapeutic results. As my old professor, A. J. Carlson, would have said, "Check and re-check and re-check your protocol, and study all the evidence you can before you initiate a clinical research program!"

Drugs, Side Effects — Anaphylaxis

When Harry Fulton, an asthmatic patient, was prescribed the popular diuretic, Hydrodiuril, for his mild hypertension, he was totally unaware of the unfortunate chain of events that lay in store for him. Hydrodiuril is a Chlorthiazide drug with many associated alterations in the body's chemical and electrolyte normals, some of which are quite significant. In many patients, the uric acid level will rise slightly. Harry's physician detected this elevation on a routine blood profile and told the patient, "I believe you have gout, as gouty patients have elevated uric acids." Harry denied any joint symptoms, but the young, unseasoned doctor said, "You are in the early stages of developing gout and we should prevent acute attacks." So he prescribed the uricosuric drug, Zyloprim, to reduce Harry's uric acid, which it did. One of the side effects that may occur with the drug Zyloprim is a widespread itchy maculopapular (elevated lesions) skin rash, extremely irritating to the patient. Dr. Jones was alerted about the rash, and without consulting the literature about Zyloprim's side effects, referred Harry to a good dermatologist. When Mr. Fulton arrived at the dermatologist's office, nervous, sweating and irritable, the doctor diagnosed his dermatological problem as "neurodermatosis" (a nervous skin disorder) and added hydrocortone for skin and Benadryl to control the itching and his nervousness. The patient continued with his Zyloprim and Hydrodiuril. However, the dermatologist forgot to caution Harry not to use any machinery requiring extreme alertness, as Benadryl makes one drowsy and decreases acuity in the performance of fine tasks. While working in his machine shop, he fumbled with his electric saw, cut a wide deep gash in his right forearm and ended up in the E.R. with twelve stitches and a prescription for Ecotrin to be taken four times daily for his discomfort. The emergency room doctor elicited no information about Harry's clinical history or medications. So

Harry went home, taking his Hydrodiuril for his hypertension, the Zyloprim for his Hydrodiuril-induced elevated uric acid, Benadryl for the itching induced by the Zyloprim, and Ecotrin for the discomfort of the sutured arm due to the accident brought on by his Benadryl depressed reflexes. As the E.R. doctor failed to tell Harry that Ecotrin contains aspirin, Harry's asthma was aggravated and he wheezed all night. It was necessary for him to use his Isuprel Mistometer for relief and had the usual tachycardia and palpitations (rapid forceful heartbeat) from the inhalation of his Isuprel, a frequent side effect of the medication. Fortunately, he did not call a cardiologist during the night as he in turn would have been prescribed Inderal, a beta blocker, to slow the heart, but many beta blockers would aggravate or induce asthma!

Thus it seems that if Harry had lost weight, went on a low salt diet, changed from a "Type A" to "Type B" person, he would not have taken Hydrodiuril, Zyloprim, Benadryl, Ecotrin, Isuprel, or possibly beta blockers. If his various physicians had asked what medications he was taking and if they had familiarized themselves with the drugs and their side effects, Harry would have avoided considerable discomfort and saved $800.

*　　*　　*　　*　　*

I was asked to check the cardiac status of Judge Bogan prior to his exploratory surgery for intestinal obstruction. At age seventy-eight he was a handsome gentleman who bore a striking resemblance to George Bernard Shaw — the thick bushy eyebrows, the well-trimmed goatee and the waxed mustache all fit this proud barrister. Bogan was a chronic alcoholic with early cirrhosis of the liver and coronary heart disease. His intestinal obstruction had lasted for four days. There was no bowel movement and no passage of gas. For the past twenty-four hours he had suffered nausea and fecal vomiting. There was no questions about his diagnosis. He had a distended abdomen and the characteristic borborygmi of obstruction (high pitched air sounds). X-rays showed the classical fluid and gas filled loops. But what was the etiology of his obstruction? There had been no previous surgery to produce adhesions, which often obstruct, nor was there evidence for volvulus (twist of the bowel). Was there an obstructing mass (tumor or cancer) not identified? Was the obstruction secondary to inflammation of the bowel, i.e., Crohn's disease (inflammatory bowel disease)? Again no evidence! Was it due to an atherosclerotic lesion in the mesenteric blood vessel with thrombosis that blocked the artery to a section of the bowel, producing necrosis and paralyzing the bowel? No positive finding for that diagnosis was forthcoming. But it was apparent if the block were not alleviated soon, his condition could very well prove fatal.

Before my examination, I re-questioned the judge, who was in intense pain and discomfort, but sober that morning. I learned that two weeks prior to his illness his only son had been found DOA from an overdose of cocaine! The judge, who apparently was a manic depressive, became understandably psychologically low after his son's demise. His local doctor prescribed Elavil, an antidepressant. Forgetting the age of the patient (older people cannot tolerate large doses of medicine), the doctor continued to increase the dosage of the antidepressant to overcome the judge's extreme dejection. But Elavil is an anticholinergic drug. This is, it depresses and blocks cholinergic nerves, which are the nerves of the parasympathetic nervous system. The normal function of the bowel requires parasympathetic stimulation. With the large doses of the anticholinergic Elavil, a paralytic state of the bowel was produced, and the intestinal obstruction ensued.

"Cancel the surgery," I told the surgeon. "The bowel can be unclocked in forty-eight hours." I then proceeded with measures to discontinue and wash out his accumulated drug, corrected his electrolyte imbalance and prescribed cholinergic drugs to activate the static bowel. The next morning, when I entered the judge's room to check on his progress, I realized that all was well. My unannounced arrival startled him and he barely had time to try to hide his bottle of Scotch under his pillow. But his breath gave away his indiscretion. "Better than those damn IVs," he asserted defensively, realizing that I had caught him — and I agreed!

*   *   *   *   *

In the practice of medicine it is necessary to use drugs for diagnosis, for prophylaxis of disease, and for therapy. There are many noxious and unintended responses which might be termed "adverse drug reactions." There are also the problems of drug interactions. That is, one drug may affect the absorption or the excretion or the biotransformation and distribution of a second drug. A drug may be inactivated by virtue of a physical or chemical change. For example, Amphotericin-B, the drug used for fungus infections and administered intravenously, is extremely sensitive to light, and unless the bottle with the medication is rendered totally protected from light, the drug will be completely neutralized. Also, if one places two antibiotics, such as Kanamycin and Methicillin into the same intravenous bottle, each counteracts the other and eliminates the desired antibiotic effect. Some drugs may precipitate others in a solution, and there are many medicinals whose absorption is inhibited by the concomitant administration of antacids. They also reduce the absorption of iron and the commonly prescribed antibiotics, the tetracyclines.

The frequently used bile-acid sequestering agents, such as Colestipol and Cholestyramine for lowering cholesterol can, if given simultaneously with digitalis, thyroid hormone, anticoagulants, or vitamins A and K, reduce the absorption of these important medications. Therefore, a time interval of two to three hours must elapse between the taking of bile acid sequestrants and other medicines.

Many anticoagulants have their effects markedly potentiated, that is, the bleeding time will be dangerously prolonged, by numerous drugs given at the same time. Thus, aspirin, sulfonamides, thyroid, anabolic steroids, and the antibacterial drug, chloromycetin, and many others can cause serious bleeding when given concomitantly with anticoagulants.

Alcohol has an additive effect on sedatives, producing marked central nervous system depression, and as is well known, will effect the person driving or operating machinery. Alcohol will potentiate the hypoglycemic (lower blood sugar) effects of the oral drugs used for diabetes and can throw the patient into low blood sugar shock.

Of course, there are a host of drugs which must not be used during pregnancy, and most obstetricians are alert to these, especially after the terrible incident with Thalidomide. Today the widely prescribed dermatological preparation, Retin-A, must not be used if there is contemplation of pregnancy.

There are many pharmaceuticals that are proclaimed as being aphrodisiacs. Notably the amphetamines, cocaine, mescaline, LSD, powdered rhinoceros horn, strychnine, Spanish fly (crushed beetle extract), Wellbutin and others. None really work and all are associated with serious side effects. Desyrel and Yocon are presently being studied by urologists as possible sexual stimulants. Use of these drugs must be under close observations by the attendant physician, as there may be a host of undesired side effects.

There are numerous medications, however, that interfere with potency. The antihypertensives, antidepressants and tranquilizers are reputed to lower sexual drives, and the extensively used ulcer drug, Tagamet, has also been implicated.

Recently we have learned that nonsteroidal anti-inflammatory drugs (NSADs); i.e., Indocin, Motrin (Advil and Nuprin) and the popular Naprosyn, can frequently block the effect of the antihypertensives. This could be a setup for a potential cerebrovascular catastrophe (stroke), and is especially risky, because several physicians may participate in the care of the hypertensive patient with arthritis. One treats the hypertension and the other prescribes NSADs for the joint problems. Also, the potential risk is extensive because all of the NSADs are available "over the counter" and hypertensive patients purchase them for pain and headaches, as well as for arthritic problems.

Also, recent disturbing publications in Belgium and West Germany have indicated a suspicious long-term effect by the use of *combinations* of nonsteroidal anti-inflammatories. It seems the researchers have evidence that their concomitant use may produce kidney problems. These findings should be considered tentative until confirmed by other studies and the analysis of the F.D.A., especially because of the widespread media advertisements and their extensive usage. Incidentally, in the study, the long-term use of aspirin produced no adverse effect to the kidneys.

The patient must be a partner in the treatment! One should not depend entirely and completely on the often harassed doctor. It would be wise for the patient to become familiar with all prescribed medications; to read about the drugs and to question physicians and pharmacists about possible side effects and contraindications.

*   *   *   *   *

When Jacob Goldman was released from the Dachau concentration camp in Germany by the Americans in 1945, his chances of survival seemed quite hopeless. Although he escaped the crematorium, he was assigned to a labor brigade, worked eighteen hours daily, was fed starvation rations, developed low grade chronic tuberculosis, lost twenty-five pounds, and suffered serious manifestations of protein and vitamin deficiencies. Ten years later, his health improved, he settled in San Antonio. His tuberculosis was inactivated by the new drugs. He had regained some of his lost weight and had overcome most of the tremendous psychological depressive insults that occurred during his internment. He developed and operated a small leather factory employing thirty hard-working Hispanic workers who were proud of their fair and congenial employer.

He married Maria Isabella Hernandez, a member of a large San Antonio family, and they had two healthy sons. She loved Jacob passionately and devoted her considerable maternal instincts towards his well-being and that of their boys.

She never allowed him to over-work, made certain that he had a nourishing diet, exercise, and vitamins. Early each morning they jogged together before opening the factory. She tended to all the office work and bookkeeping of the business, conducted a very fine home, and raised their two sons in the Jewish tradition. Early in their marriage, Maria Isabella converted to Judaism, and took her vows quite seriously out of deep respect for her beloved Jacob. Both boys were Bar Mitzvah and had read thoroughly about the horrors of the Holocaust.

In the late 1960s, Maria, who hovered over her darling Jacob and was overjoyed at his complete recovery from the traumas of his internment, began to develop a feeling of uneasiness and anxiety as she observed Jacob pursuing his daily activity at the factory. She called my office, described Jacob's symptoms, and was told to bring him in that afternoon. Initially, she was aware of the fact that he showed a generalized slowness in all of his activities and had developed a shuffling slow gait in walking. In the past month, he had also begun to stutter and drool when he spoke.

Previously, his facial expressions were lively and friendly, with broad smiles and frequent whistling. But those motions were replaced by an immobile, mask-like look. He had become quite stiff and rigid in his movements, and had some problem with locomotion. He developed an intractable tremor of the right hand, so pronounced that he was unable to sign his name legibly.

Jacob himself was aware that he was not well, complained that he felt extremely restless, had anxieties, seemed unable to sit quietly, had been having insomnia and was becoming depressed. The rigidity and stiffness increased rapidly and the tremors of the right hand at rest became quite an embarrassment.

After examination, I diagnosed Parkinson's disease and had Jacob hospitalized in the new wing at the Santa Rosa Medical Center on the eleventh floor, which was reserved for neurological and psychiatric patients. I told the family that this was a fortuitous time, bad as the diagnosis might seem, for a new drug, Levodopamine or L. Dopa, had just been developed. The drug was reputed to alleviate many of the symptoms of Parkinson's disease.

I explained to them that the condition is due to a disturbance in the part of the brain known as the substantia nigra, where there is a loss of the production of the chemical dopamine, which is necessary to control locomotive functions. The new drug, Levodopamine, produced dopamine to replace the deficiency. Thus, it counteracts many of the serious symptoms of Parkinson's disease. Maria Isabella was reassured that the disease that her husband had developed was not a result of his internment in the concentration camps, but often occurred as a consequence of aging. One other popular theory attributes the onset of the disease to complications from a slow growing virus, a residual from the worldwide 1918 influenza epidemic.

"How unfair," Maria Isabella wept to me, "how unfair. After enduring and surviving the atrocities of Nazi Germany, my Jacob was finally enjoying a normal life. Now he is to be cut down in his early sixties by this disabling disease." Nevertheless, in her usual optimistic approach to life, she reassured Jacob, "This new drug is going to cure you, and all is going to be well again." A competent neurologist who had extensive experience with L. Dopa was consulted. Jacob occupied a semi-private room with Hans Schmidt, who also had Parkinson's disease and was also a patient of the same neurologist.

On a regime of Levodopamine along with anti-cholinergic drugs and the use of Symmetrel, a good deal of Jacob's rigidity and tremor decreased. The shuffling gait improved, there was less salivation when he talked, and he began to develop some facial expressions, and began to smile again. Maria Isabella was overjoyed.

One day during the third week of therapy, when Maria entered the room, Jacob motioned to her to be silent. He signaled her to meet him in the bathroom, and closed the door so that Hans Schmidt, who shared his semi-private room, was out of earshot.

"I think," he stuttered quietly to Maria, "my neighbor, Hans Schmidt, is an ex-Nazi, and I am afraid that he is going to try to kill me during the night." "Also," Jacob reported, "on several occasions I saw him pour something into my food tray and I believe it is poison."

"Jacob," Maria said, "you are being absolutely foolish and unreasonable. Hans comes from New Braunfels, Texas, was born and raised in America, is an excellent American, fought during World War II, and actually was with one of the groups that liberated the inmates from concentration camps during the war."

"You don't understand," Jacob said, "I saw him talking last night to the nurses on the floor when they were mixing their medications, and I know they are on his side too." For the next two days Jacob refused to eat his meals. He insisted to Maria that he was convinced the staff was working with Hans Schmidt, determined to poison him!

When the neurologist and I were apprised of the problems Jacob was experiencing, we called Maria into a side room to explain that unfortunately, an occasional side effect of this wonderful new drug, Levodopa, is the development of "paranoid schizophrenia." The incidence of this complication is very small and more likely to occur in those who have had psychological problems. We felt that by juggling his medication, we could pull Jacob out of the paranoid schizophrenia and still help him with the disabling effects of his Parkinson's disease.

"How ironic," thought Maria, "to replace the signs and symptoms of such a serious disease as Parkinson's with the equally serious condition of a paranoid schizophrenia." Jacob was moved into a private room and Maria stayed with him day and night to assure him that there was no reason for his paranoia. He was assigned several meetings with a psychiatrist for the schizophrenic changes. We meticulously reduced the dosage of the new medication, and increased the anti-cholinergic drug, and soon a better balance was reached.

Although he still walked with considerable stiffness and rigidity, his tremor had lessened considerably, his psychological outlook had improved tremendously, and it was felt that he was sufficiently rehabilitated to return to work. However, it was necessary that he take an additional drug, Thorazine, a phenothiazine, that acts as an antagonist for the psychotic symptoms brought on by the Levodopa prescribed for his Parkinson's disease. We had no panacea. But with his medications properly monitored, Jacob was able to get on with his life.

During the 1960s, although most of the research in nervous system studies concentrated on Levodopa for Parkinson's disease, this was also the era of the awakening of the "antipsychotic drug" regime! Psychiatrists recognized at that time that although these newly developed antipsychotic drugs were not curative, they were extremely useful in the treatment of acute and chronic schizophrenias and the so-called "schizo-affective disorders" as well as "acute psychotic disorders." They were occasionally extended for use in organic brain syndrome, in certain cases of autism, and for patients with illogical emotional responses to environmental stimuli.

The drugs improved the patient's capacity for his adjustment to society and accelerated remission of the psychotic symptoms. They helped the patient return to normal duties and behaviors, and decreased time spent in hospitals. As doctors, we were continuously faced by problems of maintenance dosage versus therapeutic doses, versus doses that produced side effects.

There were many troublesome side effects that occurred during the early use of these antipsychotic drugs. When given in excessive dosage, or to hypersensitive people, the phenothiazine drugs produced "extrapyramidal symptoms," which are the identical symptoms of Parkinson's disease. The same rigidity, tremors, immobile facies, slowness of gait, stuttering, and salivation, etc., would occur in various degrees. Thus, successful treatment revolves around the art of effectively adjusting doses of medication.

Ultimately, with all prescribed drugs we must be ever cognizant that patient and physician are at the mercy of the pharmacists' knowledge and diligence in dispensing prescriptions, and, in hospitals, with nurses' accuracy in dispensing the medications.

*   *   *   *   *

Many of the most promising, innovative advances in medicine were accompanied in the initial stages of their developments by dangerous, unanticipated complications. In 1955, to aggressively attack the devastating epidemic of poliomyelitis, two vaccines were licensed for immunization. The Salk vaccine, which consisted of the formalin inactivated virus and the Sabin live, but attenuated, virus. Within one month after the initial inoculation of the first 400,000 persons with the inactivated virus, sixty-five cases of paralytic polio occurred. After months of painstaking, heart breaking, guilt ridden research to determine the possible etiology of the production of these precipitated cases, it was discovered that a single source of the virus had been inadequately inactivated and still contained a residual amount of the infectious virus.

Many of our dramatic, lifesaving therapeutic drugs, such as the cortisone steroids, when used in high doses over long terms, as part of immunosuppressant therapy, produce problems of "chronic steroid therapy." Patients frequently develop the round moon faces and upper back "buffalo humps," diabetes, osteoporosis and obesity of Cushingoid's disease. Even more serious are the losses, by prolonged cortisone administration, of the body's defenses against various bacteria and fungi, and occasionally the resultant change in immunity may precipitate tumor growths.

I always asked patients about any OTC (over the counter drugs) they might be taking, because of the possible undesirable effects of their combination with other prescribed medications, and I always reminded students that pregnant women must be alerted to the fact that after the fifth week of embryonic life, the fetus becomes a recipient of most medications taken by the mother.

Occasionally, innovative medical therapies have evolved from unintended uses. Lidocaine, used by doctors and dentists as a local anesthetic, was found to be extremely effective in controlling cardiac arrhythmias, and thus became a routine lifesaving drug. Minoxidil, a treatment for hypertension, was discovered to help prevent baldness and promote hair growth.

There are also racial differences in drug responses. For example, beta blockers have a twofold greater effect on heart rate and blood pressure in Chinese men than in Caucasians.

It is very disturbing to note that many successfully proven therapies have been abused by extension of their use for unwise experimental approaches. For example, chelation has been well documented as a means of chemically removing toxic metals, i.e., lead, arsenic, etc., from the body. Recently, some physicians have attempted empirically to use chelation in the treatment of atherosclerosis. This is a totally illogical approach and may even prove harmful. Experimental research must be logical, not wishful!

*   *   *   *   *

Anne Gaines was my patient for many years. She was extremely allergic and sensitive to almost every pollen produced in the San Antonio area, especially the markedly irritant cedar, a member of the juniper allergens. She would react to these various pollen antigens with severe allergic rhinitis (hay fever) and on occasion, asthma. She was also sensitive to many foods and medications. Shellfish often gave her giant hives; aspirin had been known to precipitate an acute case of asthma. She was constantly under treatment by allergists with desensitization programs that gave only fair results. It was always necessary to treat her with antihistamines, Benadryl, aerosol bronchodilators; and on many occasions, courses of corticosteroid hormones. She was a large handsome woman, with intriguing green eyes, but her nasal orifices were always swollen, and she was constantly contending with nasal drippage and sneezing. She was habitually clearing her throat of phlegm that would accumulate at the slightest provocation. Her house was dust free, as ordered by her allergist, and she could never tolerate cigarette smoking around her.

Her daughter, Barbara, was also extremely allergic, having some of the same allergic reactions as mother, and required the same precautionary measures. Barbara had an uneventful pregnancy and when her child was sixteen-months old, noted that the child also showed marked evidence of allergy. The little girl developed a rash from milk products and always had a runny nose and frequent episodes of bronchial cough and asthma.

On the advice of her pediatrician, she sought the help of an allergist who neglected to obtain a complete history of the family's severe allergic background. He was told, "I think my child is developing allergies, and I would like to prevent her from having serious problems later in life." The doctor arranged for the usual skin scratches in order to determine to which allergens little Jeannie was sensitive, and then a preparation for injectable immunizations would be made. The doctor left the room to examine a patient in the next examining room, while the nurse continued to administered the tiny dilute allergenic extracts by scratch tests. Suddenly, little Jeannie began to gasp for air, started audible wheezing, tried to cough several times, became extremely pale, and cyanotic as her breathing became more and more labored. She threw her tiny head upward, and her eyes rolled back. She had a convulsive seizure and died, all within three minutes of the inception of the skin tests!

This is an extreme example of anaphylaxis, but unfortunately these devastating situations can and do appear. The mother, the nurse, and the physician were devastated. He attempted every resuscitative and anti-allergic measure feasible, but to no avail. Had a proper family history been obtained, this tragedy might have been averted, as the physician would have used other methods of testing.

*   *   *   *   *

Gloria Sheldon was a happy, smiling, redheaded, plump, friendly woman in her early fifties, who had two grown children and an adoring husband. For the past three years, she had had severe allergic problems which were becoming progressively worse. Initially, she simply had allergic rhinitis with runny nose, sneezing and some postnasal drippage, and then began to develop asthma. The attacks of asthma responded to bronchodilators in the form of aerosols. She would take aminophylline preparations called Theo-Dur by mouth and short courses of cortico-steroids. With her various medications she became quite comfortable and found life tolerable.

A friend in St. Louis who was celebrating her thirtieth wedding anniversary invited Gloria to come to the party. Feeling much better, she was happy to attend, and accompanied by her husband, flew to St. Louis, checking into one of the large hotels. While dressing for dinner, she noticed a sudden weakness of her left arm, left leg, and an inability to speak. This lasted about five minutes and then she was normal again. She became frightened for a minute or so, but as it subsided she decided not to pay too much attention to it, thinking perhaps it was an indication of fatigue, and continued with her dressing. That evening, before retiring, she had a recurrence of the same symptoms, lasting this time about ten minutes, again with complete recovery. Her husband became alarmed and called the hotel doctor who responded immediately and told her that she had a "transient ischemic attack." This is a transient neurological defect due to a disturbance in the blood supply to one of the blood vessels of the brain. Most often, it occurs as a result of a small atherosclerotic plaque breaking off the carotid blood vessels in the neck and migrating upward to temporarily block one of the arteries in the brain. As the symptomatology did not persist, but was transient, apparently the blood clot broke up and the blood supply continued normally. But the disturbing question was the location and size of the residual plaque. Would a large one break off and cause permanent stroke?

The patient was hospitalized and a neurosurgeon was consulted who confirmed the diagnosis of "transient ischemic attack," and suggested that this patient should have diagnostic studies of the vascular tree from the neck into the brain to determine the location of the blockage and its extension. The attending physician took a "cursory history" and did a quick physical examination. She was not having any asthma at that time and in her fear and confusion, neglected to tell the staff how totally allergic she was. Unfortunately, in obtaining the history, the junior staff members did not determine the severity of her allergy and no one inquired if she was taking allergy medication.

She was taken to the x-ray department and prepared for studies for visualization of the blood supply from the neck into the brain. An injection of radioactive iodine material was introduced after the patient was positioned under the x-ray machine. Within minutes, the patient was having markedly labored breathing, with severe wheezing which became progressively worse. Soon she had total tracheal and bronchial obstruction. She went into severe shock. Her blood pressure dropped precipitously, she became cyanotic, had total respiratory obstruction, cardiac arrhythmia and expired on the x-ray table!

This again is an extreme, tragic example of severe anaphylactic reaction to a chemical. In this instance it was the iodine in the radioactive diagnostic drug injected intravenously to visualize the blood supply to the brain. Perhaps if the staff had been alerted, both by the patient and by taking a thorough complete history, to the patient's extreme sensitivities, and if skin test and conjunctival test of the iodine preparation were performed, the potential danger would have been recognized. Proper steps would then have been taken to avoid the use of this diagnostic measure and other means could have been used to visualize the circulatory system. Complete detailed histories are absolutely essential and could avoid these tragic occurrences!

$$* \quad * \quad * \quad * \quad *$$

There are many materials capable of eliciting a systemic anaphylactic reaction in the human being. They are called "heterologous proteins." They may be in the form of antiserums, such as tetanus antitoxin (horse serum produced), hormones, enzymes or the venom of the wasp or the bee. The allergic reaction may be precipitated by pollen extracts, rarely by foods, and often by diagnostic agents, which contain iodine in their formula, rendering them radio-opaque. Many antibiotics, especially penicillin, fall into this category. This life threatening anaphylactic response of a sensitized human being may appear within minutes after the administration of the antigen (the specific material to which the patient is allergic), especially if given by injection, and most especially if prescribed intravenously. Although these same symptoms may occur as a result of reaction to oral ingestion of allergens, it generally takes longer for a response. The symptoms are immediate respiratory distress with inability to breathe and spasm of the tracheobronchial tree, followed by a drop in blood pressure, and cardiac failure.

All of these manifestations of the anaphylactic syndrome are due to sudden releases of massive amounts of histamine produced by the body in reaction to the antigen. Many drugs may be offenders. Even the nonsteroidal anti-inflammatory agents, such as Indocin, Aminopyrine, and aspirin, may precipitate a life threatening episode, especially in asthmatic subjects.

If the initial symptoms are simply itching and hives, sometimes they may be controlled by small doses of adrenalin given subcutaneously and repeated in three minute intervals until the reaction subsides. If the symptoms are more severe and are not responding, then diluted adrenalin must be given intravenously. Oxygen may be necessary through a nasal catheter or through the intermittent positive pressure breathing apparatus. Aerosol dilators (solutions of various drugs which dilate bronchial tubes) and intravenous cortisone derivatives may be necessary for the acute events.

Therefore, in an allergic individual, a detailed history of various sensitivities should be taken; or when contemplating the use of a new drug with a chemical make-up of possibly being antigenic (potentially capable of eliciting allergic responses), a dilute skin test should be made before administration. Certainly this should be done before administering any serum, allergenic extracts, or penicillin. Of course, if there is already a substantiated history of sensitivity to any antigens, then the substance should be avoided. In any event, Hippocrates' ancient admonition to physicians should be heeded: "DO NO WRONG!"

All the World's A Stage

Reception Room as Theater

The Brothers

I always thought of my reception room as the proverbial melting pot, the equalizer, the common denominator for all those who entered. Whether it be the oil multimillionaire, or the McDonald's waitress, whether it be the elegant lady from Boerne or the smelly fisherman from Port Aransas, the history professor at Trinity University or the illiterate farmer from Lytle — they all have gathered there because they had medical problems and all have sought me out as their physician.

When Paul Polansky from Alice, Texas, 150 miles south of San Antonio, made his appointment to consult me about his extremely painful left arm, he didn't know what a surprise lay in store for him in my reception room. Paul, age fifty-two, was a hard-working Polish farmer who had emigrated to the United States some thirty years previously. As I learned later, Paul and his brother Joseph inherited a small farm of about 160 acres in the town of Gdansk, Poland, after the death of their father. It seems there were problems in the division of this acreage between the state and the two brothers. The wives entered the foray and soon the brothers became extremely hostile and stopped talking to one another. And so it stood for the past thirty years.

When the two brothers emigrated to the United States, they

went their separate ways. Since they had relatives in Texas, that state became their destination. Paul settled in Alice as a farmer. Joseph settled in Rosenberg about 190 miles north of San Antonio, and eventually became a very successful real estate developer and oil operator. With his success came a legal change of name from Joseph Polansky to Jack Poland. Thus, the two brothers were separated by only 340 miles, and each was totally unaware of the other's existence.

Jack Poland had developed a very severe post-herpetic neuralgia. It is not infrequent that those who develop Herpes Zoster (shingles) also develop an extremely painful neuritis as a residual complication from the previous inflammation brought on by the virus. This virus is notorious for settling in the dorsal ganglia of the spinal cord, causing inflammation along the nerve root and resulting in an eruption of blisters in the area innervated by that particular nerve. Unfortunately, when the rash subsides and the skin heals, there is often residual painful neuritis in the area of the nerve involvement.

Paul Polansky was scheduled to see me on October 14th at 11:00 A.M. for his probable cervical disk syndrome. Independently, Jack Poland was scheduled for October 14th at 11:30. Jack, a typical Type A personality, arrived at the office twenty-five minutes early. And Paul, the laid back Type B personality, arrived fifteen minutes late for his appointment. How shocked Paul was to see his brother Joseph whom he had not seen or spoken to in thirty years sitting in the reception room. They rushed to one another, embraced, hugged, laughed and cried simultaneously. And the Polish "Yak-sheh mak-sheh" (how are you) and "dobera" (I'm fine) kept floating back and forth between the two excited brothers. Then the catching up on the family, the wives, the children, etc., half in Polish and half in English went on for twenty happy minutes. It was a thrilling exhibition in the reception room and all those present were smiling and seemed to be equally gratified and almost prone to applaud this highly emotional reunion. If their appointments had been scheduled twenty-four hours apart, it might have been another thirty years before their happy reunion.

The Wives

Clayton Samuel was a bookkeeper for a large Dallas oil company who looked the stereotype. He was short and thin with balding head bent forward. He wore thick glasses for his severe myopia, and constantly had a quizzical look about him. His desk was placed adjacent to the glass wall that separated him from the boss' competent secretary. Clara was tall, with rigid posture, friendly, and rather good-looking.

Innocent flirtation through the glass partition soon developed into a romance. They were indeed an odd-looking couple, but the romance flourished. She praised his perfectionistic detailed accounting and he was fascinated with the stories she told him about the big boss and the oil development. Inasmuch as she was alert to important oil information, this was quickly imparted to Clayton who, being astute, bought up royalty all around areas to be drilled.

Within five years they were married. He became an extremely wealthy independent oil operator with his own oil company in a suite of plush glamorous offices. Clara no longer needed to work, so he hired his own secretary. Arlene was a petite, young, good-looking, somewhat sensuous female from San Marcos, Texas. Soon a romance developed between Clayton and the new secretary, who coerced Clayton into divorcing Clara, and Arlene became the instant millionairess.

The divorce was relatively friendly and Clara took her twenty-five million dollars and settled in a lush estate in an exclusive area in San Antonio. However, she did not fare too well. She came to my office one morning complaining of a peculiar rash on her face in butterfly distribution and on other parts of her skin that were photosensitive to sun exposed areas. She also complained of severe joint pains, especially in the hands and knees, headache, malaise and low grade temperature. Although her sedimentation rate was elevated, her total white blood count was considerably below normal, and she exhibited bleeding tendencies. There was albumen in her urine. The suspicion of the immune disease "lupus erythematosus" was confirmed by the positive LL cell test and the finding of a high abnormal antinuclear antibody titer.

Lupus erythematosus is a chronic collagen disorder which falls in the category of auto-immune disorders. This disease is thought to be due to a virus which develops a symbiotic relationship with the host, but the immune and hyperimmune body defenses continue unabated and produce so-called immune complexes which are floating proteins that produce all of the tissue injuries that are characteristic of this disease. Through the years, Clara developed the full-blown symptomatology of this disorder. She developed kidney complications and later cardiac disorders due to involvement of this inflammatory process in the coronary blood vessels. She also had the lung changes and pulmonary disorders characteristic of advanced stages of this disease. Ultimately she showed signs of neurological involvement of the brain. She was placed on high doses of corticosteroids and came to the office every two or three weeks to have her blood studies done. Despite her illness,

Clara maintained a friendly, cheerful, cooperative attitude. She was a courageous and delightful patient to attend.

When Clara called for an appointment one day, the receptionist put her down for Tuesday at 10:00 A.M. By sheer coincidence, the new Mrs. Samuel, Arlene, called the following week for an appointment and spoke to the nurse as the receptionist was out to lunch. The nurse looked at the appointment book, saw the name Samuel, and thought Clara was calling to confirm her previously scheduled appointment. "Yes, of course, we have you down for Tuesday at 10:00 A.M."

The new Mrs. Samuel was always disturbed when she came to my office inasmuch as she was a heavy smoker and my office and reception room were plastered with "NO SMOKING" signs. But nicotine was her problem. She had chronic sinusitis, low grade chronic bronchitis and early emphysema. And it was difficult to impress upon her the dangers of her continued smoking.

On Tuesday at 10:00 A.M., the two unanticipating Mrs. Samuels entered the reception room almost simultaneously. Each sat down at opposite ends of the thirty-foot reception room and wordlessly began throwing psychological darts at one another. The hostile barbs of eye contact were almost palpable in the room. The hostility exuded between these two women seemed to permeate the entire reception room until everyone became uncomfortable. I remembered Mr. Samuel previously asking me never to schedule the two women on the same day, but this was an inadvertent error. Although I promised him that it would never happen again, the new Mrs. Samuel was so upset that she asked to be referred to another internist. Since she was a somewhat difficult patient, did not follow doctor's orders, and refused to quit her nicotine habit, I was happy to refer her to one of my friends who had particular interest in pulmonary diseases. I thought perhaps he might frighten her and coerce her to discontinue her nicotine addiction. Two months later, however, she called my office and sheepishly asked for an appointment with the specific request that she be the only Samuel scheduled on that day.

Unfortunately, the likeable Clara Samuel's history was a continued downhill course, with increasing disability until finally, totally bedridden, she succumbed to a fatal coronary occlusion. The entire office grieved at her demise. While Arlene Samuel is still puffing away, coughing and wheezing and difficult to treat.

The Loquacious One

Loquacious Abe Greenberg was in his early sixties when he first became my patient and continued as such until I retired when he was ninety years of age. Abe was a ruddy-complexioned redhead who never really developed gray hair, but instead his red hair became brown with age. He was extremely inquisitive, friendly and a great story and joke teller. He had an exceptionally keen mind and maintained all of his faculties in an alert state even into his nineties. He survived an acute coronary occlusion in his early sixties with complete recovery and no evidence of cardiac decompensation. After a year, his ECG returned almost to normal, with only minor residual indications of damage to the left posterior coronary vessel.

Abe developed some hypertension in his later years and came to the office frequently to have his blood pressure checked and the status of his heart evaluated. I am most certain that he often came to the office because he had no obligations and loved to sit around in the reception room and enjoy warm and friendly conversations with all the assembled patients. Abe was our regular office George Burns, congenial, full of jokes and stories, and always chomping on an unlit cigar. (He had given up lighting it years before.) He was a particular favorite with my office staff who enjoyed his congeniality as well as his generous nature. He brought them boxes of candy and cookies with each visit. After entering the reception room, he would start intimate conversations with the patients. In short order, he knew their entire social and medical histories, and they in turn became privy to his life story. When patients returned for repeat visits, they would often ask, "How is Abe doing?"

When Abe met Mr. Ganz, another elderly hypertensive patient, they soon became friendly, sat next to one another and enjoyed comparing symptoms and medicines. When beckoned by the nurse to come into the examining room to have his blood pressure taken, Abe carefully took off his jacket and placed it around the armchair to reserve his place next to Mr. Ganz. He removed his glasses, placed them on the adjacent table, and then followed the nurse into the examining room. On that occasion, his blood pressure was somewhat out of control and I decided to put him on a new hypertensive medication. I told him to discontinue his Minipress and started him on the new Vasotec medication (angiotensin converting enzyme inhibitor).

Two days after this visit, Abe called me to say that the new medicine was absolutely no good for him. Since he'd started the new medicine he was continually dizzy and frequently saw double. I told him to come to the office for re-evaluation. That same afternoon, Mr. Ganz called to question me about a referral to an eye doctor inasmuch as he thought he had developed a new eye complication. For the past few days, he said, since he'd left my office, he had developed blurred vision, some dizziness, and therefore needed a new evaluation from a good ophthalmologist. Remembering that he had been at the office previously the same time as Mr. Greenberg, I scheduled his appointment to coincide with Abe's once again. The two old gentlemen lumbered into the reception room and sat down next to one another to discuss their new symptomatology. I went out into the reception room and asked Abe to hand me his eye glasses. Then I asked Mr. Ganz to give me his. I then switched the glasses, giving Abe back his original glasses and returning the proper glasses to Mr. Ganz. I told them both to go home and to call me in twenty-four hours, which they did. Each was delighted that his vision had returned to normal with no double vision or dizziness. And I entered in each chart, "Instant cure accomplished in reception room by returning to each patient his own glasses."

* * * * *

Abe was constantly telling jokes to those who sat near him in the waiting room. His favorite joke was the one about Mr. Harry Horowitz who called the doctor's office and asked for an appointment, stating, "Before I come I would like to know what he charges. The receptionist said, "Well, the first visit is $50 and the second visit is $25." He said, "Thank you very much," and made an appointment. After he arrived, he was ushered into the consultation room. As the doctor entered the room he jumped up and said, "Dr. Smith, I'm sure glad to see you AGAIN!" And with that Abe howled with delight as did the patients around him.

Office Personnel as Cast

The Three Faces of Terry

"Hi," she said, "I'm Terry Peters, your new lab technician." She bounced into my consultation room to be introduced by my receptionist. "I saw your ad in the *Texas Medical Journal* and I'm your girl! I can do all the clinical routine laboratory work you require and I have also studied up on platelet aggregation procedures for your research on the Aspirin Myocardial Infarction Grant." She bore an uncanny resemblance to the popular, wholesome, TV and movie star, Donna Reed, the proverbial girl next door, the girl every parent wanted their son to bring home. Pretty, smiling and appealing, this petite, secure young woman made an excellent impression in her clean, white starched uniform. So I agreed: she would be my new laboratory technician. A graduate of San Marcos College, she had worked three years in the Mercy Hospital there, was married, had no children, and as she was sufficiently ambitious to master the new procedures for platelet studies, I felt lucky that she answered the ad!

Terry was immediately popular with my office staff and patients. Her lab results were promptly completed and extremely accurate.

Her timid husband, Roy, was a traveling salesman and was gone for days at a time. Terry became exceptionally friendly with young Steve Samson, a bachelor neighbor at their apartment complex. He was a biochemist at a local research foundation. My receptionist soon complained to me about Steve's frequent phone calls that interrupted Terry's completion of the necessary lab procedures. They talked at length three and four times daily. Furthermore, my nosey, jealous nurse complained to me that she often overheard the conversations, which were ardent avowals of love and passion. Whenever Terry's husband, Roy, was home, the romance with the neighbor was put on "hold!"

One Monday morning Terry failed to appear for work. At 11:00 A.M. her husband Roy called to tell me his wife had been missing since Saturday. He called her mother's home, checked with all her friends, called all the hospitals, and finally reported her as a missing person to the police. Checking with Steve, he learned that Terry was last seen several days prior to her disappearance.

The following Monday she reported to work as though nothing had happened. Neither she nor Roy offered any explanation for the "lost week." But after her return, I noticed a distinct change in her personality. She was moody, quiet, introspective and tremulous. Her newly acquired profuse perspiration had an acrid odor. Her heretofore rosy complexion had a distinct yellow tinge and was unusually oily. Steve no longer called! Two weeks later, while Roy was out of town, she disappeared again, this time for four days. When she returned to work and he came back from his business trip, they had a violent argument in my office. Roy packed up and returned to Pittsburgh — his home town. Terry stayed on and for a short time was conscientious about her work. But her volatile moods soon resurfaced. The earlier noted skin changes and the offensive perspiration continued unabated. She became introspective and noncommunicative.

Once again, frequent phone calls disturbed her concentration at work. When she was unavailable, messages were left for her to call "Chris." One morning a dozen long-stemmed red roses were delivered for Terry and my nurse stealthily read the enclosed card, "To My Dear Love, last night was a blast" — signed Chris! It was apparent that Terry was again involved with someone else. This explained Roy leaving her and the termination of Steve's calls. Her work deteriorated and she became depressed, irritable, hair was unkempt, and the pallor and skin changes and perspiration became more pronounced. Our dimpled, cute Donna Reed now looked like a young "Tug Boat Annie."

During a serious disturbing talk with Terry, I learned that she had mastered the chemical technique for making LSD at home. It seemed that Steve, the biochemist, had taught her the chemical formula, and she and a group of new friends were taking this drug freely. She also admitted defiantly that she was very much in love with "Christine," not "Christopher" as expected, and had never been happier. Her marriage to Roy and the affair with Steve were mediocre sexual outlets, she explained. With Christine, she experienced true eroticism!

She confessed that she had tried very hard to love Roy, but sex with him was less satisfying than masturbation. Steve was a great passionate lover, she admitted, but he had no effect on her — "he never made me tingle." "But Christine," she said, "arouses me to ecstasies I never imagined possible. She fondles my breasts and uses her tongue so lavishly on my intimate parts. And I too can arouse her to great sexual pinnacles." "Doctor," she said, "we have great love and passion for one another."

Terry's addiction to the LSD increased, and I was totally unable to persuade her to stop. Despite my attempts to be nonjudgmental about her sex life, I was disturbed as her efficiency in the lab reached a new low. There were interminable calls from Christine, and soon she boldly came to the office to pick Terry up after work.

Christine, a librarian at one of the schools, was at least ten years older than her lover. She had straight brown hair, wore thick dark-rimmed glasses, was tall and shapeless, and had a deep masculine voice. She was curt and abrasive and had no compunction about embracing Terry in front of the office staff whenever she came to drive Terry home. An increasingly uncomfortable relationship developed be-

tween Terry and the staff. They rarely spoke to her and soon refused to
transfer Christine's calls.

Terry's status at the office deteriorated so that it was necessary to
discharge her and place another ad in the *Texas Medical Journal*. This
time I employed a young man who appeared quite virile, intelligent,
informed and was happily married. He seemed quite stable and had a
happy relationship with his wife. And for the peace in my office, I
hoped they made one another "tingle."

The Embezzler

When Dr. George Wilson and his wife, Marcy, were divorced,
Sally and I were distressed. We had been very good social friends. We
went bowling, horseback riding, played tennis, and enjoyed many dinner dates together. The divorce was stormy and therefore we knew it
would be difficult to maintain friendship with both of them. Two
months after the divorce, Marcy, a very attractive brunette, who was
an RN, came to the office to tell me that she was very bored being at
home and would like very much to get back into the medical field. I
suggested that she try the various hospitals inasmuch as she had done
work in intensive care units. She replied, "I don't want to go back to
the hospitals because I don't want to run into my husband again. I
would prefer to work in a doctor's office, and since we are such good
friends, I thought perhaps you could utilize my services."

I did not need a nurse at this time. However, since my receptionist was moving to Florida that very week, I asked Marcy if she would
like to try the front desk. Inasmuch as she was quite intelligent, had
been around doctors, was attractive and neat, I thought she would be
an asset for our office. She was thrilled with the possibility and gladly
accepted the position. For the next week she trained for the position
with the outgoing receptionist.

My patients were delighted with Marcy. She was friendly and organized. She had great rapport with the rest of the staff and was a great
bill collector. What I didn't know for several months was that she was
collecting for "herself." It seems that she became my partner. All the
checks were carefully credited and deposited. All the cash was put into
her own purse. She would credit the proper account on the books as if
it had been collected. But she never gave a receipt to anyone who paid
in cash and it was only through errors in bookkeeping, when patients
called to complain that they had been billed a second and third time
for money they had paid, that I became alerted to what was going on.

One evening Sally and I returned to the office late at night to check the deposits. We found that thousands of dollars had been credited to the books and never deposited. In each instance, these were cash collections. We were shocked, disturbed, and felt very much abused.

The next morning I called Marcy into my consultation room and confronted her with the evidence of the apparent embezzlement. She cried and said she was terribly sorry. She explained that initially she just kept $5 and $10 and $20 dollars for petty cash for her children. And then when she realized how easy it was to keep all the cash, she proceeded to so do. After having the books audited, we discovered that she'd embezzled $22,000 in the four months of her work, and it was suggested that I turn her over to the District Attorney. We were terribly hurt but I was unable to bring myself to press charges. She claimed she would pay me back, but of course I knew this was a futile gesture. Painfully, I realized there was a complete lack of ethics in her make-up.

She phoned me two weeks later to tell me that she was offered a job at the Baptist Memorial Hospital and that she knew she would enjoy it very much. I let her know that after our traumatic experience with her, I was not particularly interested in her activities. However, I did ask her on what floor she would be working as an RN. But she explained, "Oh, no, I'm not going to be an RN. I am going to be working in the business office." "In the business office?" I queried, "What are you going to be doing?" "I was offered a job as a cashier, as I told them that I'd had a good deal of experience as a receptionist collecting in your office." And then she boldly requested, "Doctor, I need a letter of recommendation to the head of the business office." This was truly the height of "chutzpa": she had absconded with $22,000 and expected me to give her a letter of recommendation! I said, "Marcy, don't you understand that I can't give you a letter of recommendation? Because if I did I would have to say yes, you were an excellent collector, but you collected all the money for yourself."

The Girl Who Couldn't Say No

When, during the Vietnam debacle, I hired Maureen Carpenter as a receptionist for my office, I wasn't prepared for the unusual series of events that would occur. She was a tall, delicate blond with an exquisitely beautiful face. Everyone thought she looked exactly like the actress Grace Kelly. She arrived from Detroit, Michigan, with her husband, who was to be stationed at Fort Sam Houston, bringing with her marvelous letters of recommendation. She had been a medical librarian and therefore was familiar with medical terminology. Also, she had been a secretary in the medical office of one of the large Detroit hospitals, so I was sure she would know her way about in my smaller office. Letters of recommendation reported in glowing terms that she was very bright, and very dedicated. In a short time she learned her way about my office and proved to be invaluable. She was extremely capable, conscientious, compassionate and was loved by patients and staff. She handled patients on the phone and in the office with exceptional skill. And thanks to her good business sense, our collections improved. I also became aware of an increase in the number of male patients who came to my office, and I suspected it was due, at least in part, to her charm and good looks.

She came to me sadly one morning telling me that her husband was going to be shipped overseas, but that she had fallen in love with San Antonio and decided to make this her home. She would wait here until he returned and would like to continue working in my office as she enjoyed the position. My patients, as well as the staff and I, were all happy that she decided not to return to Detroit.

One afternoon I overhead her querying my nurse about the longevity of prophylactic contraceptive diaphragms. Since her husband was overseas and probably would not return from active duty for two years, I was puzzled by her interest. "Perhaps she's trying to determine whether or not her diaphragm would still serve its purpose by the time he returns," I thought. And then I meditated, "Perhaps I'm being a bit naive."

Each evening before leaving my office my nurse's aide would go about making sure that all the examining beds and cots and tables had fresh linen and pillow cases changed, so that all would be ready for the next morning. The office was closed on Saturday at noon, and Sheila, the maid, did her customary meticulous cleaning before locking up.

On Monday morning, while I was preparing to do a basal metabolic rate study on a patient, I noticed that the pillow on the cot was crumpled, the linen was wrinkled and furthermore, there was a bit of brown shoe polish on the edge of the mattress on the cot. I realized this shoe polish could only get there from a position of lying face down with the feet over the edge. I also noted some stains on the linen of jelly or cream origin. Having been a fan for many years of the famous Sherlock Holmes of Baker Street, by imitation I drew some immediate conclusions. With the condition of my cot, the query about diaphragms, and with her husband being overseas, I decided that I had better have a talk with our office beauty, Maureen.

When confronted with the evidence, she readily admitted what had transpired in my office. She explained that she had met this nice-looking young soldier in her church on Sunday and that she felt sorry for him because he was fearful of going overseas and would soon be shipped out. Since her husband was already overseas, she felt a personal obligation to the boys of the service and thought it would be nice to "contribute in her own fashion." I reprimanded her and told her I would not tolerate those activities in my office. After the tears subsided, she said she would certainly not use my office for any more adventures and promised to go to church just to pray and not to meet young men. Several weeks later, a patient told me that she saw Maureen in the White Plaza Hotel late one evening, arm in arm with a young soldier and slightly inebriated. Although I knew Maureen's husband had been overseas for well over a month, I told the patient it was probably her husband. The following morning, confidentially, I told Maureen of the reported incident and she said, "But I only promised not to use your office any more." "But what about the other promise?" "You're right. That will be the end of that," she assured me.

Charles Harrison, the pharmacist, would occasionally make a personal delivery of drugs to my office whenever his delivery boy was not available and we needed medicine immediately. He was forty years of age, divorced, handsome, and enjoyed life, spending money freely on big cars, fancy trips, and probably fancy women. It soon became apparent that *all* deliveries made from his pharmacy to my office were made by him personally, and that he spent considerable time hovering around the desk, talking to Maureen. I decided it was probably just a flirtation, and being very busy did not pursue my Sherlock Holmes activities.

One morning I noticed that Maureen was quite jittery, nervous, handled the phone badly, and was irritable with the staff. After lunch she buzzed me and asked if she could talk to me privately. She came into the consultation room, eyes downcast, blushing, and timidly said, "Dr. Cooper, I'm in trouble. I think I'm pregnant." Disturbed, I asked, "Are you still feeling sorry for that young soldier?" "No, you see I was in Dallas with Charles and I forgot to take my diaphragm along." "Charles? Charles who?" "The pharmacist. You know we've been going together for almost two months." Fortunately, she was not pregnant. After this terrifying experience, she promised once again, in no uncertain terms, that she was going to say "No" to Charles and to any other applicants for her favors. She had painfully and, I believed, finally learned the error of her ways.

Sally knew all about these incidents, and again after I vowed that if approached, I certainly would say "No," we discussed how valuable and efficient Maureen was. She sincerely promised to behave, and therefore we decided hesitantly to allow her to continue as the receptionist.

After lunch one day the maitre'd of a very fine French restaurant cornered me and asked to me stop by his office to chat. I excused myself from my colleagues at the table and stepped into Maurice's office. He was an extremely attractive man, sophisticated, and immaculately dressed. He had studied the culinary arts in Switzerland and had developed an urbane, continental manner. He was a good skier, a man about town, and one who rightfully earned the reputation of being a womanizer. A delightful upbeat character, he was admired by all, and envied by many.

Once we had closeted ourselves in his private office, he closed the door, and smiling broadly, said, "Dr., that gal is a gem." "That gal?" Preparing myself for the next episode. "Yes, Maureen. She is one of the most beautiful women I have seen and I really do think she is prettier than Grace Kelly. I think I should take her to Hollywood. I know some very important people there. But she does such an admirable job in your office, that I don't feel I should disrupt it. You know I've been around, and she's the warmest, most passionate female I've been with." "Oh no," I thought, "You too?" He went on, "Al (we had developed an intimate first name basis through the years), we love to take showers together and then rub each other down with scented oils, and then go to bed. And Al, she has taught me maneuvers that even I didn't know, and you know I've been around." At this point, I thought I had to quell some of his ego. "Maurice, I believe she's taught the whole army some maneuvers of her own." He chuckled loudly, I half heartedly. We shook hands, and I left in a peculiar mood — half disgust and half envy — and concluded that she certainly was like the character in the musical "Oklahoma." She was a gal who couldn't say "No." But she was faithful to her husband in her own fashion.

Behind my colonial office building on Howard Street there are four large imposing pecan trees that produce soft-shell large pecans that are the envy of the area. Having been indoctrinated as a true Texan, I learned to love pecan pie and it was a real treat to go out on

Saturday afternoon, beat on the trees with long sticks, and collect bushels of pecans. One blustery Saturday afternoon in early fall, I drove down to the office to harvest my pecans. I drove to the back of the office, hailed my porter as he was raking leaves, and then spotted two parked cars. It was 3:00 P.M. The office had been closed since noon. One car belonged to my lab technician, Ralph, who had been on my staff for over five years, and the other car, a shabby Thunderbird, belonged to Maureen.

I knew that Ralph cleaned his lab on Saturday mornings, and wondered why he was back in the office at this time of day. Since Maureen had met with the accountant on Friday, there was no reason for her to check her books that afternoon. All was quiet in the back of the office as I entered, but as I reached the basal metabolic room, I heard whispering. The door was open and there was Ralph busily zipping up his trousers while Maureen, totally unclothed, was cowering under the sheet. We were all too embarrassed to speak, and I hastily retreated into my consultation room. Shortly thereafter, I heard the back door slam, and soon all was quiet.

When I went back to my pecan trees, my porter came to help me, and I said, "I guess I came at a very bad time." His retort was, "This has been going on for almost a year. They meet every Saturday about this time, and I was wondering how long it would be before they got caught." "How long did you say?" "About a year, Doctor." The porter proceeded to tell me that Ralph's wife knew all about the affair as she had come by on numerous occasions and parked across the street to check on him.

At the end of a long hard Monday, when the rest of the staff had gone, Maureen came into my consultation room and I thought "Here comes confession hour." By now I had determined that this "Peyton Place" environment was just too disruptive to our office tranquility. The usual sobbing, profuse tears and new promises were to be of no avail. This time I would be adamant! The soap opera would be cancelled. Maureen would be replaced. Of course, she proffered the usual story. She just couldn't say "No," and this side affair, in addition to all the others had been going on for a year. They would meet every Saturday afternoon at the office, but always replaced the fresh linens on the cot! They also met on Wednesday after office hours, each parking in a shopping center, and then registering at a local motel. "Maureen," I said, "I have just two bits of advice for you: The first is that you talk to your priest. And the second is that in the next two weeks you buy a ticket back to Detroit!"

When Maureen left, Ralph suffered considerable emotional problems. His pretty, energetic, vindictive wife divorced him. He became depressed and was unable to perform his work in the lab. I found it necessary to discharge him, and learned at a later date that he had a complete nervous breakdown. Thereafter, I tried to hire plain-looking mature women as receptionists who were closely attached to their families and went to church — to pray.

Rise and Fall of Irma

She came from the Barrio. But, at fifteen, Irma Garza was determined to climb out of the ghetto in which she had lived all her life. Like most children of "wetbacks" (illegal immigrants who crossed the shallow part of the Rio Grande from Mexico into the United States), Irma had had only a rudimentary education. At the age of twelve, these children left school and took whatever menial jobs they could find to help support their large families.

Irma was no exception. But she was bright and ambitious and determined to get ahead. She got a job as a "Green Girl" at the Robert B. Green Hospital, a position somewhat between a maid and an LVN. She was paid minimum wage (seventy-five cents an hour at that time) and for this princely sum, she kept the emergency room clean, changed linens and paper rolls on examining tables, removed discarded bandages, emptied basins and baskets, mopped the floors, replenished supplies, and sterilized needles, syringes and instruments.

During my residency at the Green, I occasionally noted this pleasant, quick moving, agile, young Mexican girl. She asked intelligent questions and seemed eager to learn.

The nurses at the hospital were impressed by Irma's attitude, and taught her to apply electrodes for taking ECGs. Before long, she became so proficient in applying them and so observant of the entire procedure that the nurses, always shorthanded, allowed her to start taking the ECGs. In the same way, she gradually learned to position patients for x-rays and the technicians allowed her to take an occasional film of the chest or abdomen.

One busy afternoon, during my third year of practice, I was interrupted by my receptionist who told me that a young woman who claimed to be an old friend from my residency days at the Green would like to see me on a personal matter. Curious, I agreed to see her, and immediately recognized Irma, the bright, industrious "flunkie" of the emergency room.

Irma said she was tired of working at the Robert B. Green. She had not had an increase in her pay in the last two years and was earning only $1 an hour. She wanted to know if I could use her services. I remembered that I had liked and admired Irma, and inasmuch as I was quite busy and could use additional help at the office, I hired her at a higher salary than she earned at the Robert B. Green. When I told her the job was hers, Irma startled me by going down on her knees in front of me, grasping my right hand and kissing it. "Doctor," she sobbed, tears running down her face, "I have prayed for this. You won't ever be sorry you gave me this chance. I thank God and thank you more than I can tell you." Embarrassed, I cleared my throat, gently disengaged my hand, gave her a moment to recover from her emotional outburst, helped her to her feet and told her to give the hospital notice and report for work in two weeks. Then I left her, still thanking me, and went to see my next patient.

Two weeks later, immaculate, starched and smiling, Irma reported for work. Her initial job was to do approximately what she had done at the hospital. She was to change the linens, sterilize, clean, take a few electrocardiograms, and help the x-ray technicians position patients. After she had been working for me for a month I noticed she was constantly in the dark room and I realized that she had learned to develop x-ray film. Soon she was taking x-rays and I found her reading my anatomy book to help her position patients accurately for the films.

Eight months after Irma's arrival, my x-ray technician's husband was suddenly transferred to Louisiana, and she left on short notice. Resignedly, I prepared to search for a replacement. Modestly, Irma told me it would not be necessary to hire a new technician inasmuch as she was sure she had mastered all the various techniques for taking the various views and knew how to develop films. Before leaving, my x-ray technician told me that Irma was as good as any Registered X-ray Technician in San Antonio. So Irma, the ambitious child of the Barrio, became my x-ray technician, with an increase in salary befitting her new status. Although not as educated as the remainder of my staff, she was highly efficient, very bright, constantly reading, and constantly learning.

About two weeks after Irma became my x-ray technician, the Texas State Board of Radiology sent out a notice that all doctors who had x-ray equipment had to employ a Registered Technician. To become a Registered Technician required high school graduation plus two years of x-ray training in a hospital under Registered X-ray Technicians and radiologists. Since Irma could not qualify for these new requirements, I was reluctantly going to have to hire a Registered Technician. I asked if she would like to do the general work she had done previously, but at her present salary. Irma was quite proud and assumed these duties in my office for the next six months, but told me she was going to be on the alert for any other possible positions that might open up for her in San Antonio.

My wife Sally had taken a liking to Irma, and on many occasions when we went out we asked Irma to sit for us, taking care of our children who were all fond of her. One evening as we left, we told her we would not be back until about 2:00 in the morning and suggested that she sleep over and offered her the guest bedroom. In the morning, when Sally went to awaken her to get dressed to go to work, she found her lying in the bed horizontally, not in the usual longitudinal position. When questioned, Irma said, "Well . . . I always sleep that way. At home we have only two beds for the kids. And since I have five sisters and six brothers, we sleep five or six in a bed and the only way we can do it is to sleep crosswise and I have never gotten used to sleeping any other way."

On most occasions when Irma babysat for us, she requested that we drop her off at the Robert B. Green, claiming that she lived only a few blocks from the hospital and wanted to visit old friends in the emergency room before going home. But one night we returned home very late and, despite her objections, insisted upon driving her home. "Home" turned out to be a two-room wooden shack near the stockyards. The aroma of the privies combined with the stench from the stockyard and the adjacent rendering plant was overpowering. Irma was obviously embarrassed to have us see the squalor in which she lived, but maintained her dignity and made no apologies. We gained greater respect for her after this experience, marvelling that she could be so cheerful and optimistic, given this impoverished background.

Before long a job opportunity opened up for Irma at the Robert B. Green X-ray Department. Since she had extensive experience at my office, she was readily accepted for the position, working under the Registered Technician. Her job, however, was the night shift. She worked from 11:00 P.M. until 7:00 A.M. without any complaints.

One evening at approximately 10:30, while walking from her home on the west side to the Robert B. Green Hospital, only about a mile away, she was struck from behind by a blunt instrument, fell to the ground, and was pulled behind a vacant store. It was very dark and she could not see her assailant, but he apparently was under the influence of alcohol, as she recalled his breath reeked of whiskey. He ripped off her clothes, and brutally raped her. When the ordeal was over, she was dazed and found herself bleeding and bruised, but managed to assemble some of her clothing and stumbled into the Robert B. Green Emergency Room. She was treated efficiently with medication for prevention of disease and hormones were given to prevent pregnancy. She was subjected to the usual routine questioning by police, by members of the rape department, by the assistant district attorney, and by psychologists, until the confusion became so great that she refused to talk anymore and withdrew into a state of catatonic depression.

She was hospitalized at the Robert B. Green and for days refused to take nourishment or to talk to anyone, and had frequent bouts of crying and hysteria.

When I heard about Irma's traumatic experience, I asked my friend, Dr. Harold Krause, a psychologist, to please see her as a favor to me. Dr. Krause had approximately six sessions with Irma, and as a courtesy to me did not charge her. She recovered sufficiently to leave the hospital and go home. After a week, she returned to her job.

But the Irma that returned to her job in the x-ray department at night was an entirely different Irma. There was a complete change in personality. She became loud, brisk, talkative, and quite free and fresh with the male x-ray technicians. They were disturbed and surprised at the new Irma. One night, she came into the lab and said to one of the lab technicians, "See that large cactus plant in the corner of the room? Doesn't it remind you of a large erect penis? And don't you think those thorns would hurt if that penis were to enter?" He was shocked to hear Irma talk in that vein, but smiled and said, "You're certainly right." During ensuing nights, it was noticed that Irma came in with an entirely different type of walk. She swaggered, making sure that her buttocks moved in rhythm. It was also noticed that her blouse was not fully buttoned, permitting a good look at her cleavage. Her pants were much too tight, and she doused herself with cheap perfume. She talked about her dates to the other technicians, and whether real or fabricated, there always were sexual overtones in the conversations. Soon she became overtly aggressive with the male employees, slapping them on the buttocks and hugging one or two in the dark room.

Irma became the sex object of the x-ray department. It was reported she had sexual experience with both patients and with technicians on the x-ray tables; that she went to cheap motels with the orderlies; and the clean up crew bragged that they had relations with her in the backseats of their cars. The heretofore shy, reclusive girl had lost all restraint.

When one of the residents of the Robert B. Green called me to apprise me of these startling personality changes in Irma, I dropped by the hospital to have a confidential talk with her. I suggested that she see Dr. Krause again, inasmuch as she was having these disturbed personality alterations. She refused adamantly, telling me that she was a new Irma and loved the new Irma, was having the time of her life, and refused to allow anyone to interfere with her new perspective on living.

Irma became friendly with a seventeen-year-old runaway girl, and soon both girls were involved in prostitution during the day. Her new friend introduced her to the upper drugs (amphetamines) and the depressant tranquilizer drugs, and she became adept at resorting to the various chemicals as she felt she needed them.

Her work at the Robert B. Green disintegrated. She made constant errors, took the wrong kinds of x-rays, was bothered too much by the eager technicians, orderlies, and so forth who had learned of Irma's sexual generosity. It became apparent to the administration that Irma was no longer of value in the x-ray department. In fact, she had become a complete detriment. Her scandalous behavior disrupted the decorum of the department and she became hostile when reprimanded. After several futile attempts to help her, the personnel director discharged her.

Now in addition to street walking during the day, she was busy day and night offering her services and earning a "non-respectable" living. Irma's new friend introduced her to her brother, Ralph, who apparently was a pimp working both prostitutes and homosexuals. He was relatively good looking, crude, virile, and very demanding. Soon Irma and Ralph became lovers and very closely attached to one another. Ralph saved the most expensive customers for Irma, and Irma began to enjoy some of the elaborate clothes and jewelry which she had never had previously.

One day Ralph said to Irma, "If you really want to get a kick out of a so called upper and really have it increase your sexual power, I want you to try this drug called LSD." And so the addiction started. LSD proved to be expensive and it was necessary for Irma to put in many hours, working day and night in her new profession.

One day, while high on LSD, Ralph suggested to Irma, "How would you like to make two or three hundred dollars in ten minutes?" Having become greedy, she said, "What will I have to do and who is the guy I have to sleep with?"

"Oh no!" Ralph said, "This time I know of a 7-Eleven convenience store that stays open all night and takes in considerable cash. I have a .38 revolver," he said, "and we could rush in there at night, scare the hell out of the clerk, grab all the money and be out of there in minutes. It will be as exciting as hell." Infatuated with Ralph and looking for new thrills, and strung out on LSD, Irma readily agreed to go along with this new adventure.

What they didn't know was that this convenience store had been robbed three times previously, and at that time an armed officer was sitting behind some boxes. He yelled, "Freeze!" Ralph turned around and tried to scuffle with the guard. Three shots were exchanged, and Irma dropped in the cross-fire. Two bullets entered her chest and one tore into her aorta. She bled freely into the chest cavity and developed cardiac tamponade.

In an ironic twist of fate, when the EMS ambulance arrived she was rushed to the Robert B. Green Emergency Room, the site of her first employment, where she was pronounced "dead on arrival."

Epilogue

"We miss you, doctor, and wish you were still in practice." How gratifying it was to find that note added to a recent Christmas card from a former patient. Almost daily, I receive requests from patients and old colleagues for a medical consultation. Plaintively, the patients complain, "Doctor, we're lost without your control of our medical problems. We're sent from specialist to specialist, more and more tests are done, and no one is 'directing the show.' Specialist number two doesn't confer with specialist number one, and no one takes time to explain my problem. And my medical bills are exorbitant!"

So why, at the peak of my career, with my medical acuity securely intact, did I give up my practice? For one, I wanted to quit while I was on top. I was painfully aware that certain physiological changes would inevitably occur with age. Hearing would become a bit depressed, vision less acute, sense of touch less defined. I would not want to miss hearing an early mitral valve murmur or rales during a *deep breath,* or recognizing an early tint of jaundice or perhaps fail to detect the tip of a slightly enlarged spleen. I could accept forgetting a name. However, forgetting a pertinent fact of a patient's medical history or not recalling a discovery on a physical examination would be intolerable.

There are other reasons for leaving the all encompassing practice of medicine: I wanted more time with Sally, for relaxation, travel, and visiting our three children and six grandchildren. And, I relished the time to write this book, and to enter in the area of chemotherapeutic

327

research for anti-cancer drugs in the non-profit Cancer Therapy and Research Center in San Antonio.

I actively practiced medicine during its "Golden Age." In the hands of the artisan, it was personal, warm, individual, malleable and enduring. Today, medicine has lost its brilliant luster. Now it is the "Age of Stainless Steel": cold, precise, sharp, mass produced and impersonal. Regrettably, today neither practicing doctor nor patient experiences the fulfillment that I enjoyed.

Your Comments On
"TAKE A DEEP BREATH"

Jane Kramer-Director
Worldwide Public Affairs
Bristol Meyers-Squibb Co.
P.O. Box 4000
Princeton. N.J. 08543-4000